MODERN OCCASIONS

MODERN OCCASIONS

Selected and edited by

Philip Rahv /

WEIDENFELD AND NICOLSON

20 NEW BOND STREET
LONDON W1

Contents

Foreword

This book is a collection of new writing—new, first of all, in the simple sense that none of it has been published before in English. Of the twenty-one writers contributing to this volume, all representative of present trends in literature and criticism, fifteen are American, three are British, one is Canadian, one is German, and one is Dutch.

This collection, while containing some experimental writing, especially in the matter of adapting the latest colloquial speech to literary purposes, is not experimental in the sense that this word acquired in the first thirty years or so of this century, that is, in the sense of fundamental experimentation with verbal and structural forms. The editor is disposed to encourage such work, but the fact is that no samples of that kind of work were submitted. It is clear that the experimentation that goes on in this period is of a different sort. In fiction, particularly, it is in the area of subject matter that innovations are noticeable; the literary energy now being expended is mostly directed towards incorporating in imaginative forms types of experience and attitudes towards experience as yet unavailable to writers before the Second World War. The "revolution of the word," popularized by the Paris magazine *transition* and its editor Eugene Jolas as well as many other literary publicists of that time, is now a thing of the past. The more elaborate and complex forms, that we have come to associate with the great names, such as Proust and Joyce, of the classic period of modernity, are assiduously studied in the universities even as their influence on the younger novelists is shrinking; perhaps they feel no need to engage with them; and in poetry, too, the tendency is for more immediate and spontaneous modes of expression. Only in the drama can one discern a movement towards renewing the medium by way of radical experimentation. But innovation is not always the product of formal experiment: there are other ways by which the vitally new sometimes displaces the old.

The term "avant-garde" has of late acquired an ambiguous meaning. I doubt whether it is very useful any longer—hence the justice, to my mind, of Herr Enzensberger's destructive analysis of it in this volume. For the fact is that from being for the most part a genuine expression of dissidence and revolt, the avant-garde has evolved in recent years into a veritable academy, and a ruling academy at that, fawned upon in the most respectable quarters even as it turns out art-objects as consumer goods. The truth is that, in the old sense of the term, the avant-garde scarcely exists now. Its cultist mannerisms are all that is left of it, and the better contemporary writers make no bones about dissociating themselves from it. The thing is, however, not to bewail the passing of the old but to heed what is creatively noteworthy in the present. My hope is that readers will discover some of it in this book.

Philip Rahv

April 15, 1966

MODERN OCCASIONS

THALIA SELZ / *The Elbow*

One autumn morning in the early nineteen-fifties when I was
twenty-four and working part-time and going to school part-time
in Chicago, I came up out of the basement apartment I shared
with my young son Sam, and I saw a building. That moment
and sight determined my career. It was an apartment house in
the shape of a square U. The sky behind it was clear and in-
tensely blue; the morning light set forth sharply the building's
angles and layers advancing from and receding into the blue
depth of the sky. As I stood there with Sam's hand in mine (I
was taking him to kindergarten), a thin curtain of smoke drifted
across the various faces of the building which my gaze encom-
passed, relentlessly and completely altering the appearance of
this ordinary structure: its color, its depth and height, its relation to every object and person around it.

It was movement which changed the building. I decided to
major in Film.

My name is Rachel, and I am short and plump with round cheeks and a sharp nose. I suppose I inherit the resilient sturdiness of the Russian-Jewish peasant woman, the other side of my mother's harping concern. Sam has that bounce, too, thank god, for inadvertently I almost destroyed it when he was five-and-a-half, the year I am going to tell about. However, he looks like his father: curly dark hair and eyes like two pots of chocolate mousse. Big, sad, articulate Jewish eyes.

Those days Mama, who lived in Queens, worried and sent boxes of clothes to Sam and me. Otherwise we would never have worn anything but grimy T shirts, jeans and thong sandals. That fall she came to visit us and sitting in our underground parlor told Heide, my sociology and psychology instructor, that I ought to marry again.

"Rachel should get married. She's a lovely girl; she's got a fine son, my grandson Sam. Samuel. She wants to make a career for herself. Very smart and talented. But a woman should have a man to look after. He should pay the bills; give her a decent apartment. Sam shouldn't be living here in this dump, with a rat and the cockroaches for company, Rachel. Sam needs to be where there's light and clean. Fresh air. He should be playing ball in the ball park. He needs a back yard. You know that, Rachel. She's so stubborn. It always had to be *her* way, even when she was three. I used to say to my husband . . ."

Meine Yiddische mama went on explaining that such a darling girl like me—even if no longer a virgin—could snag herself some young doctor or lawyer in half a sec and go live in the suburbs. If she'd just try.

Time has always fascinated me. Time and the image. Now there were two kinds of Time. One was Mama saying, "In half a second": *Rachel is twenty-four. . . . Time is passing . . . her looks, too . . . get married, quick!* The other kind of Time was Günther hiccuping drunkenly in my ear: *Ze whole universe is in flux . . . here today, gone tomorrow, nein? . . . read Lucretius. . . . Time is movement.* A composition in space (my

4

building) had been given existence in Time by the movement of a diaphanous layer passing across it.

Heide's Time resembled my mother's Time, for it too was fraught with fear; its arena, however, was less dramatic. There she sat, facing my mother, as monumental as a Roman matron. She was a young widow. Her husband had been an Italian professor of music. Of him she would say, "Often he was an hour late for supper: he had to practice. But a schnitzel doesn't wait! Food must be eaten hot. You should all sit down at the same Time. When I was a child in Zurich the entire family assembled at the door to the dining room one minute before the dinnerbell would ring. My grandfather said I was late because I came when the gong sounded. He used to get very angry with me. *Think* if I had come an *hour* late!"

What was remarkable to me was the quality of infinite change which the drifting smoke lent to such a static object as an apartment house. But let us regard the film from a societal standpoint, as Heide liked to say. It is basically a cooperative endeavor which distinguishes it from the other arts (except, of course, architecture). The idea of subordinating my contribution to an idea of the whole, so that the finished work would be better than any single individual could make it—why, it was like working together to make a new society! I can't tell you what excitement we generated all together!

One sign of our intimacy and mutual respect was the fact that we called all our professors by their first names, to their faces. Just as Sam called me Rachel because that way we were supposed to have a more honest relationship.

But there was more to the idea of the School than that. You see, an idea can infuse your life with meaning; properly realized, it can alter your whole existence. The School had been founded in the late thirties by a great educational experimenter. It was neither an art school in the usual sense nor a school of design; this man, whose memory we all revered, believed that if art and the new technology were married their issue could be a splendid new society in which each item would be both beautiful and useful. Let an object be truly functional and its form must necessarily be pleasing. The end product was to be an environment so functional and at the same time so esthetically satisfying that it could not help but revolutionize the attitudes of the people living in it. Thus the world would fill up with happy, handsome, healthy, useful, loving, possibly even good, human beings.

We had to take certain academic subjects, of course. Our founder, dead by this time, had wanted us to be whole men and women. (More men than women, because most parents were afraid to expose their daughters to such an experiment.) So Heide, née Heidelotte Schlossheim, came from Zurich via N.Y.U. and Berkeley, to teach us about society and psychology. We studied art history, music (the twelve-tone scale), even English. Most of the students wrote at least a little poetry which they tacked up on the bulletin board outside the men's bathroom, but the letters home for more money were an awful mess. (I had gone to a conventional college for two semesters, so I could write a little better than the general run.) And god knows, we all needed money except for Irene R———, who was a real R———, too: a grandniece. Günther said she looked like a thoroughbred racehorse (imagine saying such a thing about a girl!). He said that because all he knew of American literature was Hemingway and because he had a crush on her just *because* she stank of money and family. The rest of us stank of poverty and the comfortable ghettos in Queens and Brooklyn and Rogers Park and Glendale we had left behind. I could have had a nice Jewish doctor or lawyer, for several came around, but I dare say I looked dirty. I was dirty. We were up to our ears in everything in that School. Half the time my hands were stained blue or black or red, and I couldn't afford a manicure. Besides, who had the time? There was a bathroom at home, all right, but Sam and I shared it, as we did the kitchen, with a Mexican couple and their teen-aged daughter who lived down the hall. Not to mention all those cockroaches and Ludwig, the rat.

Sam christened him Ludwig after he had known Günther for several weeks. I knew Ludwig a long time but I only saw him twice: once galloping down the hall; and one starry morn at two or three when I got up to go to the bathroom I found him crouching tense with power along the rim of the bathtub. He was dreadfully ugly and much larger than I had imagined from his frolicsome tumbling in the pots and pans at night.

The next day I described him to my English classmate, Jessica—in front of Sam, which was stupid. I knew it was stupid as soon as I had started, but I was so used to doing that sort of thing. Jessica said, Chin up, everyone's life had at least one rat in it and I was lucky mine kept to the bathroom. Sam was looking scared but Jessica's daughter Kay popped out:

"Yes, but Mama, she already has Günther."

Only six years old. Sam laughed boisterously, but perhaps he really did get the joke. At least he knew there was one and he relaxed.

But how did Kay know I "had" Günther? Indeed, did I "have" Günther? Did anyone? Jessica wouldn't have told her. She didn't confide in her child. In addition to English reserve Jessica had some very clear notions about the place of children. Yet at the same time she knew well, I thought, how to share with Kay. If she were painting or working on some messy project for Visual Design she would strip Kay to her underwear and set her in the middle of spread-out newspapers with pots of paint and a brush and paste and scissors, and the two of them would work together companionably for hours until it was time for Kay to go to bed.

Kay was six, a half year older than Sam. No one knew or cared where her daddy was, for Jessica's family was well enough off to send her money. She and Kay had to live frugally, but unlike me, Jessica could afford to go to school full-time, and she enjoyed life. She dated regularly, bringing her boyfriends home to the two-room apartment she shared with Kay, but they were friendly, well-behaved Jewish fellows who came from affectionate families, liked children, and never made scenes. She didn't date the faculty, I suppose because she considered it bad form. She never said so to me because she wouldn't have wanted to be rude, but it was evident by the distance she kept between herself and Günther, for instance.

None of the rest of us was able to manage. The faculty had always slept with the students. It was a School tradition. Every class had one or two exceptionally pretty girls who were chosen by this or that generally unmarried prof. They went everywhere together without embarrassment; sometimes they lived together; occasionally they married. These girls were almost always very intelligent and talented, but of course they tended to grow prideful in the manner of girls who have been raised above their station. The rest of us vied to become their friends; they knew everything worth knowing, and it wasn't overlooked that they might have some small influence on grades and scholarships.

My relations with Günther were not so simple. Günther was German; he said he didn't believe in "such American tribal customs as going steady." Accordingly he played the field, dating students and faculty interchangeably; he didn't, however, seem much drawn to the outside world. Or only if she had a cold all the time and no breasts and worked like a dog for some fly-by-night enterprise that underpaid her without conscience. There were a few such girls in my time, but they had to be able to adapt to our small world, and it wasn't easy. Not only did Günther drink and whore around; he occasionally blackened the eyes of the lady he was currently living with. He never once struck me, but then we didn't live together.

Günther was thirty-five when I knew him. He had come to this country in the late forties as an exchange professor, and he had stayed. He wasn't old enough to have studied at the Bauhaus, which had been dissolved by Hitler in 1933 when Günther was sixteen, but as soon as the Wehrmacht occupied Paris he sought out Wassily Kandinsky; shortly, however, he was transferred to the Russian front, where there were no improper humanistic distractions, and he spent the rest of the war there.

Like most Germans who were not refugees from Hitler, he wouldn't talk about the war except to say that it "stinked. The whole goddam, son of bitch sing stinked. The Russian is a good fighter though. We fought Russians and Americans and English, and I saw our men fight. And the Russian is the best fighter I am seeing. He is so brave it seems stupid. You shoot and shoot and they keep on coming. Admirable, but stupid. I hate to fight, yah? except when I am terribly angry about somesing. Or have *hunger*. I like girls and hard liquor, especially Bols, and movies. I don't like to fight, though I can do it if I must, but it is stupid to be so brave as those Russians were. But I admire it. To be a man; yes, that is important."

It is also important to have one. I was only twenty-four, but my first year in college, when I was seventeen, I had become pregnant with Sam, who was inoculated into me by a serious young fellow student in biology named Nathan. He legitimatized the unborn Samuel, but six weeks before delivery date he disappeared. I actually carried his photograph with me into the labor room. Mama came and cried at my bedside after Sam was born, telling me my life was ruined, but fortunately at that age you don't believe them when they tell you such things. Sam weighed in at eight pounds six ounces, and he was magnificently ugly, but he had those chocolate mousse eyes, too. When he was three weeks old Nat suddenly reappeared out of the rest home where he had taken refuge and tried living with Sam and me for six months. He quit school and took a job as laboratory technician to support us, but there was no future without a degree. Nat's family was on his neck; *meine mamale* wept even harder; I wept; Sam wept though only at feeding time; and finally Nat disappeared into Greenwich Village to do some significant research; returned for a few days; left again; came back; left. I can't even remember if I ever really loved him.

Günther was the head of the Photography Department, and although he had made his reputation as a still photographer he was much more interested in making movies. He had already shot one ten-minute documentary—just some Negro children jitterbugging in the slums around the School, but it had an easy breathless rhythm echoing the rhythm of the dancers' wild gyrations, and when he entered it in the Cannes film festival that year it won a prize and was shown around thereafter. So he borrowed more money to make another, longer film. This one was to last forty minutes or so—a fantasy. Günther was becoming interested in experimental photography, not for the sake of the experiment but for what it could provide of an original visual experience. He was, I found, relentless with his beginning students in allowing no tricks of any kind in the developing room. He said you had to learn to shoot first before you could unshoot. I was fascinated with myself and the School and my secondhand Rolliflex when I enrolled in the Photography Department, but one night at a party I was sitting in a semicircle of others at Günther's feet, listening to him grunt and watching him guzzle beer, and suddenly I began to be fascinated with him, too.

Günther bent his shaggy blond head and looked down at me, and I noticed for the first time that this Nordic giant had great black, mournful Jewish-style eyes.

I believe I was actually wearing a dress that night: a cheap cotton but it had a low neck and looked good on my small though much too plump self. Anyhow we were all so young and worshipful, black or brown or blonde, even grubby and occasionally suicidal, we must have constituted an overwhelmingly tempting force, all in a crescent at his feet.

At two or three o'clock in the morning he kissed me in our hostess' kitchen. It was a real kitchen, too (instead of a hotplate), with a regular pantry toward which he beckoned me silently, his head nodding with drink. Günther kissed with what I fancied was a distinctly European style—long, smooth, diving kisses into the neck and below the shoulders. I was inexperienced and impressed, so we lurched home together.

He insisted soddenly but unswervingly that we go to my place instead of his, and I must have been drunk because I agreed. However, I had to leave him up on the street for a few minutes while I plunged into the greasy stink of that basement to pay my baby sitter, the thirteen-year-old Mexican daughter Luisa, her twenty-five cents an hour, and then shoo her away down the hall to her own apartment. I checked Sam in his curtained alcove off our parlor, but he was sleeping with a deep abandon, arms and legs in every direction. Then I called softly up to Günther.

During his lovemaking Günther blurted out several times a strange phrase which sounded like *ka-ve leena*, but he was far too drunk to do anything but grunt and paw around. As I showed him to the door he staggered back against the wall, stuffed his big hands desperately in his pockets for a pack of cigarettes, found one, successfully extracted a cigarette at last, triumphantly raised a match to light it, and—Ach Gott! It was broken, limp, crooked like an index finger.

Günther plucked it from between his lips, dashed it to the floor, ground it furiously under his heel, and hissed, "Son of bitch! Nussing works tonight!"

As he went crashing like a sick bear up to the street, the curtains to the alcove parted and Sam trotted out, pouting with sleep, grinding a fist in one eye, dewy with that sweet sweat of young sleep, his cheeks still plump as a baby's.

"Rachel, dwinka wa'; who zat man? Who was here?" he finally enunciated with the clarity of alarm.

"Just some nice person who brought Rachel home."

He crawled back into his cot again, and I collapsed across the bed in my underwear, not having been so far gone as to neglect carefully hanging up my party dress in the closet along with Sam's and my boring jeans and his wool suit with the long trousers that my mother had sent him for his fifth birthday.

The next afternoon when Sam got out of kindergarten and I had finished my editing stint for the day (I worked five mornings a week for a trade publication downtown), I trotted him into the main reading room in the public library, and we looked up *ka-ve leena* in the unexpurgated **W**ebster's. All I found with the aid of two years' Latin in highschool were *cavum, cavus: any recess or chamber* plus *lena: a procuress.*

I thought: Oh, my goodness! Decadent? But a classical education. Also German: **W**ehrmacht, master race, and all that bull.

I didn't expect Günther would feel especially pleased at the sight of me in Photography Lab that afternoon. Sure enough, he strode around erect and chilly, giving the best students hell for nothing at all. I averted my eyes. Still, I was curious. At five-thirty after most of the students had left, he approached with the stiff-legged walk peculiar to his generation of male Germans and invited me to "a small gathering" in his studio the next evening. It was to be, he explained briefly, "a social experiment. Ve are conducting un inwestigation of a new art form called *skip-reading.*"

About nine o'clock, then, the following night we gathered in Günther's barnlike loft whose windows—a good two stories tall —looked down upon the delicious, shabby glitter of Division Street. There was no scene I liked better than this network of filthy streets where streetcar tracks still lay embedded in the old asphalt; where the gutters swirled continually with refuse— rinds, loose dirt, bits of paper—spinning in tiny twisters or puffing in a wild, malicious arc right up into one's face; where the store windows looked as if the narrow, deep shops behind had vomited up into them every scrap of tawdry merchandise they carried; where the Hot Pastrami signs were even more menacing than the Hernia Braces and Post-Surgery Breasts, and the passers-by all appeared to be poking and prying without ever finding what it was they were looking for. There was always some female Presbyterian bum asking you to read the title on the movie marquee to her because she couldn't quite pick it out, which was why she went to the movies every afternoon and twice a day on Saturdays and Sundays.

Günther gave a short introduction while we all sipped politely at our beer cans. There were eight of us: Heidelotte Schlossheim, who was eyeing me with some surprise; the president of the Student Council; Morris, the other member of the Photography Department and his brand-new, sullen bride; a stunning freshman named Sue-Ellen Bogan, who smoked cigarillos with éclat; and a visiting photographer who lived alone somewhere in the Arizona desert and took pictures of what he called "found objects." This was the first time I was to hear the expression, though it quickly became chic. But his work was excellent; those soft yet lustrous clusters of seemingly unrelated objects, all refuse yet gathered poetically together as though time or chance or the photographer himself, maybe God, was seeking to establish a pattern in universal chaos.

He sat like a solemn old child with a thick book in his lap while Günther spoke of "poetic compression" and "intuitive structure." I wasn't really listening; I was just staring at Günther's big-boned face with its high Slavic cheekbones and massive forehead. If ever a brow "shone," it was that brow: it got oily when he was tense, which was most of the time. It was a dedicated forehead, probably a little insane. Just the same, those speech fragments of his bore the stamp of a certain superrational lingo. He was talking about "social experience" and "community art form," and where had I heard that before?

Then Günther sat down beside Heide right across from me, and the Visiting Photographer placed his book with the spine between his knees and suddenly opened it like a wizard cracking the Book of Doom.

"I'm going to read from *Don Quixote*," he said. "It's one of my five books I keep on the shelf at home, and it's always new; it's always different."

"But it's always the same, too?" queried Morris, Günther's colleague. "I mean, like you told us, it is The Book? Itself? The true, whoever that guy was, Cervantes?—It's a great book; I read it once myself, but it's so goddam long. This way it's shorter anyhow."

"I feel it's the true *Don Quixote*," said the Visiting Photographer. "I *believe* this is It, the real thing, the spirit of that book. And you can find it in a million combinations. That's why it's always new. Listen—"

"I haf read Hölderlin this way," murmured Günther to the ceiling. "In German, of course."

"Hermann Hesse?" asked Heide. I wondered if she were serious.

"No," said Günther. "But Heine. It doesn't seem to vork so vell mit Goethe."

"You can do it with poetry?" breathed Sue-Ellen Bogan through her cheroot fumes.

Günther allowed himself a smirk. "You can do it vis anysing." In horror I thought I saw him wink at her, but the Visiting Photographer was growing irritable. He snapped, "Listen!" and began to read:

"*When Don Quixote saw what it was, he was speechless and remained as if paralyzed from head to foot—*" Snap went the book a quarter of an inch farther along. "*On the other hand, I note that Amadis of Gaul, without losing his mind or committing any acts of madness—*" Snap! to page 310. "'*I did not think, beauteous Camila,' he answered her—*" Snap! "*—in accordance with my means—*" Snap! "*Still others compose their pieces without giving a thought to what they are doing—*"

"There! That's it!" yelled Morris, fortunately covering the burst of nervous giggles which erupted out of me at that moment. "He meant we should read it like this."

"That's only our interpretation," said the Visiting Photographer. "Just the same, I see what you mean—" He put his head to one side and scratched his eyebrow.

"You mean," pressed Heide, "a great work of art is truly universal? (I'm just trying to understand.)"

"This is the way—it—" began the Visiting Photographer, but he was more used to his finder than to words.

"This is the way it proves its universality," I piped up smartly.

14

Günther sent me an approving look. Those two semesters in a regular college hadn't been for nothing.

A frown creased Heide's milky skin. "I see. You mean that it speaks to us out of its own times."

"*He* speaks to us. The guy. The creator him-self!" bawled Morris, who wasn't drunk. Merely enthusiastic.

"Why did you just go forward?" asked Morris' wife suspiciously. "I noticed you didn't really skip around. Was there any reason for that? I mean, you didn't by any chance *plant* those passages ahead of time?"

"Honey!" protested Morris.

But the Visiting Photographer was not put out. "You can do it any way you like," he said earnestly. "I read from front to back this time because I guess I'm self-conscious about reading in public; a bunch of us desert rats get together there and read aloud sometimes but, like, we know each other—"

The president of the Student Council wanted to know what were the names of the other four books on his shelf.

"*The Bible, Ulysses,* Proust—*Swann's Way*—and *War and Peace,*" he answered promptly.

"You don't need *Ulysses,*" cried the irrepressible Morris; "it's written that way."

"You should add some Nietsche," advised Günther.

This raised a new problem. Emboldened by my recent success, I remarked that of these works only *Ulysses* had originally been written in English. Didn't translation interpose another intelligence between the intuitive consciousness of the creator and that of his reader? Sue-Ellen Bogan purred smokily that one could hardly call the King James version of *The Bible* a mere translation, it being virtually an original work in its own right. Günther wanted to know, did they use the King James version? Morris said, Suah, suah, did he think they were gonna read it in Jewish, for Chris' sake? Heide nervously interpolated something about Greek and Hebrew, Morris please; I noticed she was still watching us as if we might go off like defective firecrackers, so I took another swig from my beer can and suggested that while any interference by a translator was unfortunate, some of the original intuitive power would certainly get through, just as the greatness of a really great old film will manifest itself in a bad print or even in a version that has been pitifully mangled by some brutal censor. For which I received a rare smile from Günther. He had a three-cornered smirk that for an instant gave his broad face the self-sufficient humor of a cat's and made him even more delectable.

Sue-Ellen wished to hear further and lit a new cigarillo expectantly, so the Visiting Photographer asked her to read from any book which Günther chose from his shelves. Günther brought her the *Sonnets of Aretino* with a new smile this time, one that I might characterize as both curious and ironic. He then sat down next to me, so that I came to only intermittently and listened to Sue-Ellen's skip-reading with skip-hearing.

She laid aside her smoke and stretched out delicately on the rug. While she read she would from time to time toss her long red-brown hair to this side or that: she is the only person I can recall who had "chestnut tresses," and she knew it and was disgustingly narcissistic about weaving them in and out of your sight all the time. She had been divorced once—some said an annulment, which gave her history a special flavor of child rape and secret frustration. They said she was a countess, too, and if she hadn't been magnetic as well as absorbingly beautiful she would have been unbearable. But in class discussions she could invest words like *methodology* with magic, partly by means of her low, musical voice, partly by accompanying each clause with some slow, sinuous movement of her long, slender torso. I am *so* small, and I'll bet she practiced all that ahead of time in front of the mirror. She dressed with the simplicity one finds only in the smartest shops; she obviously had no more problem with alimony than she did with kids. I heard her read:

"Seven traitor years I now have thrown away—"

And later (I had been listening to Günther breathe):

"*Sleep, Ariosto!—bastard scoundrels—Togli il Lauro . . .*"
Then suddenly she seemed to get involved. She skipped from
"*There is, they say, a certain occult sin/That dwells in monas-
teries—*" to "*My fingers are but stragglers at the rear. . . .
They've wandered through a tufted valley near—*" Whereupon
she continued with the rest of that sonnet. Then she stopped.

Morris said, "Wow!" while his wife curled up in her chair and
sulked at her own fingers. Heide suddenly stood, and I saw that
her Nordic skin had blushed a soft rose madder. "I must go,
Günther. I prepare my mid-term now, and I do not want to stay
up all night."

She left with a worried, reproachful look in my direction. I
heard her sturdy tread descend step by step the echoing wooden
staircase to the street. She was too old to run down, skipping
three steps in a row like me. How I must have squatted there in
my jeans, fat as a toad with triumph! But this broke up the party.

Except for me. Günther was not drunk; he bent on me com-
manding looks to stay; I very much wanted to; so I did. Because
of the Aretino sonnets I wondered if he might not have what I
fancied the French meant by "special tastes" in those novels,
and which Aretino certainly had, and I began to feel apprehen-
sive: what to do in such an emergency?

Some time later while he was in the bathroom I picked up the
volume and read some of the other sonnets. Lying on my stomach with nothing on and kicking my heels in the air. When he
came out and found me he laughed with a paternal pleasure.
Since—to my considerable relief—he had not seemed to have
"special tastes," I asked him why he had given this particular
volume to Sue-Ellen for skip-reading.

He lay on his back beside me and lit a cigarette, looking as a
cat might if cats lit cigarettes. "Because I vanted to watch her
face, her attitudes. In embarrassment, maybe, or concurrence.
Yah? I wish to know who she is. Zey say she is a Lesbian but I
do not sink so. Just wery, wery narcissist, like all actors. She is

not an actor yet, but she is waiting for a director. I sink I will use her for my film. I wish to explore her. Ve will see if she agrees." And then he added with cool frankness: "I am somesing of a voyeur, yah? Every artist is a voyeur. Let me look at you. —Oh, Rachel, I sink zat you are wery beautiful."

I have been off-hand about this, but he was my professor, I was by no means so experienced as I pretended, and I wasn't at all sure how I would feel and above all how I would be able to behave in class the next day. Going home on the streetcar at two or three in the morning, while Heide no doubt labored to finish our mid-term, I shivered in the chill compounded of autumn, early morning, fatigue, and nerves. There was no moon to be seen above the dying neon lights. I was exhausted but strung up high with that painful excitement that comes from too many cigarettes and a new stimulus. Maybe I should swear off smoking, to please my mother. At each corner some bum, forsaken by his comrades, lingered like a sentinel. I had begun to invest the slightest fragment with romantic portent, as one does when at last one falls in love.

I was in love. I continued to feel kisses. I smelt Günther on my flesh and swam drunkenly in the memory of his heavy shoulders. When I got back to my basement at last Sam was up—at three-thirty in the morning, furiously entrenched in his flannel pajamas at one end of our rented sofa while Luisa pleaded with him.

"Sam, little boys should be in bed."

"No!"

"Why don't you want to go to bed, Sam?"

"I'm not tired. I wanta play. I'm hungry. You go out all the time."

"Sam, Rachel's tired. I'm too tired to talk to you. Now go to bed before I get mad and give you a swat."

"I don't care. I wanna play, I wanna play." His voice was rising.

"Sa-um!" My own voice was rising. We glared at each other,

he from under his lids with pure, unmanageable, male malevolence. There was something even then about the square set of his five-year-old jaw that frightened me off. It said, Don't tamper. Don't aggress me, you pushy female, you. Frankly, it always weakened my position.

"If you go to bed now, like a good boy, and go *right* to sleep like Rachel's pet, I'll sing you three songs."

He set his lips and thought, while he inspected me with the long, cool gaze of a contemporary. "O.K. But I want my dolly, too."

I brought his doll: a foolish, provocative virgin with copper curls.

"Sing 'The Big Rock-Candy Mountain,' 'I've Been Working on the Railroad,' and 'Jesus Loves Me.'"

"I don't know 'Jesus Love Me.' Where did you hear that, Sam?"

"In kindergarten."

It was a public school, and I realized it was my duty as a freedom-loving American-Jewish-Protestant-Atheist to write a letter of protest to the principal. One more thing to do!

"Then sing me about the little lord Jesus. Luisa always does."

"What about the little lord Jesus?"

"You know. *Away-ee inna maim-jer* . . . What's a maimjer?"

"Manger. Where animals eat. What other songs does Luisa sing you?"

"Just that one. Her prees said not to. What's a prees?"

"Quiet down. A priest is the boss of a church. A church is where people pray to God. I don't really know that song, Sam."

A lie. Shortly before meeting Nat, I had conducted a brief but intense affair with High-Church Episcopalianism, even going to service (secretly, of course) three or four times a week, and I had memorized not only whole sections of the *Book of Common Prayer* but also a dozen or so hymns and anything repetitive, friezelike, and solemn that smacked to me of this ritual. I was very much ashamed of my conversion now—as much for the transitory quality of my affections as for the original unfaithfulness to my parents' vitiated Judaism—and I tried to pretend to myself it hadn't really happened, but Sam wasn't going to let me off the hook so easily.

"Don't you know any songs about Jesus? I like Jesus. He's good to little children. He watches them when they're asleep. So does your guardian angel. Yes, he does. Luisa *says*. Why does Jesus eat in a maim-jer? Won't the prees let him eat in church?"

"Oh, Sam, shut up, for Christ's sake. I've been up all night, and I've got classes tomorrow. Rachel has to go to school and work *hard*." What with drink and cigarettes and Günther and guilt and above all a wallowing self-pity, the tears came into my eyes. "I'll tell you all about Jesus and church tomorrow if you'll be a good boy and settle down now, while I sing." I knew if my mother had been around there wouldn't have been any of that nonsense about Jesus, anyhow. She would have had an answer even if it were the wrong one: Jesus was a *guter mensch* till he got in with the *goyim*, Sammy.

When I finally bent to kiss him good night he said, "You smell funny, Rachel."

"Beer and cigarettes, doll."

"No," said Sam, "*that's* not beer and cigarettes. I know how those smell."

I got a Satisfactory in Heide's mid-term, but with a Warning. (The School didn't give conventional grades.) I went to see her about the Warning as soon as I could make an appointment; I was applying for a scholarship the following semester, and I didn't want to jeopardize my chances. But as luck would have it I went straight from a meeting with Günther. He had telephoned me that morning at eight-thirty. "I can see you in one hour. Yah?"

I was annoyed, but you have to allow for unfamiliarity with the idiom. "I work. I have a job, Günther."

"You must go?"

"N-no—"

"Then do not go," said Günther with unimpeachable logic, and hung up.

But I was paid by the hour, which Günther couldn't know, and I was still standing helplessly at the telephone when Sam came out of the kitchen, chewing on his toast and margarine. "Rachel, who was that?" (I might as well have been married to him for all the freedom he gave me.) "Was that Günther?" Whom in the meantime he had met.

"Yes."

"He talks funny. Why can't he talk English?"

"He didn't learn English when he was little like you. He learned it only a couple of years ago."

"I'm not so little," said Sam. "Guess what?"

"What?"

"I just heard Ludwig."

"Who the devil's Ludwig?"

"The rat. That's what I call him. Ludwig. Luisa does too. He's under the sink. Right now."

After dropping Sam off at kindergarten I spent the morning skip-reading among other things with Günther. Of course I thought the skip-reading was nonsense. I *think* I did. At first I couldn't see why the obviously intelligent if slightly nutty Günther indulged in this latter-day insanity. He claimed it helped "provoke a flow of images, yah?" That morning I had begun to feel sure enough of myself with him to rail at him for meddling so pointlessly with the structure of a work. He shrugged, told me not to be so worshipful, and advised me to read Apollinaire.

"Ze natural state of ze uniwerse is disjunctive. Even a stone is alvays in a state of separation of its elements—vun from ze ozzer. *Nicht?*"

"But that's so—unstable."

"Yah. Zat is life."

Then he rolled his head around on the big bed that also served him for a couch and gazed thoughtfully at the enlargements of stills he had nailed up on the walls. There were by this time three of Sue-Ellen Bogan, whom he had persuaded without the slightest difficulty to act as the heroine of his new film. *Heroine* is not quite the word; *central image*, perhaps; *springboard* —*muse* of a sort.

"I shall build ze film around her—her attitudes—movements. What zey suggest. She is fantastic. She changes like *eine wolke*. A cloud, yah? I do not know—I cannot sink of anysing else."

This was hardly flattering, though I could tell well enough what it was Günther liked so much about me. But I would rather have heard him say he couldn't "sink of anysing" but me, and for a moment the regret actually flapped across my brain: *if I were tall and glamorous and Irish now, instead of dark and stumpy and Jewish—*

Delicately I brought up the question of a script, for in the School we deplored "literary influence" and talked about truth to the material and filmic quality. We admired *Variety* and *The Last Laugh*; a showing of *Potemkin* in the School auditorium brought a standing ovation at the conclusion of the Odessa steps sequence; and *The Passion of Joan of Arc* and *Le Chien Andalou*, while admittedly great, were considered to teeter on the brink of decadence because they were made just prior to the advent of sound movies. Günther said yes there was a script by a young west coast poet, but it was "secretive." He spoke truer than he knew, for later he showed me the script and it was so secretive as not to reveal to this reader any coherent meaning at all. How he managed to do what he did with that script I'll never know. Maybe it was Lady Sue the Countess of Bogan, after all. I mean, what that damned narcissistic posturing of hers brought out in him: one takes off from the most unlikely spot. I remember he slapped the foot of the bed that morning and exclaimed:

"When she lies down here, right avay I get a wolume of ideas und nussing stands still und everysing is in flux—like life, like art."

But oh, I didn't like to think of her lying on the foot of that bed. It gnawed at my entrails. Yet I wasn't at all sure they were having an affair. Everyone *said* she was a hard nut to crack, too. Still, could Günther's exploration of her be logical or complete without her giving in? I didn't believe it, yet Günther himself had told me about a famous French painter who had gone to the brothel every week without anyone knowing whether he went to sketch or to have a woman. I told myself it didn't matter and went right on being jealous.

Before I left that day for my appointment with Heide he pulled down the shades upon Division Street and showed me some rushes. This is so much the exciting part: all of that jumble just waiting to be put together. I love it as I love the smell of paint, or the red girders swinging through the air when a building's going up, or those alphabet blocks with which children learn to spell. I can stand for an hour upside down reading newspapers on the floor, about nothing, about cosmic disaster or Miss Felicia Rinehart's nuptials. Just the letters moving together to make the words. Those were magnificent frames, too, some of them; I could see a little of what he was about, and it was all so exciting I wanted to make love again.

I am afraid I hung on him before leaving, so that he had to shake me off, though he tried to do it tenderly. But while I was still standing in the circle of his arms he got a guilty, restive look on his face and mumbled, "I do not onnerstand vat it is you vant—"

Heide's blonde hair was frazzled with fatigue by the time I saw her. She had three lectures in a row on Wednesdays and office hours the rest of the afternoon. She lumped her classes together so she could spend long stretches of time with her son, who was Kay's age. Her husband, the Italian professor of music, had died of a heart attack during what Heide called "a sordid affair" with a much younger girl.

Heide was in her late thirties: a handsome woman in spite of looking so tired most of the time. She possessed the strong, regular features of a classical bust; actually, because of her big, straight nose and full, pretty lips and her flaxen hair weirdly arranged in a high ruff of upended, corkscrew sausages, she did look very much like a marble head on a postcard someone recently sent me: "A noblewoman of the Flavian age," which for some self-immolating, grimly amusing reason I have kept around just because it reminds me of Heide.

I told her about the scholarship application; I asked what I had done, or not done, to deserve the Warning; I wailed that I couldn't afford that sort of thing.

She held a long yellow pencil suspended horizontally above her desk blotter between the thumb and index finger of each hand, and she bent her head and shook it back and forth over that pencil as if it were me on the rack, which it was.

"They say always the same thing: they can't *afford* it! I cannot afford to have poor students, and you really can't afford to debase your intelligence by turning in such a lazy work. The research paper you have just given to me—I read it last night. I am sorry to tell you, but I am always direct: it is bad. It is not good. You are not going to half the important sources; the sources you do use, you misquote or you—let's say it right out now—you plagiarize. Rachel, what is the matter wis you?"

By this time I was crying; she handed me a Kleenex out of her middle drawer just like a psychoanalyst, so I told her about Günther and staying up late at night and working five mornings a week and trying to raise Sam right and botching that, too, and altogether I said far too much while she sat there like a weary goddess.

"Listen," she said at last, "I am Swiss for many generations; maybe that is why I am so bourgeois, but this way of living looks ab-so-lute-ly crazy to me! I have a child of my own, and I feel you are not structuring the reality situation with regard to yourself or Sam. You feel inadequate as a mother because you are acting so (I am perfectly sure that you are not really inadequate); you feel inadequate as Günther's mistress—"

"No, not mistress," I said hastily. "We're not living together, and anyhow, I don't really feel inadequate that way—"

"What way?"

"Well, you know, the screwing part—"

Heide flushed. "Rachel, I have been married too and I am living a good ten or twelve years longer than you and I can tell you that screwing, as you say—well, believe me, there really is more than *that* to a good relationship between a man and a woman."

At this point I wanted to say, I don't know why exactly, *What* more? But all I did was whine, "I don't know what a good relationship is. I never really *had* one with a man."

"Of course not," said Heide swiftly. "If you have been having a good relationship with a man, you would know what to look for now."

It was on the tip of my tongue to say, Did *you*? But I didn't. I was too contrite. I knew she was right, but I had no idea what to do about it. You don't tell someone like Günther that you're not going to sleep with him anymore because you can't have a good relationship with him. Besides, he was the head of my department.

A fact which Heide, realist that she was in certain ways, recognized immediately. "You will be having to work this out," she admonished me, "but please: no more late drinking parties or skip-reading or that kind of crazy stuff."

"I thought you believed in skip-reading," I exclaimed.

"That night I am just keeping an open mind," she said with dignity. "I am informing myself and trying not to seem prejudiced. But it is ab-so-lute nonsense. It must stop!"

"How?" I asked weakly. But it seemed to me that Heide was superhuman, that she could do anything once she decided it was right. I felt I could, too, if I just followed in her footsteps, in her very large footsteps, rather like walking in the deep snow when you are a child, in the tracks of your parent.

As I left her office she added comfortingly, "Now do not worry like a goose about your scholarship. Maybe you will get one, after all."

Within two weeks Heide had persuaded my landlord to board up Ludwig's various means of ingress so that he no longer thumped and crashed among the pots and pans. Of course I was grateful, but in a way I missed being able to brag about him. She advised me which of my friends were good for me and which weren't: Jessica she approved of, although she thought Kay too precocious a companion for Sam, but "he will be having to work that out for himself, too, Rachel. You cannot make all his decisions for him, can you? After all, he is a big boy, now, isn't he, Rachel?"

"Do you really think she's precocious? I know she told him to pull her pants down and feel her there the other day, but isn't that normal at their age? I mean, the books say—"

"An only child," allowed Heide. "Father unavailable and frequent though temporary and brief separations from the mother. I admit there is apt to be more masturbation and sexual fantasying in all our children for these reasons. Nevertheless, I would like to experiment with Sam by having him to play with my Frederick two or three times a week. Both of them are needing male friends. Too many women—" She shook her head.

"Women are nice, too," I protested.

"Of course! What do you think? I am a woman myself, but a child is needing to form relationships in his sexual peer group, believe me."

I believed her and trotting up that long flight of wooden stairs to Günther's, related to him what was transpiring in my basement.

"Yah?" he said. "I sought, Sam seems like a wery nice child. What is wrong wis him?"

"Well, he *is* terribly excitable, Günther. I mean all this waking up at night when I'm out and telling me how to live my life and all. Heide says he's not really emotionally disturbed. He's just suffering from too much displacement of the father image. He thinks he's the male who runs things, and then he keeps discovering he isn't and that fills him with anxiety. She says he needs his problem to be settled one way or another. Either he needs a responsible father or he needs to know that he *is* the household male."

I waited, but all Günther said was, "Yah, it sounds like 'household god.' But I sink he is a nice child. I like zat he is excitable. I like zat you are excitable," he added grinning. "Zis good for us, *nein?*" Then he added musingly, "It is because you are a Jewess."

"*What?*"

"You haf ze Jewish racial warms' (warmth)."

"I thought it was Russian."

"No; zat is your courage. You haf a simple, peasant courage. But ze sexual power is racially Jewish. Ze better sexual union is ze Nordic wis ze Jewish. *Alvays!*"

I felt flattered but a little uneasy. And he had specified sexual union, only. Well, good God, I guess I didn't really want him to propose! In the School we believed in personal freedom, lonely as it often was. We knew the only true commitment could be to art and our ideas for a better world. But I lay there breathing him in and dying of some kind of longing while I considered my plight as a poor, defenseless divorcee, and I must have looked forlorn because Günther said, "Vat is wrong?" and thought I wanted to make love again.

I understood that Günther was clinging to me as a kind of buttress at this time in his war of the imagination over Sue-Ellen. I supposed he wanted to possess her, if he hadn't got there yet; or maybe he felt about her as men do about their wives when they're big with child: this is the Holy Grail and you dassn't touch it. Nevertheless, he was deeply "involved" with her. They would have long discussions and he would shoot a sequence; then he would summon me by telephone to make love. This made me decide theirs could only be a "spiritual" affair. Was he really making love to her when he was making love to me? I didn't know for sure. If he was, it was just as true that when he was shooting Sue-Ellen he was expressing postures, movements, rhythms, even whole moments that he had experienced on the big bed with me.

But sometimes he seemed to have us so separated out it was unnerving. He might remark that it was about time I went on a diet or when was I going to stop playing the role of the cute kid and assume my responsibilities; then I would go home and cry, trying to keep Sam from noticing that my eyes were puffed up. Which wasn't easy because he saw everything, that boy. I know it sounds silly that I could cry over such trifles, but I would think: if that is Günther's way of being intimate, how perverse! And how perverse of me to go back to him! And I would long for some kind fellow my own age, some man who was still partly youth without being unnatural, someone who was what I was and who would be willing to help lift the load a little. But I was so many things! Where was someone to satisfy them all?

Like the other girls in the School, though, I dated often because of the surplus of men, and usually I had a good time. I felt the distance I still had to travel in time was safely infinite. Heide didn't think so. About the time Sam started playing with Frederick she began casting a critical eye on my boyfriends, but for a while I wouldn't listen to her. I liked the bums, the ones who tied their trousers with rope because they'd mislaid their belts or couldn't afford one. Besides, I suspected her of unconscious double-dealing. How could she like that solid young man with all the boring virtues when everyone who had been around at the time swore what a no-good charmer the Italian professor of music had been?

But Heide was honestly trying to help me. She supervised Sam's and Frederick's hours together in a way that was new to me. She played with them if she felt they required it, and she saw that their toys were sturdy and constructive and that they got outdoors during at least a portion of their meetings. She believed in walking, and of course Sam didn't—he was American. But he consented to stump along beside Frederick with his mouth pulled to one side in a grimace until he had to rest or was able to turn them home again because his "leg ached." She decided Sam wasn't using his native capabilities any more than Sam's mama was, so she offered to teach him German, since she was already teaching Frederick. For a time Sam resisted, but eventually he too succumbed. None of us urgent, vigorous human beings was able to stand up to Heide for long. Even Günther began to listen to her, and this is finally what I want to tell about. Even he. Children of fire and/or energy that we were, we lacked direction and above all self-assurance. And she had both energy and direction, and she knew that God who knew how to ski and spoke four languages, albeit none of them well, but who lived in a German-speaking canton, she knew that He was on her side. Which is only a nasty way of saying that it probably never even occurred to Heide that there was more than one true way (hers) of looking at any problem.

At first I didn't realize how provocative Günther was to her, though the conversation always seemed to come around to him —but I thought that was my fault—while she listened avidly, leaning forward, her mouth open, a slight frown of concentration sullying that marble brow.

Often she would comment, though never at length as if sparing me. "Obviously you have an excellent *sexual* adjustment . . ." she would say, leaving it at that, or, "The fact that the sexual act is so central to your relationship reveals your basic insecurity with each other." Just try to stand up to remarks like that for a while! Once she said darkly, "Neither one of you fully trusts the other, which is always true in such sado-masochistic relationships." I jumped a foot. It's one thing to sense a fact yourself, but quite another to have indecent language used about it. I couldn't have been more shocked if I'd been my own mother.

But I trusted her. I believed she didn't mean to upset or hurt me, and I still believe it. Just as she was monumentally insensitive, so was she innocent of willful destructiveness. She couldn't help herself, that's all.

She wanted to know about Günther's film. I explained as well as I could: it did not have a plot in the usual sense (I'll say it didn't!) but rather attempted to explore the fantasies—or were they realities?—of a beautiful, narcissistic young woman. The central theme was her accidental meeting with a mysterious stranger whom she believes she has not only met before but actually made love with. Yet she can't recall precisely how or where. Günther had impressed a brawny Product Design major into service as the Stranger; to save money he was keeping the Product Designer's appearances at a minimum, but frankly, I don't think that was the only reason, though I dare say Günther couldn't have admitted that he was jealous. The emphasis was on a filmic development of the heroine's moods and dreams, rather than on her actions; or perhaps it is better to say that Günther wanted to show, within the span of forty minutes and by every photographic means at his command, how indistinguishable are actuality and fantasy.

I told Heide that if he had had enough money he would have expanded it into a feature-length film utilizing a series of baroque and rococo settings, for he was interested in art history and like many Germans devoted to the baroque. Indeed, his idea for the film grew partly out of this fascination with a style in which sculpture and painting and architecture were so subtly integrated both with one another and with the surrounding space. In which the decorative moldings, while lavish, didn't obscure the structure but simply helped to orchestrate it. In which carving and pulpit and pillar and ceiling flowed so organically into one another that even in its minor monuments one was seldom conscious of an actual transition.

Heide asked if she might see some rushes. I carried her request to Günther, who said solemnly, "Of course," and got upon his face the most curious expression of self-solicitude. He was as shy and tentative as a virgin when I brought her up one evening; he acted as innocent as the lamb delivering himself into the care of the Alpine shepherdess. Gone were satire and what he liked to call his "masculine hardness." I couldn't figure out what he expected to get from her unless it were more admiration; didn't he have enough of that from me and his other students?

The lousy, narcissist bastard!

Heide watched with great seriousness the sequence he showed us. It was one of Sue-Ellen's most Garboesque passages, and Günther explained that among other things he was engaged in his film in stylistic play. He and Sue-Ellen had spent hours in the middle of the floor surrounded by stills from Garbo movies while they attempted not only to reproduce and define but to poeticize further certain of Garbo's characteristic attitudes. It was as though they were saying: "Look again! This isn't as dated as you think. The past and the present, even in this most evanescent of art forms, are one. And her gesture, which has become a classic, meant this—and also this."

The artist often returned to earlier forms, said Günther. Sometimes in an attempt to find the strength of a simpler or harsher period. Sometimes for parody. Sometimes to embroider, to continue and elaborate upon the central image of another time, to extend the flight of fantasy in another direction.

"But we must be original," cautioned Heide. "We must be careful not to plagiarize, even spiritually," casting a stern glance at me.

"If ve are vat *you* call 'original' zen ve are not artists," said Günther shortly. Then he relented and explained to Heide that to use the work of another artist consciously as a springboard was not to plagiarize (she looked relieved and nodded vigorously); it was like fertilizing oneself with the sperm of another, at which point she looked distressed and muttered something about the ambivalence of the image revealing a confusion of attitude.

Günther heard *ambivalence* and shouted, "Yah, yah! Zis is exactly what I am shooting. Ze essence of ze baroque, even more of ze rococo!"

And they were off together, for this was one ardor Heide's European youth enabled her genuinely to share, though I never could understand how her spirit really took flight up there among those scrolls and clouds, those flying waves, the yearning angels, orgiastic statues of the saints flickering like white fire and the gold, the gold, the joyous, heavenly gold.

Imagine those sturdy Swiss ankles clomping relentlessly up Jacob's ladder!

As soon as I reasonably could, I bounced up and said briskly to Heide, "Well, let's go!"

The evening had been a fizzle as far as I was concerned; Heide looked unusually warm and desperate; Günther, embarrassed and a trifle sly. He kept glancing cautiously in my direction and I thought, Oh God, he's treating me like a wife! Who wants it? So I strode rudely downstairs without saying goodbye to him.

The next day I was sorry and telephoned to apologize, but unfortunately he hadn't even noticed.

A few days later Heide approached me with a problem about Sam. She was concerned, she said, about his overactive imagination. I was still annoyed with her and snapped, What did she expect of my son? She continued as if not hearing me, and probably she hadn't really listened, that since it was approaching Christmas and there were better programs for children on television right now Frederick had been allowed to watch more frequently, and the other day she had overheard him describing to Sam the birth of the Christ Child in the manger, which he had witnessed rather, I dare say, in the spirit of one of those superficially technical medical programs so popular nowadays. And Sam had said, you should see what Kay and I watch on *our* TV, "and then," said Heide, "he describes the most fantastic jumble of things you can imagine—but you don't have a TV set, I think, Rachel?"

"No."

"Does Jessica?"

"No."

"Is there anyplace else he would have been watching?—You don't go with him into bars—?"

"Oh, for Christ's sake!"

"He said he saw animals eating in a church—"

I burst into laughter while Heide stared and then said hesitantly, "You don't think there is something too—too—? I mean, he insisted and when Frederick was saying you're nuts, you're cuckoo—the way these men talk to each other!—you know you don't have a TV set, Sam was yelling I do too! it's a great big console set! Now what do you think of that?"

I described for her the Catholic Luisa singing a famous Protestant hymn in defiance of her priest, and I must say Heide had the grace to laugh, but then she came back to Sam's basic insecurities because we were poor and had lived so long with Ludwig and because of my own ambivalent cultural attitudes, all of which meant that he compensated through fantasy, and she said, Wasn't it interesting that Sam had immediately invoked Kay as his accomplice, and I asked with mock innocence, Why, since they still played together?

I was furious! I told myself she was a veritable Matterhorn of Monotony and Mediocrity and everything else that began with an M that brought out the worst in me. Especially Marriage and Monogamy! For what, I asked myself, could someone like Heidelotte Schlossheim want to do with a man like Günther unless it were to marry him? And once married to him, would she continue to put up with me? She would not!

But what about Günther? For two more weeks he continued to call me; meanwhile the students had started to gossip: he was seen having coffee every day with Heidelotte Schlossheim;

someone had seen him escorting her to a revival of A *Night at the Opera*; someone else had run across him in a crummy north side bar at 2 A.M. chug-a-lugging draught ale with Miss Schlossheim. I paled and wept into my pillow. I fumed and waited frantically for the telephone to ring, pacing our two rooms till Sam grew jumpy and complained he couldn't play with me around. I decided that none of my dates had been any fun at all compared with a mature man like Günther and that even if he would have been hell to live with at least I would never have been bored, and what a relief to have someone besides my parents helping to support Sam. Sam needed a father, didn't he? (Some father!) Well, I needed a husband! At which point I always ran up chin first against reality: some husband Günther would have made! A tantrum-throwing, hard-drinking, woman-chasing husband was better than none, wasn't he?

No, said a cool little voice inside; not for you; you're always in flux yourself. And remember, slyly added that same small, chilly, bitch-voice, you're only twenty-four; you needn't get married for another ten years; just think, you can have a ball for a decade!

This always cheered me up so much I'd go out to buy ice cream for Sam and me.

Just the same, my meetings with Günther became invested with a kind of new poetry; shall we call it skip-screwing? We *could* call it skip-loving. Realizing this delicious morsel was about to be withdrawn from my sweaty clutch, I gave this bad relationship, this aborting love affair, this most imperfect structure, this piece of life—I gave it everything I had. Jessica shook her head over me; she found it a foolish waste of energy, but Jessica wasn't only more rational than I; she derived less pleasure from poetic statements. I felt about these last two weeks with Günther as I felt about a series of photographs I was then making of water: water in pools, in fountains, in running streams, in the gutter. Rain falling, stagnant ponds, the thin glass sheet of a breaker after it has flung and spread itself on the sand and just before it rushes out. The magnified close-up of a drop of water under the microscope is one of the most beautiful things—most immensely full of experience—I have seen. And then it moves, coalesces with other drops, separates and joins others again.

Don't think I was only playing games with myself. Like many self-absorbed people Günther could be enormously responsive when he felt himself to be truly needed. This need to be needed was his Achilles' heel, and by this time I knew it and consciously used it to hold him. It was in his beautiful eyes. Where did they come from, King Günther, your beautiful sad Jewish eyes? Like the eyes of the wise child who has lost something—not knowing exactly what, but knows for sure it will never be given back, and continues to long for it just the same.

Often during those last meetings when we were making love, he seemed to be listening for a new sound. Very carefully, almost holding his breath. It was more moving for each of us because it was about to end, and each of us knew that. But gently we never said a word to each other of ending till the time came, so as not to hurt, not to break the spell. When suddenly that solicitous stillness was no longer necessary because something happened—a small series of things, really—which abruptly changed my whole feeling and catalyzed his.

Jessica and I decided to give a party in the week after New Year's in Sam's and my apartment. For, after all, it was Sam's too, which became part of the problem. Jessica couldn't have the party in her apartment because her building was slightly nicer, and the other tenants made sure it stayed that way by giving Christmas presents to the janitor and by calling the police. But Luisa's parents were no strangers to noise, and anyhow I put them under obligation by inviting them. Sam was to spend the night in their apartment in the care of Luisa, while they spent the night or a good part of it in my apartment drinking their very own contraband tequila.

It was a lovely plan! Jessica felt that a party of twenty people would just about take care of the invitations she owed, and I felt that it would pack the space to capacity, and right then I needed it packed to capacity because I was beginning to feel lonely. Maybe I wanted to *show* Günther and Heide. I invited them separately, anticipating that they would come together, which I was surprised to find they had the good manners not to do. Jessica and I laid in a supply of rye bread and sliced salami and bologna and cheese and pickles. Then I fed Sam an early supper while he glowered at me and threatened to lie awake in Luisa's room till the guests came.

"You'll be asleep; this is a grown-up party, darling. There won't be any children here."

"Kay'll be here."

"Oh no; Kay's going to stay home in bed like a good girl."

"Then Frederick will come."

"No, sweetheart. Frederick will be sleeping too. Just like you. All the little children will be asleep."

"Why?" said Sam. "Why will the children be asleep when the grown-ups are having a party?"

"You have your social life during the day, darling; the grown-ups have theirs at night." I really felt I was on top of this situation.

"It isn't fair," grumbled Sam. "Damn it!"

As a special treat I let him wear his new (gift from my mother, of course) red-and-white clown pajamas for Luisa's delectation and sent him into her warm, smelly apartment at eight o'clock. The guests were safely invited for nine, but I knew the first of them wouldn't arrive until nine-thirty. This gave me time for a leisurely bath in Ludwig's old garden, where he had romped and gamboled.

At nine Jessica arrived with the food, which she had stored in her refrigerator because I had to share mine with Luisa's family. We set it out on a small table in my parlor, and at nine-fifteen her date appeared with a large brown bag full of unsightly ice cubes, the size of ABC blocks, and two cartons of rented glasses. He was one of Jessica's hearty, decent guys, who liked to take care of women, as can be seen from the fact that he was footing the bill not only for the ice and the glasses but also for a fifth of bourbon, which we put out proudly together with half of another bottle of bourbon, a pint of gin, and a gallon of cheap red wine. This was going to be a fancy party and we all talked together in a sprightly fashion till the doorbell rang at nine-forty-five.

It was Heide, bearing a small can of smoked oysters and another of liver paté, and I was touched. She was wearing a pretty green velvet frock with the wide, low neck and long, full skirt then in fashion, and it suited her sturdy, maternal figure. Her hair had been freshly done in the strange style she affected, and I could see by the crisp care bestowed on all parts of her person that it was important to her to look well that night.

We had asked twenty people, but I think each of them must have brought at least one friend. By eleven-thirty, when Günther showed up, already slightly high from another party, both my tiny bedroom and our parlor were jammed; there were twelve people (I counted) on Sam's cot in the alcove, while the overflow had sluiced off into the kitchen and hall. I fixed Günther a drink with the pint he had brought and then attempted to mix drinks for others to cover my agitation. But Günther wouldn't let go and hung on me, nuzzling drunkenly (he wasn't that drunk) in my neck while he looked around one of my ears to see what effect this was having on poor Heide. Oh, he was all of four years old, all right! I pecked him angrily on the cheek and shook him off, but it is very hard to loose yourself from the particular odor of the skin or the particular feel of such-and-such a suit when you've grown used to it through frequent reacquaintance, and when you know it's about to depart for good. For bad. Forever. For the 326th time I asked myself as I chucked ice into glasses and swished the liquor around, what it was he saw in Heide. I knew he needed a mama, and she would make him a good one, but what about bed, transcendental experience, the skipping upon the mountains and through the rill?

Oh, blessed be that tufted valley near!—And a tear dropped into the horrid Southern Comfort which was like fire and brimstone, while the voice of wisdom soothingly reminded me that ours was not a good relationship because all we had done, all we had wanted to do, was to cling together and screw and as the healthy part of my person had begun to understand this was not mature. Something else beginning with M. . . .

At midnight Sue-Ellen Bogan swooped in on her broomstick, accompanied by the stalwart Product Design major with his splendidly hairy lower arms. Sue-Ellen was wearing something dark and soft and clinging; her hair hung over one eye and more or less down to her feet; she drew back this chestnut drape with the slender third finger of her left hand and lifting her stupendous eyes to Günther began to purr about *La Nausée*, which she implied she was reading in the original. (I dare say she had read a précis in the original.)

I saw Heide's face go wild for an instant. I hadn't known she was capable of such primitive emotions, and I felt a hush descend on my own snappish envy. Couldn't she see how Günther had sobered in two sentences? That it was his intellect and his esthetics that were involved (I hoped); or was this what she resented? I watched him bending over Sue-Ellen, discoursing quietly; I wasn't sure his film would be really good, but I knew that at this moment he was an earnest, good man. Which was no guarantee that within two seconds he might not have grown more horns than the African rhinoceros, a realization whose acceptance made me feel as omniscient as the Buddha.

I went solemnly into the hall, and threading my way among guests, climbed the stairs to the street. I was holding an almost empty glass in my hand; I had no coat; it was the first week of the new year. How the knives screamed against my flesh, but I hardly felt them. I wanted to see how our party was going, and the only way was to listen out in the street. Two of our guests joined me, and we held our breath at the comfortable roar of noise from below stairs, expecting to see a patrol car draw up any moment. We three embraced; we kissed lovingly; who they were I'd forgotten by dawn; I think I knew one of them, but it was so loving, truly loving, just the same. Then we strolled, arms about one another's waists, like the Three Graces down the street against that terrible wind, skidding on the strips of ice where feet hadn't worn it away. I stubbed the toes of my evening slippers against the hardened chunks of dirty, gritty, city snow. At the corner we stopped before a window in which hung black lace panties and G strings dripping with purple fringe and brassieres with red satin hands appliquéd on them. The window drew us like a magnet, but if it had been daylight any one of us would have been shy about going in, I more than the men because the salesgirls always contradict you about your size, upping the hips and downing the bosom no matter how you're built. Declaring with curled lip, "Oh, we don't have that in *your* size," implying that your size couldn't even be manufactured.

How does a man feel, I asked aloud, when he requests his jock strap by size? So because we were all drunk and thoroughly objective, we began to argue this point before the window which had been left dimly alight with the lights of two o'clock in the morning. It was so beautiful, my Babylon. From the mountains of Armenia to the deserts of Arabia, how I loved my city then!

Until some dumb Daniel, huddling in the shop doorway, a shivering prophet hunched against the cold, crept out onto the sidewalk and trotted about us like a caged hyena. "You're all damned," he said matter-of-factly. "You'll all go right t'Hell in the stench of fornification."

We pricked up our ears. We were so drunk, but each of us had clearly detected fornification. Like a grim new possibility.

"You got it wrong, man," said one of the Graces. "It's *fornication.*"

Daniel (unhearing): "Our lord Jesus Christ died for me on the cross which is the tree of life I'm saved praise Him amen."

"Barbaric practices," said the other Grace. "Self-sacrifice, which is simply an inversion of the straightforward pagan custom of human sacrifice. What the hell was He trying to prove, anyhow?"

Me: "I'm *cold*—!"

Our spirits sunk, we trudged back slipping and sliding through the desolate, through the dead and ruined hanging gardens where the twigs rattled in their casings of ice. I still clutched my glass, but the imprint of my hand on it was the only warm thing about me now. Downstairs the guests were drawn up in two parallel ranks on either side of the hallway, leaning forward and peering toward that point on the floor at which their own lines converged. Where lay on his back the great hulk of Günther, roaringly drunk like a sweet, dear, little teeny-weeny newborn, sloshing his drink about through the air, pouring it over his hair. Suddenly he perceived two exquisite nylon stems stepping along delicately past and over his head. Maybe he got a blurred glimpse up Sue-Ellen's skirt.

Günther went mad. He rolled over, grabbed those long, beautiful legs, and holding Sue-Ellen firmly in place began caressing them and moaning something incomprehensible in German or Bantu or pig Latin. His hands went up and up and they went down, when all at once Madame Moon lost her balance and tumbled all over his face and chest in a flurry of shrieks and flailing legs, and suddenly the door to Luisa's apartment flew open and Sam stood there in his red-and-white clown polka dots, wide awake, eyes glaring, the thunder in his curly hair.

"I can't sleep. For Chris' sake, shut up!" Then he saw me, where I leaned with sunken head against the shoulder of one of the Graces.

"Rachel," he yelled and started to bawl. I tried to hide; I huddled away from him, but he was howling like one of the damned. "Rachel, make them go home! Cuddle me! I'm tired! I wanna sleep! Luisa—Luisa—" Hiccuping his sobs.

I found his mother in me. I started to rush to him. I wanted to swoop him up in my arms, to dash away with him to some safe and secret place, but how stumbling my advance. I couldn't seem to pick him up; it was as though there were blankets tangled all around my arms. He clung to me, wailing into my skirt, pressing his face against me so that the tears soaked through the cloth and wet my stomach. Someone picked him up and carried him into the parlor, while I trailed haltingly after and he screamed his head off. The revelers fled from his alcove, scattering peanuts and salami in their wake. We put him down, and there was Heide beside me, helping to cover him.

"Stay with him," she whispered, pressing me down by the shoulders into a seat beside his cot. I think I remember her adding, "You will reduce his trauma," but I'm not sure. I held his hand while he sobbed more quietly now, and she shooed everyone out of the parlor, shut the door into the bedroom where two or three couples were making ritual love on my bed, and turned off the parlor light. Then she marched resolutely into the hall, crouched down beside Günther, who was sitting up and leaning against the wall, and murmured something into his ear. It must have been powerful, for he struggled tottering to his feet and made for the bathroom—just in time, too.

I don't remember the guests leaving. Perhaps I fell asleep, for I seemed to come to much later, and at first I couldn't imagine what had aroused me so sharply except my own discomfort. I was cramped into my chair without a pillow, still cradling Sam's small paw. The lights were out, except for the January moonlight, which crept in even here. The door to the hall was shut. The spicy odors of salami and cheese lingered powerfully in the air. I moved my foot and my shoe skidded: in the moonlight I could see rinds scattered over the floor among the puddles of spilled drinks.

Suddenly I heard a cat race down the hall and fling itself against our closed door. Cat? Whose cat? It took me about twenty foggy seconds of feeling something wrong but not yet groping toward it to realize with a certain shock that Luisa's family didn't own a cat. Nor did we. Someone must have left the door to the street open, so that a stray pet had slunk in, attracted by the redolence of spilled food.

There it came again: a wild dash and wham! against our door. I jerked to my feet in horror, suddenly wide awake. Those weren't soft cat pads thudding on the hall floor. These were tiny nails that clicked sharply as they raced. That compact body, crazed with hunger and more nerve than any cat ever had, hurling itself against the thin plywood panel again and again, intelligent, determined, and tireless—I had seen it once tearing down the hall like that and I knew it was our rat, come back for his dinner, for his inheritance. Somehow the cover must have come off his hole; perhaps one of our guests, souped up with the random energy of alcohol, had torn it off in a game.

Here he came once more, and I knew that if he were strong enough to keep it up for a few more minutes, if he threw himself often enough and hard enough and high enough up toward the door handle, eventually the loose metal tongue in the catch would give, would click wearily back, the door would burst open, and Ludwig would be on us, eager for the fulfillment of a pact. And not just upon me, but upon my Sam, who had done nothing to deserve this hellhole, this mess of squashed cheese and sticky salami shreds, these salted peanuts in his bed, this stink of stale liquor and cigarette smoke—nothing at all except to be born into it under the ugly conjunction of Nat's and my own unlucky, irresponsible planets.

Oh no, I didn't think this through, but I had a sudden frightful vision of Sam as a grown man, hating and withdrawn, ungiving, unloving, unloved, doomed and damned, or hanging by the neck like one of my classmates or blowing his brains out like another. What the goddam-it-to-hell was the matter with all of us anyhow, that we had brought ourselves to live in this way? And suddenly Sam sat up in bed, whimpering "Rachel, what's that? What's THAT, RACHEL?"

From somewhere I found the common sense to answer

lightly, "Oh, it's only that idiot Ludwig after some salami on the floor," and I stepped quickly to the door and pressed the metal button that locked it.

"Just in case," I said; "he's so eager . . ." And I giggled.

"He needs something to eat," sighed Sam sleepily, sliding down onto his pillow again; "or he'll be hungry, poor Ludwig," and away he went murmuring into dreamland.

I crept around the room, searching till I found my old-fashioned office typewriter, and this massive machine I dragged to the foot of the door, just to make sure it stayed shut; then I sat down beside Sam once more, where I remained till dawn, with a blanket about my legs and the silence around me to think and watch Sam in.

When he woke about six-thirty he smiled to find me sitting there. Then he stretched. Then he frowned.

"Y'know what Luisa said last night? She said everyone at the party would prow'bly go to Hell. That's what she said. Except her mother and father because the prees' would make 'em do peanuts. What's it mean 'do peanuts'?"

I straightened out Hell (no such thing) and peanuts (penance), and I remember that when, after breakfast, I led Sam in his snowpants up into the blue-and-white winter morning we found two lines of colored kids swinging hands in the street and chanting with the greatest assurance, "*London Bridge is all broke down, all broke down, all broke down . . .*"

By suppertime I had prevailed upon our landlord, an Indian from New Delhi, to cover up Ludwig's hole again. He muttered as he did so something about *students and Jews* until I said sharply something else about the Housing Authority which shut him up fast enough. Maybe he really had suffered from students and Jews, but I had suffered from a rent-gouging landlord, and I was going to set my own corner of the world up right.

I did not see Günther privately for the rest of the school year. He didn't phone, nor did I want him to. There were some painful withdrawal symptoms, but I treated myself sensibly, accepting dates with any halfway decent men who asked me, and being especially nice to the milder-mannered, less imaginative ones. I continued, of course, to see Günther several times a week in class, where we mutually maintained a gently impersonal attitude. If one of us caught the other watching him, he would look away and perhaps compress his lips. At the end of the semester he gave me a very strong recommendation for a scholarship, which I had honestly worked hard to deserve, and this, together with Heide's efforts in my behalf made such an excellent impression on the Scholarship Committee that I was awarded a full-tuition grant, almost unheard of in mid-year when funds were apt to be spoken for. My parents were impressed in spite of themselves and scraped up enough extra cash for me to quit my job. I tried to justify everyone's good faith, and in April a small group of my photographs, the Water Series, was shown in one corner of a dinky gallery not far from where I lived. But I was proud, and so was Sam; my fellow students looked at me with respect and sought out my company; and my instructors smiled approvingly when they passed me in the hall. Günther said nothing to me, of course, but I knew he had gone to see the exhibit because I found his Flying Dutchman scrawl in the guest book.

About this time I made a note of a disturbing dream which seemed to contradict my burgeoning self-possession. To make a point in class about the traveling shot Günther showed us a brief excerpt from his own film in which the mysterious Stranger rode a horse while the camera moved along beside him.

That night I dreamed I was sitting in an Elizabethan inn in an English town; through the casement windows I could see a procession passing by in the street. It was composed of a number of small but superb horses, each ridden by a handsome rider in uniform. Tied to each horse, in an extraordinarily strained position, was a prisoner who appeared to be awake, though in an exalted state or trance in which he not only felt no discomfort but actually seemed very happy. Some were fixed before the saddle upon the horse's neck; others were tied beneath the horse. Yet faces of riders and bound ones were equally serene. I turned to others in the room: what did this mean? Who were these riders? The answer came: the bound men were the vestrymen of the local cathedral—an imposing and exceptionally beautiful structure—who had been apprehended for accepting bribes for their bishop. They were being taken to judgment by the riders.

At which point I awoke, feeling a kind of shock and then a profound unease as I sensed from this dream, which I couldn't fully decipher, that I was still not free of Günther.

Meanwhile Sam continued his healthy walks and his healthy games with that solid townsman Frederick, who every week more and more resembled Heide and less and less what legend retained and projected of his romantic papa. At my urging Sam kept up his German lessons, too, though in a careless fashion.

I remember one afternoon when Heide was drilling the boys in Sam's alcove while I mounted photographs on our dining table. Heide pointed to her mouth and the boys exclaimed in unison *"der Mund,"* to her eyes—*"die Augen,"* to her nose— *"die Nase,"* to her elbow—*"der Ellbogen"* chanted Frederick, while the impious Sam cocked his head to one side and chirruped *"der* Sue-Ellen Bogan, ha ha ha!"

Heide proceeded to the knee without flicking an eyelash, but I gave him a look; he knew that Heide and Frederick had packed their tent and gone to live with Günther above the neon lights. And he also knew that Heide didn't approve of Madame Bogan's appearances in that studio. He knew because Frederick had told him so the day before; I knew because I had been eavesdropping from my bedroom, though I would have surmised it anyhow.

"The whole movie's been shot already," Frederick had explained importantly, "but she keeps on coming back to help with the editing. Know what a editing is, Sam?"

"I know all about the movies because Rachel takes me lotsa

times—RIGHT, RACHEL?—and anyhow, Günther took me once."

"Günther takes me alla time," retorted Frederick, and they regarded each other truculently across the shade of Günther. "Anyhow," Frederick continued, "Mama doesn't like it because Sue-Ellen comes up to *are* place—"

"It's not your place," corrected Sam; "it's Günther's. I was there once."

"I live there," countered Frederick," and it's *ares*, and Günther's gonna buy me a bicycle inna summertime—"

"Fucker!" jeered Sam: a *non sequitur* if ever I heard one.

So I called, "Now, boys! Let's be nice to each other."

"Fucker *back!*" hissed Frederick. I hadn't known he had it in him, and for one moment I wished his mother could have heard him; but then she would have said I taught him. "So my mama says Sue-Ellen is using Günther to feed her ego," continued Frederick, whose command of his mother's vocabulary was extraordinary and who, like his mother, would never let go of a subject until he had roped it, tied it, and fried it. "And Günther says my mama is subverting the fantasy, as well as the human body—"

"For Chris' sake," asked Sam reasonably, "whaddaya mean, Frederick?"

"I don't know," said Frederick, shrugging.

"Boys," I exclaimed, "how about if I read you a story?" For I had begun to hurt again somewhere and was eager to get them off this dangerous topic before I should hurt worse and Heide return from class, perhaps catching a phrase accidentally as she came downstairs. "Sam has a nice new copy of *Peter Pan*—"

"It's gonna be on television," said Frederick; "I'd rather watch it on television."

"Me too," said Sam.

"When is it going to be on television?" I asked.

"Saturday night. I'm gonna watch it."

"Please can I watch, too?" pleaded Sam. "Please?"

"You can watch it," I told him.

"With Kay?" Who in the meantime had acquired a second-hand TV set from one of Jessica's providing boyfriends.

"Kay's a stupid-head," said Frederick.

"She is not," flared Sam.

"She is too. She's a stupid-head dummy. I'm not gonna let her ride my bike when I get one."

"You better! She's my best friend," cried Sam.

"You're not even supposed to play with her," countered Frederick coolly.

"Sam may play with her whenever he likes," I declared to the unseen presence of Heide. "I like Kay, too; and I like you, Frederick. Very much. You're nice."

"O.K.," said Frederick negligently, "but I still don't like Kay. She makes up stories. That isn't right. We should always tell the truth," he added as firmly as his mother.

Poor lamb. I knew he couldn't help what he had become, even less than could Günther who was, after all, old enough to know he mustn't fling his sacred images in Heide's unswerving path. After this discussion and the incident of *der Ellbogen* I was able to relish for at least two days my own luck and good sense in having avoided such an alliance. Not that it had ever been offered to me! Still—

No, I didn't envy them their uneasy household. I understood how much a part of Günther must have needed Heide's stalwart *hausfrau* loyalties—just the plain mothering all men, but especially German ones, require so much—but I also understood that dangerous other part of him. You can do only two things with heroes: give them room to be heroic or execute them. It's no good just trying to trample on their spirits: you end by trampling on your own. Within Günther's guzzling waywardness there lurked—there even lived self-sufficiently for many hours each week—a hero, and there were disturbing suggestions in

Frederick's remarks that Heide was trying to trample him underfoot. Please keep off the heroes!

Yes, I told myself that it was none of my goddam business, but my soul (was it?) suddenly soared up out of that basement. I wanted to press down the rat-ridden walls with the palms of my hands. I did the next best thing. I went to the museum with Sam, and while he inspected Victorian toys I stared for a long time at an Indian relief in red sandstone from the second century A.D. A tree goddess, naked except for the thin robe flowing from her shoulders. She stood cross-legged upon a kneeling monkey, superbly thrusting forward her high, globed breasts. It was a difficult stance she held. For balance one hand rested upon her round hip, the other she raised ritualistically above her head and—serene in this extraordinary pose—she looked back at me, at all of us. This proud and naked, self-sufficient self, smiling in her trance. What was it that spoke to me? I went out humming.

As I stood with Sam, waiting for the bus on that broad, bright avenue in front of the museum, I remembered the anecdote Günther had told me about the painter he had known in Paris during the war. The man was virile and happily married to a pretty woman young enough to be his daughter, but every Tuesday afternoon he went to a brothel. No one being absolutely sure whether he went to buy him a girl or to draw. For the artist all the senses are alive in the eye.

That night I plucked down books of poems and read till two. I played records and read Yeats and Dylan Thomas. I read the agonized sixteenth-century quatrain—*Christ, if my love were in my arms, And I in my bed again!* I read Keats, with English Lit. I annotations ("picture of spiritual life as compensation for pangs of love")—

> *Who are these coming to the sacrifice?*
> *To what green altar, O mysterious priest,*
> *Lead'st thou that heifer lowing at the skies,*
> *And all her silken flanks with garlands dressed?*

I played more records, sipped vinegar-wine, and read Yuan
Chen speaking out of the eighth century:

And tonight my love who died long ago
Came into my dream as the pitcher sunk in the well.
That was why the tears suddenly streamed from my eyes,
Streamed from my eyes and fell on the collar of my dress.

The tears didn't stream from my eyes, but they plopped down,
one or two, on the page while I exulted in having lived and
loved and lost. The pain was gone in the poetry. —Steady,
warned the brand-new voice of sobriety.

I went to bed at last, sleeping poorly because I was all souped
up, but the next day I worked hard. It was Saturday, which for
us at the School was the same as any weekday except that I had
to find something for Sam to do. However, I'd begun to imitate
Jessica in these matters because I found her method worked. I
would park him in one of the workshops while I attended class:
there was always someone around to keep an eye on him, and he
liked tinkering with the scraps and shavings. He would make
miniature projects while he waited for me; then we'd have a
sandwich together in the lunchroom where the big boys gathered around to kid him. Sam loved Saturdays. He would hurry
to pull on his jeans in the morning; then he would swagger up
and down the hall with the exaggerated rock of little boys when
they imitate the walk of men. I began to see how he would be
when grown, and I loved it.

In the afternoon I sent him to play with Frederick while I
finished a layout for Visual Design. Where those kids were concerned Heide had the eye for detail of a Swiss watchmaker, and
anyhow she offered. What if it was up at Günther's? I felt sure
enough of myself and Sam not to let that bother me. (I admit
that when he came home I asked him if there were still any
photographs of Sue-Ellen up on the walls; he said no, and I was
glad and sorry to hear it.)

That evening he went to Jessica's to watch *Peter Pan* with Kay, while I continued working, only trotting over to pick him up at bedtime. By this time I was tired and depressed; after such a day of lonely labor I should have liked to turn to some loving man; you give so much to your work; but I had Sam and he was full of *Peter Pan* and aerial triumphs, and he made me feel that I wasn't such a failure of a woman as I might have been.

I slept as though I had taken a sleeping pill, for many hours, and when I awoke I felt relaxed, like a pond. It was Sunday morning in the late spring. The true heat hadn't yet come, but already the parks were as succulently green as if they'd been nursed in a hothouse. You wanted to sink your teeth in the trees and bushes. Sam and I went for a long walk in the warm breeze, and spent an hour in one of the school playgrounds we passed. Coming home for lunch we met Luisa returning from late Mass, carrying her prayerbook and looking as if she'd just eaten butter. Maybe she'd finally confessed our party. The knees of her nylons were filthy: she bitched proudly about that priest taking forever to get through Holy Communion.

After lunch Sam looked at the funnies while I worked some more, easily and swiftly, without fatigue, as sometimes happens when all true labor's been done before, maybe when you were quite unaware of it. At such times you feel it pours, that's all. When I finished in mid-afternoon I was as light as a bubble. Too light almost for plain living.

Heide dropped by to leave Frederick with us for a couple of hours while she went somewhere with Günther, and I felt so lovely I phoned Jessica and invited Kay over, too. At once they began to play *Peter Pan*; at least Sam and Kay did while Frederick glanced at the funnies and poked at one of Sam's puzzles and aimed a space gun and tried his hand at solitary Chinese checkers. I went into the kitchen to fix them hamburgers for supper, and by and by Frederick was in there also.

"They're playing *Peter Pan*," he said.

"I know."

"Sam is Peter Pan and Kay is Wendy, and Sam is teaching Wendy to fly."

"You could be John or Michael. You could be Captain Hook."

"They can't fly."

"John and Michael learned to fly. Not Captain Hook."

"I mean Sam and Kay can't fly."

"They're pretending."

"But it's not true."

He wandered to the kitchen door and stood as though with his feet many yards apart, watching the other two while they climbed up onto Sam's cot, yelling, "Watch me, Wendy," and, "Have some more fairy dust," and, "Hey, look out for the pirate ship," then leaping to the floor and running around to climb back up and jump down again.

"That's silly," said Frederick.

But they were hallooing too loudly to hear him.

I bent down to put the buns in the oven when I felt a tug at my elbow. It was Frederick. "Hey, they think they can fly. They can't fly!"

"No, not really."

"Can they?"

"No, Frederick. They're just pretending. Wouldn't you like to be in the game? Here, I'll—"

"Heck, no," said Frederick. "That's babyish. Pretending they can fly!"

"Don't you think they're having fun?"

"Jumping off the cot like that," Frederick went on scornfully, "—that's cuckoo. They can't fly."

"Do it like me, Wendy!" yelled Sam. "Just wiggle your elbows and fly—Wheee-e-e-e!" Crash! to the floor. Thumpaty-bump! came down Kay after him.

"Hey, isn't that nutty?"

"They're *pretending*, Frederick." In spite of myself I was beginning to lose patience. "Sometimes it's fun to pretend."

"Flapping your arms like that. They're not flying—"

I gave up. Poor doll. It occurred to me how he would bore his wife someday, and I began to be sorry for her instead. Maybe she would be enough like Heide not to mind.

"That's really cuckoo," said Frederick. "Fairy dust. —Whyn't we play Chinese checkers? I like to play checkers. Günther's gonna teach me to play chess. Chess is hard but I betcha I'll beat 'im. But chess takes a lotta time to learn. You have to be patient."

"I'm sure you will be, Frederick."

"Sam's not patient. Sam couldn't learn chess."

"No," I said with a rueful smile. "Sam's not patient." It's taking Sam's mama years to learn patience. But I didn't say that.

"Günther's patient."

"Is he?"

"He's patient with *me*—"

Ah, the wisdom of the very young. A month ago my eyes would have filled to hear the unconscious reproach I fancied in that remark, and to imagine what I might have been depriving Sam of. To wit: a father. But today I merely smiled. I was glad Günther could be patient with Frederick, but I didn't think he could have been patient with my son, who was in certain ways a little like him. Maybe Günther needed a son who showed promise of becoming a solid citizen. The young Telemachus. I just hoped Frederick would be patient with Günther.

"Supper's ready," I said to Frederick. "Call Peter Pan and Wendy."

"They're not Peter Pan and Wendy," said Frederick, gazing up flatly into my eyes. "They're just Sam and Kay."

That night Luisa sat with Sam while I went to a party. My mother had sent me a new suit: tight blue silk with gold buttons. Very classy, and for once it didn't have to be shortened. I wore orange pumps and felt as if I could bounce.

I don't recall much about the party. There were lots of people to talk to, corners to smile in, walls to lean against; potato chips in bowls on the floor and a couple of dips, into one of which someone accidentally stepped around midnight; a cluster of about ten people with preoccupied expressions sang folk songs; I joined or not as I felt like it, and at every turn it seemed there was someone nice who was eager to talk to me. I felt as though I were floating, and I loved everyone. When Heide and Günther came in quite late I loved them too, differently but equally. I smiled at them and went on mixing and laughing and chattering, and when I caught Günther's eyes I saw no reason not to laugh into them also. It's important to me to record that I felt right then toward Günther precisely as I felt toward every other physically attractive and pleasant-mannered male at that party; all were being nice to me; why should I differentiate?

Now occurs a blank. A cloud, or rather a kind of haze. There are a couple of hours I don't remember, but they couldn't have been unusual in any way, for when memory picks me up again I am half-lying on the floor (there were never enough chairs, of course) and still wearing my new blue silk suit but not my orange pumps, which are somewhere in a corner. I still feel perfectly happy—if anything, happier. I am mildly groggy, but my head doesn't swim; I haven't drunk or smoked too much; I *am* sleepy, though; it must be late; it has been a long day. Someone says something to me; I lie back—I have *been* lying down; I look up, see Günther's equally happy, smiling face; he looks ineffably kind; no, this isn't the effect of liquor but rather that of the consciousness of good works: I have done a fine job on my layout and been sweet and helpful to everyone I know, and the *pleasure*—how can you express that urge to give back the delicious happiness you feel? Except by letting Günther with his so-beautiful, immensely kind eyes kiss me as he seems to be leaning over to do. Perhaps I hear a few murmurs of surprise; I'm not sure because I really don't remember anything except that I came back to consciousness of my blissful state in the midst of kissing Günther what seemed to have been a long, long time.

Slowly I drifted down, away from his mouth, seeing as I did so, far up in the air, looming over us, high high above the back of Günther's golden head, the silent, awful face of Heide. She reached down, touched him on the shoulder; he struggled to his feet, and shambled after her.

That's absolutely all there was to it, but I felt sick to my stomach immediately. I admit it: the first thing that popped into my head was my scholarship. I would certainly lose it now!

This was Sunday night. On Wednesday I learned in School that Frederick's right arm was in a cast from his shoulder to his wrist and that he and Heide had left Günther. Jessica described a scene she and a few other students had witnessed that morning in the Faculty Common Room. They were passing by; the door was open; they heard a crash and the explosion of voices.

Heide and Günther were standing four or five feet apart; an Eames chair—wooden—was lying on its side just beyond her, as if it had been thrown at her.

Isolde was drawn up proudly, chin aloft. "I am ab-so-lute-ly through! If you had even tried," she said more quietly and bitterly, "I would try to stay with you. But you continue to see that girl—that two-penny actress. You are drunk at least one quarter of the time. You go suddenly off to a bar, a cabaret, a strip joint, god-knows-where all by yourself. You don't even do me the courtesy of asking me once to go with you!"

Günther's shoulders slumped; he turned aside as though to deflect these accusations upon someone better able to bear them, but there wasn't anyone else in the room, so he sank down on a couch and rested his head in his hands.

"You say you are just looking, just thinking, just taking pictures, just I-don't-know-what! Do you think I believe that? I've been married before: I *know*. You get mad, curse me; yes, you even hit me. Almost I had a black eye, but thank Gott that didn't happen. And then you find Rachel again and right in front of everyone, you shame me: you make love in public. Like two drunks. You're disgusting. Maybe you even waited till you knew I was watching! Why—*why?* I know she doesn't mean that much to you, so I don't understand! Please tell me—what is it? Why do you do this? I DON'T UNDERSTAND."

Heide took a vast breath, as if drawing all the air in the room into her lungs and then went on, an octave lower. One thing she had, Jessica said, was operatic control.

"And now the last straw. My Frederick, my own son, who has been through so much hell already in one sordid business after another with his father. He comes yesterday home from school; he finds you with Miss Bogan. You are *talking*—on the *bed*. Do you expect me to believe this? In front of my child—your *son*. Yes, Günther, *your son* . . ."

"But ve *are* talking," Günther finally cried. "Jus' zat. Only ve talk. Ve onner-stand sings in zat way. I *need* it. Nussing wrong!"

"Your son came home from school, Günther. You should have asked him: do you need to go to the bathroom, do you want a banana? Instead you *talk* to this conceited idiot—on the *bed*—"

That bed seems to have made her angrier than anything else.

"—and you don't watch him. He begins to play this crazy game he learned in that neurotic household. He *flies* off one of your stupid ladders—that horrible place is full of everything, I-don't-know-what, flapping his arms like a crow! Did he think he was an angel? He breaks his elbow: thank Gott he doesn't kill himself. I am lucky; I know I am lucky, but just the same, you are the one who is responsible. And you know it! That's why you throw chairs at me! Because it's your fault. Guilt, Günther! *You* are the reason I am leaving you!"

Exit Heide, past open mouths. Exeunt: Günther eventually stood up and staggered out to his favorite bar a block away and got drunk for four days.

This incident took place a week before exams. I still had a few more classes with Heide, and I made up my mind to go to them and do as well as I could on the final. I was scared: she looked so withdrawn and hard—almost terrifying—those last days, but I should have known I had nothing to fear. That's one trouble with these moral people; they can't allow themselves the sensual delights of revenge, which *does* make you suffer if you have a conscience. Actually, she had sense enough to realize her quarrel wasn't really with me but with Günther (of course, it was with herself, but I don't think she got that far), and she passed me with a high enough recommendation to ensure my scholarship.

I tried to thank her by sending Sam with Jessica and Kay to visit little Icarus. They took him presents and wrote their names on his cast; he seems to have been somewhat subdued but already pursuing a regimen which would not only quickly restore him to normal activity but give him an even more efficient right arm than he had before.

A week after finals my telephone rang: Günther in a low voice sounding contrite. My knees trembled and my feet dragged, but back I went! Right up that long, long, arrow-straight flight of wooden steps.

An old barrel painted white stood upended beside the bed. On it he had set out a pint bottle of whiskey and two little glasses.

"*Prosit.*"

I lifted my glass. "To you and your film, Günther. And to me, too. To both of us."

He shot me a glance out of the corners of his eyes. "I vant to run off for you zis sequence, yah?"

In my mind's eye I saw her writhing on her tree, suddenly in the greatest pain, and I felt a weary letting-go in myself. I watched his sequence—it was very good—and after that and a little more whiskey we made love, but it wasn't as it had been. Not for me, anyhow.

"Somesing is ze matter?" he asked gently.

"I don't know." I sighed. "I've changed, I guess. I'm sorry, Günther." I kissed him in the soft flesh of his neck and put my clothes back on.

No more strain. I thought: I'm through pulling Günther, or

anyone else, together. I'm through paying for who I am and who he is, and that's that.

Günther finished editing his movie by midsummer. In late August it was shown at the film festival in Venice, where it aroused enough critical ire to win an award and to ensure its continuing on to the festival in Edinburgh, by which time the critics had grown sufficiently used to it to praise it and give it first prize in its classification. It success encouraged him to seek backing for a full-length feature, which turned out to be too long and much too pretentious. Still, everyone talked back and forth about it, and he went on making movies.

He now lives comfortably in *all* of an elegant Roman palazzo, having married the much younger daughter of his backer. One of those rich, beautiful, good-natured, capable girls upon whom good old Gott has truly smiled and who should be reserved from birth to be wives for artists, since they are the only ones tough, cheerful, secure, and maternal enough to stand the strain. —He's made three superb feature-length films in the last ten years: a considerable achievement for any artist.

At thirty-six I actually earn my living making movies. I have a partner; we've formed our own company; we free-lance. Shorts: not always good but in each of them there's one good thing I wanted to do. Now for the future. I have an idea and a notion of where I can get the money. In a sense I feel myself to have reached the very stage at which Günther was when I met him. It's amazing what you can do if you simply have an idea. And then the energy!

But the other day Sam telephoned me from his prep school up the Hudson. "Guess what? I've been accepted by Princeton!"

We shouted together over the telephone.

"Something else. Dad's definitely agreed to pay the tuition."

"Sam, are you really seeing Nathan?"

"We're in touch all the time. I'm urging him to go into analysis. You too. It's about time you got married again, Rachel.

You'll never really make it, you know, till you establish a permanent relationship with the right kind of man."

"I love you, my son, but you sound like the textbook for Psych. I. Let me handle my own love life, please."

"Aw gee, Rachel, it's Time you settled down! You need the security. You're a woman, aren't you? This free-love stuff went out with the Charleston—"

"—which I notice has come back in."

"What?"

"Nothing, dear. You just reminded me of someone else."

I tried to go back to work, but all the rest of that evening and the hours since then my youth has hovered around me like a cloud, obscuring and altering every one of my movements. Sam is right, of course, but how can I turn into someone else just like that?

A puff of smoke! and there they stand—Heide and Frederick —looking at me with pained surprise.

I stamp my foot and snarl at them :"Why couldn't you learn? Did you think you had Forever?"

At first I really thought Heide was learning. She didn't return to the School in the fall but took a job teaching in our city college system and moved with Frederick to an attractive apartment. His arm healed sublimely well, and one day he said he wanted to see Sam. In a voice tense with I-am-being-adult-about-this Heide phoned to invite us over. I didn't want to go but we did, and after twenty uneasy minutes I brought myself to apologize for my behavior that night, because I could see that she thought it would be cathartic for me to apologize.

She said brusquely: "My Gott. Sink nussing of it. But sank you just the same."

I blew my nose. The air was cleared.

I noticed that she had far more of an accent than the year before, and it transpired that her current boyfriend was a refugee from Vienna. I wondered why he had increased her accent, whereas Günther hadn't, and finally decided he must be a more sympathetic individual.

He was. He had huge violet eyes of a kind almost indecent in a man and he was velvet-voiced and tender with Heide. But he couldn't live with her. He couldn't marry her. He had this and that responsibility. Asthma, I-don't-know-what. One day some little thing fresh out of high school got pregnant by him and married him, and Heide trudged on in flat-footed agony to the next. The Passion of Heidelotte Schlossheim. Dragging Frederick her cross with her. She is now in her mid-forties and living in Hollywood, where she supports an alcoholic movie actor fifteen years her senior. Frederick wants to be an astrophysicist when he grows up, but he grew up so long ago that he must be ready for retirement now.

Me? I want—

What do I want?

I know that if it hadn't been for Heide's humorless, dogged devotion to duty at a crucial point in our lives, Sam and I might have gone down the drain.

Yes, she got in our way with her tiresome emphasis on health. If we slept the sleep of the healthy we wouldn't have visions, now, would we? And where would the world be without our lovely flying machines?

Oh, the hell with the world. Where would *we* be? We're the world, part of it. *Our* hanging gardens. Our fleshpots, the temple prostitutes. Babylon, who stretched from the banks of the Euphrates even as far as Egypt, thou wert glorious above all! Israel, what bitchery hast thou wrought!

But oh god I'm sick of living alone! I want to end the strain.

ROBERT LOWELL / *The Vanity of Human Wishes* / A VERSION OF

JUVENAL'S TENTH SATIRE

FOR WILLIAM ARROWSMITH

In every land as far as man can go,
from Spain to the Aurora or the poles,
few know, and even fewer choose what's true.
What do we fear with reason, or desire?
Is a step made without regret? The gods
ruin whole households for a foolish prayer.
Devoured by peace, we seek devouring war,
the orator is drowned by his torrential speech,
the gladiator's butchered by his skill
at killing. Wealth is worse; how many pile
fortune on fortune—like the Atlantic whale,
they bulk above the lesser fish and die.
For this in the dark years and at the word
of Nero, Seneca's high gardens fell;
Longinus died; a cohort of praetorians
besieged the Lateran. No soldiers purge

a garret. If you take a walk at night,
fingering a little silver, be prepared
to think each shadow hides a knife or spear.
You'll fear each wavering of the moonlit reed,
while beggars whistle in the robber's face.

Almost the first and last prayer made in all
the temples is for wealth: "Let my estate
stand first in Rome!" But who drinks arsenic
from earthenware? Fear death each time you lift
the jeweled goblet, or when vintage wine
purples the golden bowl.

                        Which wise man shall
I praise, the one who laughed, or he who sighed
each time he left his house? But all men smile,
I marvel any finds sufficient tears.
Democritus could laugh till he was sick,
and yet in those days in his little town,
there were no fasces, litters, canopies,
no tribune bawling from the tribunal.
What if he'd seen the praetor riding high
in his triumphal car across the Circus,
dragging his palm-embroidered robes of Zeus,
a gold-stitched toga, and a cloud of dust?
What if he'd seen him in his cardboard crown,
a millstone that no mortal neck could bear—
there elbowed by a sweating German slave,
crowding the praetor to deflate his pride?
And now the eagle on its ivory staff,
the hornblowers, the herd of toadies mixed
with citizens of Rome, in snow-white robes,
his dearest friends, the lackeys in his pay.
Democritus could laugh at everything;
his neighbors' self-importance made him smile,

he even found amusement in their tears,
and by his tolerance and courage proved
that honesty and wisdom can survive
the smothering air of a provincial town.

When Superstition shouted for his head,
he laughed, and left her hanging in her noose.
Why do we hunger so for vicious things?
Our wishes melt the statues of the gods.
How many men are killed by Power, by Power
and Power's companion, Envy! Your long list
of honors breaks your neck. Statues follow
the rope and crash, the ax cuts down the two
wheeled chariot's wheels, and snaps the horses' legs.
Fierce hiss the fires, the bellows roar, the head,
all-popular and adored by all once, burns—
Sejanus crackles, and his crude bronze face,
the second in the world, melts down to jars,
frying pans, basins, platters, chamber pots.
Hang out your streamers, lead the great chalked bull
to the high altar at the Capitol—
men lead Sejanus on a hook, and all
rejoice. "What flannel lips he has! No man,
I tell you, ever loved this man!" "But tell us,
what was his crime, friend? Who were the informers?
What witness swore away his life?" "No witness!
A wordy long epistle came from Capri."
"Tiberius spoke, enough, I'll hear no more."
But what about the Roman mob? Their rule
is always follow fortune and despise
the fallen. One thing's certain, if the gods
had spared Sejanus, if some accident
had choked Tiberius in his green old age,
the mob would hail Sejanus Caesar now.

Now that we have no suffrage left to sell,
we have no troubles; we who once conferred
legions, fasces, empires, everything,
are simply subjects; restlessly we ask
for two things: bread and circuses. But listen—
"I hear that many more are going to die."
"No doubt about it, they have built the fire."
"My closest friend, Brutidius, looked white
just now at Mars's altar, Caesar stirs,
I fear fresh heads will fall for negligence."
"Quick, Caesar's enemy is still exposed;
let's run; there's time to trample on the corpse."
"I'll bring my slaves for witnesses; no paid
accuser shall drag me haltered into court."
Thus, thus, the secret murmurs of the crowd—
would you be cheered and flattered like Sejanus?
Be rich as Croesus, give the curule chair
to one, and armies to another? Would you be
Tiberius' favorite, while he sits and suns
himself at Capri, fed by eastern fags?
Surely you'd like to have his lances, cohorts,
blue-blooded knights and army corps of slaves.
Why not, friend? Even if you never wished
to murder, you would like to have the power.
But would you want to shine and rise this high,
if ruin's counterweight must crush your life?

Who would prefer Sejanus' rod of office
to being mayor of Gabii, or Fidenae,
some country praetor smashing crooked weights,
wearing a threadbare cloak at Ulubrae?
Let's say then that Sejanus was insane;
wanting authority and wealth, he added

story on story to his towering house—
so much the higher for the blinding crash!
What ruined Crassus, Pompey, he who scourged
Gaul and the torn Republic with his lash?
What brought them down? High places and the art
of climbing, wishes answered by the gods,
who send few kings to Pluto without wounds,
still fewer cherished by their people's love.

All through the summer holidays, each schoolboy
who worships wisdom with a penny fee,
and one poor slave to lug his sack of books,
prays for the eloquence and name and fame
of Cicero and fierce Demosthenes;
yet eloquence destroyed both orators,
this, this condemned and drowned them in its flood.
Eloquence lopped off Cicero's right hand,
and cut his throat, but no cheap shyster ever
dirties the Roman rostrum with his blood.
"My consulate, how fortunate the state":
if this were all you wrote, you might have scorned
the swords and vengeance of Antonius.
Yes, all in all, I like such pompous verse
more than your force, immortal fifth Philippic!
Dark too the murder of the patriot Greek,
who stunned the men of Athens with his words,
and held the hushed assembly in his palm.
Under unfriendly gods and an ill star,
your blacksmith father raised and sent you forth,
red-eyed and sooty from the glowering forge,
from anvil, pincers, hammer and the coals
to study rhetoric, Demosthenes!

War souvenirs and trophies nailed to trees,
a cheek-strap dangling from a clobbered helmet,

a breast plate, or a trireme's figurehead,
or captives weeping on the victor's arch:
these are considered more than human prizes.
For these Greek, Roman, and barbarian
commanders march; for these they pledge their lives
and freedom—such their thirst for fame, and such
their scorn of virtue, for who wants a life
of virtue without praise? Whole nations die
to serve the glory of the few; all lust
for honors and inscriptions on their tombs—
those tombs a twisting fig tree can uproot,
for tombs too have their downfall and their doom.

Throw Hannibal on the scales, how many pounds
does the great captain come to? This is he,
whom neither Africa, nor the Moorish sea,
the stagnant Nile, nor Ethiopia's
thick elephants could hold. He set his hand
firmly on Spain, then scaled the Pyrenees;
when snows, the Alps, and nature blocked his road,
he derricked rocks, and split the mountainsides
with vinegar. Now Italy is his;
the march goes on. "Think nothing done," he says,
"until my Punic soldiers hack through Rome,
and plant my standard over the subura's
whorehouses." What a face for painters! Look,
the one-eyed leader prods his elephant,
And what's the end? Oh glory! Like the others,
he is defeated, then the worried flight,
the great, world-famous client cools his heels
in royal anterooms, and waits on some
small despot, sleeping off a drunken meal.
What is the last day of this mighty spirit
whose valor turned the known world on its head?
Not swords, or pikes, or legions—no, not these,

his crown for Cannae and those seas of blood
is poison in a ring. March, madman, cross
the Alps, the Tiber—be a purple patch
for schoolboys, and a theme for declamation!

The world was much too small for Alexander,
butting against the limits of the globe,
as if his kingdom were a bull's corrale;
however, when he reached his final city,
a grave was all he wanted. Death alone
shows us what tedious things our bodies are.
Fleets climbed the slopes of Athos (such the lies
of Greek historians), yes, and paved the sea;
wheels rumbled down an avenue of decks,
breakfasting Persians drank whole rivers dry—
that's how the perjured laureats puffed their songs.
But tell us how the King of Kings returned
from Salamis? He whose amusement was
whipping the winds, and bragging how he'd drag
Neptune in chains, and branded to his throne—
a lovely master for the gods to serve!
Tell us of his return. A single ship,
scything for sea-room through the Persian dead.
That was his sentence for his dreams of glory.

"Give us long life, Oh God, and years to live,"
in sickness or in health, this is our prayer;
but age's ills are strong and never fail.
Look at the face, deformed and paralyzed,
unlike itself, it's skin a hide, gone cheeks,
a thousand wrinkles like a female ape.
Youth is unique: each boy is handsomer
than the next one, or cleverer, or stronger,
but old men look alike, their voices shake
worse than their fingers, every head is bare,

each snivels like a child; they mess their bread
with toothless gums—how heavily they weigh
upon their wives, their children, and themselves!
Even the fortune hunter turns them down,
now food and even wine are one more torture,
a long oblivion falls on intercourse,
the shy nerve, pumping, drops like a wet leaf,
though tickled through the night, it cannot rise.
What do you hope from your white pubic hairs?
Sex hounds you, when it's power is gone. Or take
the loss of other senses—the best voice
strikes on the drumming ear like lead, the harp
of the best harpist screams like a ground knife.
What good are bosoms jingling with gold coins,
the front row in the concert hall, when you
can hardly tell a trumpet from a drum?
The boy announcing visitors or meals
half kills himself with baying in your ear.

Now only fevers warm the thinning blood,
diseases of all kinds lock hands and dance,
even their names escape you—let me list
the many lechers Oppia will love,
slow-coming Maura drain a day, how many
schoolboys Hamillus will crouch on, the partners
Hirrus will swindle, the sick men Themiston will kill
this autumn—I could more easily count
the villas bought up by my barber. This
man has a sagging shoulder, that a hernia,
another has a softening hipbone—here is one
with cataracts, another's spoonfed: listen,
they yawn like baby starlings for their swill!
But the worst evil is the loss of mind;
then we forget the names of slaves, the friend
we dine with; our own children's faces blur

to one dim presence, then the will's rewritten:
All goes to Phiale, so lulling are
the acrobatics of that quick, moist tongue
that used to sell her body in the streets.

Let's say you keep your mind, you'll live to see
your wife and sons laid out, the ashes of
brothers and sisters shut in marble urns.
These the rewards of living long: repeated
groaning that fills an empty house, yourself
in black, a ghost, disaster on disaster!
Nestor, if one believes the lines from Homer,
lived longer than a crow—how fortunate,
outwitting death and tasting the new wine
a hundred autumns! Was this all? Fate's grace,
and his long thread of years were all too much
the day he saw his son, Antilochus,
flame on the pyre, asked, why he'd lived? "What crime
have I committed?" Peleus felt the same
for great Achilles, and Laertes for
Odysseus. What of Priam? Would that he had died
the day when Paris launched his robber galley;
he would have met his city's shades, with Troy
still standing, Hector and all his sons on hand
to bear him on their shoulders, with Cassandra,
unravished, free to wail the song of mourning.
What good was his long life? He saw his house
go down in ruin, Asia burning—fire
and sword! He put on armor, then the poor
old doddering soldier fell before his altar,
like some old ox discarded by the plow,
craning his neck out for his master's ax.
But Priam's death was human; Hecuba
survived him to die barking like a dog.

I pass by Mithridates; why repeat
Solon's old saws to Croesus—take our own men,
take Marius. Age brought him prison, exile,
weeks on his belly in Minturnae's marsh,
a last day begging bread in conquered Carthage.
Did Nature ever raise a Roman higher?
Did Rome? if he had died with all the pomp
of war, his army marshaled out to cheer him,
one foot descending on a Teuton's back?
How provident was the Campanian fever
for Pompey; but the tears of many cities,
all praying for his life, prevailed. He lived,
his stars preserved him, and a eunuch's scab
cut off his head. Was Lentulus so tortured?
Was Cethagus? Or even Catiline,
whose corpse lay undishonored on the field?

The nervous mother passing Venus' altar
prays for good-looking sons and lovelier daughters.
"Why not?" she says, "Latona bore Diana!"
Why not? And yet Lucretia's fate forbids
us to desire her face. Virginia
would swap her figure for Rutila's hump.
A handsome son has shy and trembling parents.
Breeding seldom saves beauty. But suppose
a simple household teaches him the fathers'
virtues and Sabine manners, say that nature
moreover makes him kind, intelligent,
with warm blood rising to his cheeks—
what better gifts can nature give the boy,
all-giving nature, gentler than his teachers?
And yet the boy will never be a man.
Some prodigal seducer will seduce

the parents—money never fails its giver.
No overweight tyrant castrates the deformed.
Trust Nero, Nero had an eye for beauty:
he never picked a spastic or a lout.

Move on though, revel in your breathless beauty.
Soon you will seek more calloused hands to guide you;
you'll fly to women. Chase the iron foot
of Mars, who stumbled in the cripple's net,
risk the worst punishments the laws allow
an injured husband—often the revenge
outdoes the law: The cuckold kills the lover,
chops off his balls, or jams a mullet up
his arse. Then choose a widow; soon you'll have
her money, all her unloved body has
to give. What can Catulla, what can Chloris
deny your greasy prick—sad sacks in heat,
their conscience washing out between their legs.
But beauty never hurts the good! Go ask
Bellerophon, go ask Hippolytus.
Chastity couldn't save their lives from Phaedra,
or Sthenoboea, faithful wives, then scorned
lovers screwed on to murder by their shame.

Now tell me what advice you have to give
the fellow Caesar's consort wants to marry—
the best man, the most beautiful, an old
patrician house could raise, soon caught, soon shoved
from life to death by Messalina's eye?
She's long been seated, and her bridal veil
rustles, the lovers' bed of purple roses
rustles quite openly inside the garden;
by ancient rule, a dowry of a million
brass sesterces must now be counted—clerks,
lawyers, the thin-lipped priest, attend on tiptoe.

"What, did you want a hole-in-corner marriage?
The lady has a right to her religion.
What will you do? Speak up! Say no, you'll die
before the lamps are lit. Say yes, you'll live
until the city hears, and someone squeals
in Claudius's ear—he'll be the last in Rome
to know of his disgrace. Meanwhile obey
your love, if one or two days' life mean much—
whatever's best or costs the smallest effort
to bring your fair white body to the sword."

There's nothing then to pray for? If you want
my counsel, let the gods and Zeus provide:
What's best, what serves us, only He can know.
We're dearer to the gods than to ourselves.
Hurried by impulse and diseased desire,
we ask for wives, and children by our wives—
what wives, what children, heaven only knows.
Still, if you ask for something, if you must
buy holy sausages and dedicate
the tripe of bulls at every altar, pray for
a healthy body and a healthy soul,
a soul that is not terrified by death,
that thinks long life the least of nature's gifts,
courage that takes whatever comes—this hero
like Hercules, all pain and labor, loathes
the lecherous gut of Sardanapolus.
Success is worshiped as a god; it's we
who set up shrines and temples in her name.
I give you simply what you have already.

HANS MAGNUS ENZENSBERGER
The Aporias of the Avant-Garde

translated from the German by John Simon

To count himself a member of the avant-garde has for several lifetimes now been the privilege of everyone who covers empty surfaces with paint or sets down letters or notes on paper. Not everyone has availed himself of this opportunity. Whoever undauntedly sticks the label *avant-gardist* on an author like Franz Kafka is already seduced into negligence by that mouthful of a word; it would have stuck in Kafka's craw. Neither Marcel Proust nor William Faulkner, neither Bertolt Brecht nor Samuel Beckett—none of them, as far as we know, has invoked that vocable, which nowadays, to be sure, every laundry list lays claim to, but on whose meaning, as if it were settled once and for all, hardly anyone of the crowd who mouth it stops to reflect.

This is true of the partisans of the avant-garde no less than of its enemies. They differ in their judgments but not in their

Published in German under the title *Die Aporien der Avantgarde,* © Suhrkamp Verlag Frankfurt am Main, 1962.

premises. Both sides help themselves uncritically to a critical concept that struck it rich in Paris over a hundred years ago, and has since passed for a touchstone of which it has not been expected or demanded that it undergo a test itself. The minds that it separates from one another have a way of lapsing into a permanent debate whose beginnings are lost in a mist and whose end can be held off ad libitum. Names and catch phrases change; the schema remains the same. Since Swift's *Full and True Account of the Battle Between the Ancient and the Modern Books* (1710), this controversy has lost some of its originality and brilliance; what remains is that modest abstraction for which, all along, it was willing to settle. The cast-iron stances of the contenders, no matter on which side, are of a depressing innocuousness; they remind one of the figures of middle-class family drama to whose antiquated conflict between father and son they would reduce the march of history. Commonplaces like the ones about the impetuous youngster whose ears will yet be pinned back, about the excesses of youth and the wisdom of maturity, and about the enlightened traditionalism of age that looks back with a wink on its own rebellious past are characteristic of the entire sphere of such discussions with their lack of a sense of history. Unhistoric, not merely hackneyed, is the blind trust they are happy to put in the threadbare concept of generations, quite as if it were the life of the arts, rather than that of trichinae, that is subject to the biological law of the life cycle; or as if the content of a hymn by Hölderlin or a play by Brecht could be read off the author's "vintage." Whoever distinguishes between old and new, or old and young, in such comfortable fashion, agrees by his very choice of criteria with the philistines. To him, the simplest dialectical propositions must remain inaccessible. That the durability of works is always determined only by their immanence in today's creation, which simultaneously devours and rejuvenates them, remains unfathomed, indeed unfathomable, even though this insight could be gleaned at the starting point of all European thought: "The old, veering round, becomes the new, and the latter, veering back, the former." The statement is to be found in Heraclitus.

The argument between the partisans of the old and those of the new is unendurable, not so much because it drags on endlessly, unresolved and irresoluble, but because its schema itself is worthless. The choice that it invites is not only banal, it is a priori factitious. The semblance of a timeless symmetry with which it surrounds itself is invalidated by history, which has as yet overtaken every unhistoric position and given it the lie. For no sooner do the arts enter the gravitational field of totalitarianism than the harmless tug of war about the avant-garde, or rather what passes for it, assumes murderous traits. The symmetry of the old and the new, that timeless mirror image, is brutally broken in two, and its real substratum becomes manifest. No avant-garde has thus far called for the police to rid it of its opponents. The "healthy forces of preservation" are the ones that have persistently sanctioned censorship, book burning, bans on publishing, indeed murder, as the extension of their criticism to other means; they purport to be liberal only until the political conditions permit, or rather command them to talk of a breach.

Only when it has come to that (but it has always come to that on the other side of the fence) do the categories of Progressive and Reactionary in the arts come into their own. To be sure, they are scarcely less questionable and shabby than those of the Old and the New; moreover, so many cardsharps have been operating with them that there are indelible black marks against them on the books. Nevertheless, they can lay claim to their historicity; they are not suited to the analysis of biological but of historic processes. So long as somewhere in the world esthetic questions are settled by force—so long, indeed, as such a procedure can be reckoned with as a real possibility—they are indispensable; in other words, everywhere and for an unforeseeable length of time. They require no metaphysical foundation. Their usefulness is simply and solely heuristic.[1] They require, there-

[1] Where obscurity is mistaken for profundity, the elegant modifier *shallow*

fore, constant reappraisal: like every indispensable device, they imperil the user as soon as he relies on them blindly. What most profoundly distinguishes the progressive attitude from every reactionary one is precisely its relation to doubt. The readiness to revise all solidified theses, to examine endlessly its own premises, is the essence of all progressive criticism. Reactionary criticism, on the countrary, considers itself, so to speak, naturally and everlastingly in the right. It is exempt from reflecting on its presuppositions. As complaisantly as it adapts its judgment, from case to case, to the nature of the powers that be, as unshakably has it established what is to be considered beautiful, sane, and constructive.

Only after coming into power does it reveal its brutal countenance. Until then it operates in the underbrush of conventicles, on the unsurveyable terrain of textbooks and "education in the arts"; in the open, it observes certain precautions. Under democratic conditions, reactionary criticism sees itself constrained to deny its own existence. It even admits tacitly to its canon of imperishables what it previously denigrated: the moment a modern work is no longer new, no longer risky, it is claimed as a "contemporary classic" by that very criticism which for decades tried in vain to strike it dead with its "rigid yardstick." Once annexed to the heritage that must be preserved, it is truly deprived of its life, that is, removed from criticism and exhibited as an embalmed holy relic. Whatever he cannot lick, the reactionary critic will join, and even thinks thereby to demonstrate

---

is usually held in readiness to describe enlightenment. In such a climate of thought, it may be needful to note that the concept of the progressive can do without any kind of roseate halo. It does not in the least presuppose optimism or the conviction that man strives—perhaps even under constraint!—for perfection. Whoever clings to such a belief is merely negating a negation whose real effects can scarcely be denied in the teeth of the universally planned return to the Stone Age. Even the person who would stick to his guns and refuse to join the general regression seems to be straining forward against an escaping multitude: he functions as a troublemaker. Thus the concept of progress is an obstacle to those who practice regression.

his magnanimity. As long as he cannot enforce his doctrine with police assistance, he finds himself willing even to sign a truce and passes himself off as a mediator and man of common sense who stands "above the press of things." Social pluralism becomes, for the time being, an esthetic pillow; in the dark of freedom, all cats are gray. Every work has its justification along with every other one, trash "complements" the masterpiece, and with the obligingness of all judgments the critical faculty itself is made to vanish by sleight of hand.

Neutrality of this ilk, which likes to answer to the name of "openmindedness," condemns itself. At the first sign that esthetic questions are about to be adjudicated by the power of the state, it flaps over into what it has secretly been all along. In the face of a rule of terror, whether exercised by a Goebbels or a Zhdanov, there can be no tolerance; which, for reactionary criticism, means that tolerance for the victims of that terror can be dispensed with. Such criticism rests untroubled on its certitudes as long as it sees to it that the yardsticks of its Beckmesserdom are always calibrated according to regulation.

The prescriptions are always the same: "The emphasis must be placed on questions pertaining to a world view." The work of art is nothing in itself; it functions merely as the "representative" of the currently demanded "*Weltanschauung*," which it must "adequately reproduce." "What matters is not the specific, artistically formal manner of writing, but this stand in terms of an ultimate world view." Opportunism that makes common cause with the stronger battalions is candidly appealed to: "Affiliation with the determinant tendencies of the times, which, sooner or later, will be the ruling ones," is what the writer must seek, placing himself "on the ground" designated to him by reactionary criticism. He is thus given the "concrete plumb line" by which he can hang himself, and "the justified, world-historic optimism, so extraordinarily fruitful for art" will then come about on its own. The arts are there to supply "lifelike realism" and "all-embracing positivism" and "to fashion man's future from within." "The will and aptitude for the creation of such a positive, new reality" facilitate "the choice between social health and sickness." "From that there follows"—verbatim!—"such a heightening of the watchtower" that it can no longer be doubted what sort of strait jacket the watchman intends for the arts: the avant-garde, or whatever that term means to him, is "decadent," "perverse," "cynical," "nihilistic," and "sickly." This vocabulary will be well remembered from the *Völkische Beobachter*, and that the state of mind it expresses has not died out in our land is demonstrated by every second glance into the newspapers that appear between Bonn and Passau. The quoted phrases did not, however, sprout from fascist dung; they were not culled from the *Neues Deutschland*, either. The man who wrote them passes for the most intelligent, distinguished, and courageous literary critic whom Communism can point to anywhere; they appear in Georg Lukács's book, *Against Misunderstood Realism*,[2] which could not come out on the other side of the Elbe, for to the cultural police that has the word there it seemed still not reactionary enough. To be sure, Lukács objects—in a language that, probably unjustly, claims to derive from Schiller and Goethe—to the "ever more pronounced stepping-into-the-foreground of the pathological" in literature, but he does not opt for the therapy that customarily follows on such pronouncements and consists of liquidating the patient. Lukács does not by any means reach for his gun when he hears the word *culture*. He has kept within him a remnant of that bad conscience that the most intelligent "representatives" of reactionary criticism bring to it as a dowry. It stirs in vain.

The "artistic striving" of such criticism does not manifest itself only in that its language, under whatever party insignia, gets tattered and rotten. This criticism can dispense even with the knowledge of what it defames. The goat turned gardener need not concern itself with botany. It separates herbs from weeds with its horns. What passes for healthy is most likely to be the

2 *Wider den missverstandenen Realismus* (Hamburg, 1958).

mediocre: Theodore Dreiser, Sinclair Lewis, Norman Mailer, Romain Rolland, and Roger Martin du Gard are for Lukács the quintessence of modern literature. To what unhappy misconception Thomas and Heinrich Mann may owe their appearance on this roster of those given a clean bill of health remains inscrutable. Sickly and decadent, however, in contradistinction to the apple-cheeked author of *The Black Swan*, are Dos Passos and Beckett, Montherlant and Kafka, Proust and Jens Rehn, Koeppen and Jünger, Gide and Faulkner—about as nonsensical a collocation of names as could possibly be conceived.[3] Tonsure is administered over the self-same unclean comb to heads that, for content and quality, for style and provenance, simply cannot be compared. Lukács calls this pocket comb "avant-gardism"— naturally without taking the trouble to analyze the term.[4] Nor have Hanns Johst and Will Vesper made the art of discrimination any harder for themselves.

Neither Western nor Eastern exponents of such criticism, on whatever bastions they may ply their trade, are competent to criticize the avant-garde. Their verdict about what is healthy or sick—about people or the degenerate—must be implemented by the police, or it remains without significance. With every one of their anathemas, they attest to their lack of authority.

In the face of their censure, whose aim is nothing other than censorship, solidarity goes without saying. Every work deserves to be defended against its suppressors: this tenet precedes all

[3] That all classical writers, without any exception, bask in "health" goes without saying. The "heritage" from Homer to Tolstoy must serve as a bludgeon with which modern literature is given whatfor. But not only the illustrious writers of the past are recruited as witnesses for the prosecution; Lukács does not hesitate to put into the witness box the American popular novelist Louis Bromfield, who is good enough for him to testify against Proust.

[4] This negligence takes its toll when Lukács writes, "Lenin repeatedly criticizes the sectarian point of view, as if something of which an avant-garde has become fully conscious could be taken over by the masses without further ado." So quickly, then, can a concept be cured of its ills, if party discipline demands it.

esthetic probing, and even the most superfluous "experiment" may have recourse to it. A criticism that considers itself progressive must weigh all the more carefully its rights and duties precisely as regards the most advanced production. If it is content with turning the verdicts of the culture wardens upside down, it thereby makes them seem only more justified. Whoever denies the bailiffs of unjust power their competence cannot simultaneously vindicate himself by reference to their pronouncements. Solidarity can be valid in the arts only as long as it is not used as a carte blanche. What proclaims itself the avant-garde is by no means immune to criticism. There is much evidence for this term's having become nowadays a talisman, which is to make its wearers proof to all objections and to intimidate perplexed reviewers. What is most revealing is that the term, to this day, has not been analyzed. Those who would be happiest to eradicate it have never specially concerned themselves with what the avant-garde actually is. That is understandable. What is queerer is that its followers have hardly contributed more to the definition of that which they admire than have its foes. The concept *avant-garde* is in need of elucidation.

Under that catchword, there appears in all [German] dictionaries, in token of its military derivation, a pair of crossed daggers. Older works of reference do not even recognize the figurative meaning:

> *Avant-garde, advance guard, vanguard,* that segment of a marching troop which the latter (the main body) sends some distance forward. . . . An a. subdivides itself frontward into ever smaller divisions, down to the spearhead marching at the very forefront. Each of these subdivisions serves the purpose of gaining for the larger one following it more security and time. . . . The flung-out smaller divisions must govern themselves as to their movement according to the larger ones that follow them.[5]

[5] Brockhaus, *Konversations-Lexikon,* Vol. II (14th ed.; Berlin: 1894).

The transfer of this strategic concept to the arts was first effected in the fifties of the past century in France. The metaphor has since dislodged and obscured the original sense of the term; it must, however, accept the fact of being taken at its word. The objection that it wasn't meant that way comes ready to hand but does not matter. The figure of speech preserves what its users have forgotten; analysis merely brings to light what presuppositions it drags along. The concept of the avant-garde is, like the word itself, a composite.

Its first component poses no conundrum. The field in which the avant-garde moves is history. The preposition *avant*, conceived spatially in the technical military sense, returns in the metaphor to its original temporal significance. The arts are regarded not as historically unvarying activities of mankind or as an arsenal of timelessly extant "cultural goods" but as a continually advancing process, as a work in progress, in which every single production participates.

Now, this process has a single direction. Only that makes it possible to differentiate advance guard, main body, and rear guard. Not all works are equally far "forward," and it is by no means a matter of indifference which position they occupy. The pathos of the concept feeds on the notion that the place at the spearhead of the process distinguishes a work, endows it with a rating denied other works. What is being compared is not really present performance with the past. To be sure, the avant-garde metaphor does not exclude the dull and inferior view that whatever came earlier can, for that very reason, be thrown on the junkheap. But it cannot be reduced to vulgar worship of the latest thing. Included in the concept is the nonsimultaneity of the simultaneous: precursors and stragglers are, at every moment of the process, simultaneously present. External and internal contemporaneity fall apart. The *en avant* of the avant-garde would, as it were, realize the future in the present, anticipate the course of history.

This conception has its justification in the fact that art without a moment of anticipation cannot even be thought of. It is contained in the very process of creation: the work is preceded by the design. The design, the project, does not disappear in its realization. Every work of art, and the masterwork in particular, has in it something unfinished; indeed, this necessary residue makes up its durability: only with it does the work fade away. An inkling of it is the prerequisite of all productivity. The idea of fame has its roots here. It has always been the notion of posthumous fame, not to be compared with mere celebrity during one's lifetime. Only subsequent generations can fulfill the work of art that juts, uncompleted, into the future; only they can, so to speak, redeem anticipation through fame. The works of antiquity were created in this confidence. It is stated explicitly in a widespread literary *topos*: the poet's apostrophe to posterity.

With the development of historical consciousness, this faith in posterity begins to decline. No doubt, there opens before any work, even the least significant, a prospect of a new immortality: everything can, indeed must, be preserved in mankind's memory —but as a "memorial," as a relic. That brings up the question of surpassability. Eternal survival in the museum is being bought with the prospect that henceforth the march of history can stride across everything without extinguishing it. Everyone becomes aware of the process of steady advance, and this awareness, in turn, becomes the motor that accelerates the process. The arts no longer find protection in their future: it confronts them as a threat and makes them dependent on itself. Faster and faster, history devours the works it brings to fruition.

From now on, the arts are cognizant of their own historicity as a stimulant and a threat, but this change of consciousness is not all there is to it. The triumph of capitalism turns it into a hard economic fact: it brings the work of art into the market place. It thus enters into a state of competition not only with other mechandise but also with every other work of art. The historic contest for future recognition becomes a competition for present purchase. The mechanics of the market imitates the devouring course of history on a smaller scale: it is geared to a rapid turnover in accord with the scant breath and crude eye of planned economy. The anticipatory moment of art is cut down to a mere speculation; its future is charted like that of stocks and shares. Historic movement is observed, comprehended, and discounted—a market trend upon whose correct prediction economic success depends. In the long run, however, the consciousness industry does not content itself with merely letting its augurs survey the market place of the arts. It attempts to insure itself against changes in the weather by creating it. If it does not exactly invent tomorrow's trend, it certainly proclaims and promotes it. The future of the work of art is sold before it has even occurred. What is steadily being offered for sale is, as in other industries, next year's model. But this future has not only always begun; it is also, when tossed out into the market, always already past. Tomorrow's esthetic product offered for sale today proves, the day after tomorrow, a white elephant and, no longer sellable, wanders into the archives in the hope of the possibility that, ten years later, it might still be palmed off as the object of a sentimental revival. Thus the work of art too is subject to the industrial procedure of built-in obsolescence: its afterlife is immediately cashed in on and cashiered; indeed, it is transmogrified, by way of publicity, into a forelife, which the work inherits before it even appears on the scene. Its afterlife is factory-made. The proposition concerning the nonsimultaneity of the simultaneous is realized by training the clientele to become a vanguard that insists on being served the newest thing and demands the future, so to speak, as consumer goods.

As suppliers of this industry, writers, painters, composers assume, economically speaking, the traits of employees. They must "keep in step with the times" and always nose out the competitors. To keep in the forefront, they must not "fail to connect." This explains why fifty-year-olds let themselves be described as young authors. Such an economic disposition obviously invites contemptible maneuvering. It gives rise to an avant-garde as bluff, as escape forward, with which the main body, for fear of being left behind, falls in. The type of the fellow traveler who would like to pass for a forerunner becomes prominent; in the rush for the future, every ram fancies himself the bellwether. The man on the treadmill remains unremittingly the object of a process that he thinks he is, as subject, in control of.

These economic consequences, however, merely reveal an aporia that is posited with the very concept of an avant-garde in the arts. What is questionable is not just its commercial exploitation but also the very *en avant* with which the avant-garde presents itself. For just who, other than the avant-garde itself, is to determine what at any given time is "to the fore" remains an open question. "The flung-out smaller divisions must govern themselves as to their movement," if we may trust the Brockhaus, "according to the larger ones that follow them"; but that means, as soon as a spatial movement is translated into a temporal one, governing themselves according to an unknown body.

Of course, it is possible to verify without much trouble that there exists at all times a rear guard. It coincides without fail with what reactionary criticism recommends as healthy. Its physiognomy can be described down to its minutest traits, for in them it is only the all-too-familiar that epigonously recurs. An extreme, very-well-explored example is the popular novel, which always reiterates older, exhausted patterns in distorted fashion. This does not actually devaluate what previous epochs have produced; devaluated, rather, are the suppliers of this rear guard, which likes to justify itself—but always unjustly—with reference to tradition. Its unassuming, petty bourgeois wing is shielded from every objection by its stupidity; in Communist countries, it enjoys state protection; in neocapitalist society, it supplies, hardly observed by the public eye, the proletariat, which, by universal demand, has been rechristened "lower middle class." How this majority of the population is being provided for, without dissension, with fifth-hand esthetics, can be studied in the catalogs of the large department stores and mail-order houses. At the forefront of this inarticulate rear guard is to be placed that "elevated" one, which consists of "culture-bearers." Its speciality is the aristocratic gesture with which it purports to "attend to spiritual interests" and defend "values"; its shadowboxing with modernity, of many decades' standing, needs no elucidation, and its points of view have become known *ad nauseam*.

On the contrary, it is not possible to discern a vantage point from which one could determine what is avant-garde and what isn't. All the efforts of the consciousness industry to detect a trend in the historic movement of the arts and elevate its prognostications to the level of a dictate misfire as speculation; at best, it is by chance that it scores any bull's-eyes. The actual process puts to shame not only the impotent attempts of the Communists to plan it but also the cleverer endeavors of capitalist economy, which would steer it by means of advertising and market manipulations. All that can be affirmed is what *was* "out front," not what *is* there. The work of Kleist or Kafka remained invisible to the contemporaries not because they refused to "go with the times" but because they went with the times. This does not mean that, in the arts, what contains futurity must go unrecognized. The notion of the unrecognized has, in any case, taken on an old-fashioned coloring, ever since the capacity of the reproducing apparatus has become greater than existing production, and since, consequently, anything at all that anyone writes or paints is indiscriminately and suspiciously publicized. That in this way every work—let alone one that anticipates the future—is done justice to cannot for a moment be entertained; there is no authority before which such justice can be pleaded or, like a tariff regulation, implemented. Where the word *avant-garde* is being construed in the present tense, a doctrinaire formulation results. Whoever becomes rigid about objective necessity, the demands of the medium, and compulsory evolution is already in the wrong. Every such doctrine relies on the method of extrapolation: it prolongs lines into the unknown. Such a procedure, however, will not get even at a political or economic process, because it is applicable only to linear, not to dialectical operations, to say nothing of an esthetic process, which can be apprehended through no prognosis, not even a statistical one, because its characteristics are determined by leaps. Their spontaneous appearance defies any theory of futurity.

The model according to which the concept of the avant-garde orients itself is invalid. The forward march of the arts through history is conceived of as a linear, perspicuous, and surveyable movement in which everyone can himself determine his place, at the forefront or with the hangers-on. What is overlooked is that this movement leads from the known into the unknown, that, therefore, only the stragglers can indicate where they are. Nobody knows what is up front, least of all he who has reached unknown territory. Against this uncertainty there is no insurance. Only someone willing to suffer the consequences of error can get involved with the future. The *avant* of the *avant-garde* contains its own contradiction: it can be marked out only a posteriori.

The metaphor of the avant-garde, however, contains not only temporal but also sociological determinants. These are expressed in the second component of the compound term.

> *Guards* is the name given, other than to the bodyguards of princes, in many armies, to elite troops distinguished by excellent supplies and especially brilliant uniforms (cf. *Elite*); they are usually garrisoned in capitals and royal residential towns. Guard means originally an enclosure. . . . Napoleon I must be considered the actual creator of the g. Tradition puts into the mouth of its commander, General Cambronne (to be sure, without foundation), the saying, "The guard dies, but does not surrender." [6]

Every guard is a collective; that is the first thing that can be deduced from this word. First the group, and only then the in-

[6] *Ibid.*, Vol. VII.

dividual, whose decisions are of no consequence in the undertakings of the guard, unless he be its leader. For every guard is most rigorously divided into the one who issues the commands and passwords of the day and the many who receive them, pass them on, and obey them. What all who belong to it have in common is discipline. Without dictates and regulations, it cannot manage. To abide by them is not always easy, but it does relieve the member of the guard of many worries. Along with his freedom, he delegates to the collective body doubt, fear, and insecurity; he feels surer about his cause, which is no longer his concern but that of the whole. The protection that the guard vouchsafes is enjoyed, in the first place, by the guard itself. The guardsman has not only duties but also rights—to be exact, prerogatives. To belong to the guard is a distinction. It is an exclusive league of men; the enclosure keeps others out. Every guard, and so too the avant-garde, considers itself an elite. It is proud not only of being ahead of and further on than the others but also of belonging to a distinguished minority.

The guard's vocation is combat. In it, and only in it, does the guard prove its worth. Not productivity but contest is its *raison d'être*: it is always militant. Here the transfer of the concept to the arts leads into some difficulties. What adversary does the vanguard expect to encounter on the terrain of history if it alone, and nobody else, operates in, or into, the future? What enemy army could it meet there? Enemies should not be lacking to anyone who forsakes the safe, allegedly so "healthy" grounds of mediocrity; but these adversaries seem to be located in back of him rather, and aside from the fact that he will not exactly see his purpose in life as fighting the likes of them, it just will not jibe with the idea of a guard that its only foe should be the tail of that very column it has the privilege of leading.

The concept of the avant-garde was applied not only to the arts but also, over half a century later, more felicitously and sensibly to politics. In 1919, Lenin defined the Communist Party as the avant-garde of the proletariat.[7] This formula became part of the international Communist vocabulary.[8] It pinpoints what the avant-garde metaphor sociologically comprehends, or rather, uncomprehendingly drags along. The role played by Sorel's concept of an elite in the development of Lenin's theories is well known. Very much in Sorel's sense, the party is to Lenin a strictly organized, elite combat unit, where absolute internal discipline is a matter of course; no less obviously, it is entitled to a privileged position vis-à-vis the outsiders, the mass of nonparty members. Here the avant-garde metaphor is thought out with sharp consistency down to its last detail. At one point only does the figurative meaning diverge from the literal one: the Communist avant-garde need not "govern itself as to its movement" according to the main body, but conversely, it is at the same time the general staff according to whose plans the entire operation must proceed: it enforces the dictatorship not only *of* but also *over* the proletariat. Understandably, if the revolution is to be "carried out" in the name of the majority but against its will, what is required is not so much muses as a bodyguard. In all other particulars, however, the Communist concept of an avant-garde is strictly relevant. What is forward is determined once and for all by an infallible doctrine, and the adversary at whom the vanguard action is directed is established and really there.

Beside Lenin's well-defined application of it to politics, the concept of the avant-garde in the arts appears to be somewhat confused. Least convincing is its collective trait. Clearly, a historic process has many collaborators, so many that it would be ridiculous to speculate about just how many individuals at a given period "constitute" a literature. But as much as every literature is a collective effort, as little is it to be visualized as a

[7] Vladimir I. Lenin, *Works*, Vol. XXXI (Berlin: 1958), p. 28 ff. Later incessantly reiterated.
[8] Hence the amusing terminological difficulty that presents itself to all Marxists when they write about esthetic matters: avant-garde in the arts is to be damned, but avant-garde in politics is to be respected as authoritative.

troop organized along disciplinary lines and sworn to a doctrine. Whoever participates in it enters forthwith into a direct relationship with the process as a whole; he can consign his freedom and risks to no group outside of himself.

The avant-garde metaphor does not contain the slightest reference to a revolutionary or even rebellious intent. Nothing is more glaring than this lack. For as yet every group that made use of the concept, in the arts as in politics, viewed itself as a *Fronde* and proclaimed the overthrow of existing conditions. No avant-garde program but protests the inertia of the merely extant and promises to burst esthetic and political bonds, throw off established rule, liberate suppressed energies. Freedom, gained through revolution, is heralded by all avant-garde movements. It is to this claim, which it does not even express, rather than to its future-orientedness, rather than to its promise to form an elite, that the concept of the avant-garde owes its emotional appeal. This aspect too was thought out more acutely and thoroughly by Lenin than by all the writers and painters. From what the Communist avant-garde would free its partisans and everybody else is made clear beyond any doubt; its revolutionary character will not be denied by its worst enemy. By contrast, it remains vague and blurry just what freedom the manifestoes of the artistic avant-garde have in mind and what the word *revolution*, frequently though it may appear in them, is supposed to mean there. All too often these manifestoes sound both grandiloquent and innocuous, as if they had no other concern than to scare off bourgeois conventions, which, in any case, are nothing more than ghosts. The cry for absolute freedom rings peculiar when the question involved is whether or not fish may be eaten with a knife. The propensity for revolutionary rhetoric may reveal the surface nakedness of the avant-garde; it does, however, cover up its central aporias. Only where it ruthlessly formulates its aims and methods, as with Lenin, do these aporias become apparent.

In much the same way as Communism in society, the avant-garde in the arts would enforce freedom in doctrinaire fashion. Just like the Party, its believes itself to have taken, as a revolutionary elite, which is to say as a collective, a lease on the future. It disposes with the indefinable in the most definite manner. It arbitrarily dictates what will be valid tomorrow and, simultaneously, submits, disciplined and will-less, to the commands of a future of its very own contriving. It proclaims as its goal total freedom, and surrenders, unresisting, to the historic process, which is to relieve it of that self-same freedom.

These aporias lie in the concept *avant-garde* itself. They can be verified empirically in all groups that have had recourse to it, but they have never become more flagrantly apparent than in that which today exhibits itself as the avant-garde: in tachism, in *art informel*, and in monochrome painting; in serial and electronic music; in the so-called concrete poetry; and in the literature of the beat generation.[9] These movements have in common the more or less obstreperously announced conviction of being "out front," their doctrinaire bias, and their collective state. That their names have become, in the course of a few years, catchwords, indeed trademarks, stems not merely from their accord with the consciousness industry; these terms were launched with premeditation as handy slogans. Avant-gardism, nowadays, is brought into currency overnight as coin of the realm. All the more reason for examining the coinage a little more closely.

It is to Jack Kerouac, the supreme commander of the Beatnik sect, canonized by his partisans as Holy Jack, that we owe the

---

[9] This assertion is not a wholesale dismissal of whatever counts itself a part of the above groups, or is so counted by others. In this essay, the assertion can be elaborated only with regard to certain literary phenomena; an analysis of corresponding conditions in painting and music would go beyond its competence. Theodor W. Adorno has written about *"Das Altern der neuen Musik"* ("The Aging of New Music"). The essay stands completely by itself in contemporary music criticism for its acuteness and uncompromisingness. It is reprinted in the volume *Dissonanzen. Musik in der verwalteten Welt* (*Dissonances: Music in the Bureaucratic World*) (Göttingen: 1956). For the questions of nonobjective art, cf. Hans Platschek's excellent *Versuche zur modernen Malerei: Bilder als Fragezeichen* (*Essays on Modern Painting: Pictures as Question Marks*) (Munich: 1962).

following maxim, which he posited in his "Credo" together with a "List of Indispensable Remedies" for the writer: "Be always idiotically absentminded!" The sentence can serve as motto for the current mass productions of tachism, *art informel*, action painting, concrete poetry *in toto*, as well as for a large part of the latest music. Kerouac goes on: "My style is based on spontaneous get-with-it, unrepressed word-slinging. . . . Push aside literary, grammatical and syntactic obstacles! Strike as deep as you can strike! Visionary spasms shoot through the breast. You are at all times a genius." [1] To be sure, the avant-garde bares its breast with so much naiveté (even if false) only between New York and San Francisco. The harmless simplicity with which it proclaims barbarism has a downright endearing effect in contrast to its European counterpart. Here indeterminacy expresses itself in a petrified academic jargon that dishes out delirium as a seminar report: the proffered texts form "a system of words, letters or signs, which obtain their meaning only through the personal contribution of the reader. . . . They are arbitrarily disposed in the sixteen directions of the quadratic square and alligned in a chance sequence . . . they possess stringency only through the swirls of motion and the assent they evoke in the reader . . . when carried through with rigorous consistency,

---

[1] *On the Road* (novel) (Hamburg: 1959) jacket copy; also *The New American Poetry, 1945–1960*, Donald M. Allen (ed.) (New York: 1960), p. 439. The sociological equivalent of esthetic indeterminacy is blind mobility, which is expressed already in the title of Kerouac's novel: change of locale as an end in itself; furthermore, a programmatically fostered promiscuity and obsession with the use of narcotics. The reverse side of this anarchic attitude is the strict code to which the members of the group must submit. There is stern differentiation between them and the outsiders, the so-called squares. To Norman Mailer, who has joined the movement, we owe a repertory of its principal rules in the form of a handy tabellation. These rules extend, among other things, to articles of clothing, philosophers, eating places, and jazz musicians that the hipster must favor. This code is meant in utter earnest; Mailer will not be found guilty of the slightest irony. With equal determination, the group celebrates the secret language of its own invention, whose expressions act as passwords. Here no swerving is allowed, and "uninhibited word-slinging" becomes fixed ritual.

they debouch into the black stone, the last standstill, as the no-further-enhanceable complex motion. Are, thereby, concrete form, uninterruptedly centered point, objective duration in nature (as materia-l *sine qua non*) guess whyyyy." [2]

That reads like a translation of Kerouac's catechism into occidental culture-gibberish. The translator keeps strictly to the prescriptions of the original, which, to be sure, is garnished with eruditional flotsam, but to whose intellectual exiguity he remains absolutely faithful. Mobility raised to an end in itself reappears as "swirls of the no-further-enhanceable complex motion," and the "visionary spasms" turn into "the black stone guess whyyyy." In both cases, mystification demands "carrying through with rigorous consistency," and the precept "Be always idiotically absentminded" lays claim to stringency. An idea of the possibilities this avant-garde opens up may be gleaned from the following "text":[3]

```
ra ra ra ra ra ar ra ra ra ra ar ar er ir
ra ra ra ra ar ar ar ka ra ra ar ar ar er
ra ra ra ar ar ar ak af ka ra ar ar ar ra
ra ra ar ar ar ak af ab af ka ar ar ra ra
ra ar ar ar ak af ab af ab af ak ra ra ra
```

This result does not stand in isolation. Works of the same stamp are available in such quantities that it would be unjust to name the begetter of the specimen, even though he has already made a bit of a name for himself with his output. Since, however, it is hardly distinguishable from the outpourings of his companions, what should, rather, be considered the author, insofar as this word still applies, is the collective: in such texts the guard brings itself into being. It can be seen at a glance (and this in itself justifies the reproduction of a specimen) that the sociological aporias of the avant-garde are repeated in them

---

[2] *material I* (Darmstadt: 1958). [The last two words in the German text are *ahne warumbe.*]
[3] *Ibid.*

quite accurately on the formal level; indeed, they perfectly consume themselves in their reproduction. Indeterminacy appears as doctrine, retrogression as progress. The milkman's bill masquerades as inspired madness, quietism as action, chance as prescription.

That these characteristics apply not only to "concrete poetry" and the literature of the Beat Generation but also to the self-declared avant-garde in all the arts is demonstrated by an international album in which it draws its self-portrait and which purports to be "at once account, documentation, analysis and program." It contains a list of basic concepts and categories, which are supposed to be equally valid for literature and painting, music and sculpture, film and architecture (insofar as such distinctions are still permissible). The following should be noted: improvisation, chance, moment of imprecision, interchangeability, indefiniteness, emptiness; reduction to pure motion, pure action, absolute motion, motoricity, *mouvement pur*. Arbitrary, blind movement is the guiding principle of the entire album, as emerges already from its title. That title applies insofar as the avant-garde was all along bent on movement, as conceived not only by the philosophy of history but also by sociology. Each one of its groups not only believed itself to be anticipating a phase of the historic process but also saw itself always as movement, motion. This movement, in both senses of the word, now proclaims itself an end in itself. The kinship with totalitarian movements lies close to hand, their center being precisely, as Hannah Arendt has shown, empty kinetic activity, which spews forth thoroughly arbitrary, indeed manifestly absurd, ideological demands and proceeds to implement them.[4] Kerouac's appeal, "Strike as deep as you can strike!" is so utterly innocuous only because it is directed at literature, and because literature, like all arts, cannot be terrorized by the likes of him. Transposed onto the plane of politics, it could serve as a device for any fascist

[4] Hannah Arendt, *Elemente und Ursprünge totaler Herrschaft* (Frankfurt: 1958); Amer. ed.: *Origins of Totalitarianism*.

organization. The impotent avant-garde must content itself with obliterating its own products. Quite consistently, the Japanese painter Murakami contrives a large painted paper screen destined for his work, which is "the piercing of several holes in one instant"; "the work of Murakami made a mighty noise as it was being pierced. Six holes were torn into the strong eightfold paper screen. This was done with such speed, in a single moment, that the cameramen [!] missed the exact instant. When the six holes were there, he had an attack of bloodlessness of the brain. 'I've been a new man ever since,' he later murmured." [5]

All avant-garde groups incline toward the adoption of obscure doctrines of salvation. They are, characteristically, defenseless toward Zen Buddhism, which, within a few years, spread rapidly among writers, painters, and musicians of this cast. In its imported form, Zen Buddhism serves to confer upon blind action an occult, quasi-religious consecration. Its teachings are transmitted in *exempla*, the so-called *mondo*. The punch line of the best-known *exemplum* consists in the master's answering the metaphysical questions of a disciple with a stick or a slap in the face. Murakami's "action" too may be considered a Zen precept. It points to the latent acts of violence in avant-garde "movements," which, to be sure, is directed first against the "materials" with which they are dealing: they blindly toss about paints, tones, or word fragments rather than hurling hand grenades or Molotov cocktails.

The reverse side of this susceptibility to extremely irrational, supposedly mystical teachings is the no less extreme faith in science that the avant-garde proudly sports. The indeterminacy of its "actions" always pretends to be exact. It tries to convey this impression by means of a terminology for which the most diverse disciplines have been ransacked: along with vacuum and absolute motion, there are catchwords like *constellation, mate-*

[5] *Movens. Dokumente und Analysen zur Dichtung, bildenden Kunst, Musik, Architektur* (*Movens: Documents and Analyses of Poetry, Plastic Arts, Music, Architecture*). Edited in collaboration with Walter Höllerer and Manfred de la Motte, by Franz Mon. (Wiesbaden, 1960).

rial structure, *correlogram, coordination, rotomodulation, mi-croarticulation, phase-shift, autodetermination, transformation,* and so on and so forth. A laboratory smock enfolds the breast shot through with visionary spasms; and what the avant-garde produces, whether it be poems, novels, pictures, movies, constructions, or pieces of music, is and remains "experimental."

Experiment as an esthetic concept has long since become part of the vocabulary of the consciousness industry. Put in circulation by the avant-garde, used as an adjuration, worn threadbare and unelucidated, it haunts artistic conferences and cultural panels and reproduces itself through reviews and essays. The obligatory modifier is *bold,* but the choice of the ennobling epithet *courageous* is also permitted. The most modest reflection reveals that it is a case of plain bluff.

Experimentum means "that which has been experienced." In modern languages, the Latin word designates a scientific procedure for the verification of theories or hypotheses through methodical observation of natural phenomena. The process to be explained must be isolable. An experiment is meaningful only when the variables that appear are known and can be controlled. There is the additional requisite that every experiment must be susceptible of rechecking and must at every repetition yield the same unequivocal result. That is to say, an experiment can succeed or miscarry only with regard to a previously exactly defined goal. It presupposes reflection and contains an experience. It can in no way be an end in itself: its intrinsic worth equals zero. Let us also set down that a genuine experiment has nothing to do with boldness. It is a very simple and indispensable procedure for the investigation of laws. It requires, above all, patience, acuteness, circumspection, and diligence.

Pictures, poems, performances do not satisfy these requirements. The experiment is a procedure for bringing about scientific insights, not for bringing about art. (Of course, every publication can be considered an economic or sociological experiment. Under this heading, success and failure can be established quite accurately, and most publishers, art dealers, and theatrical managers do not hesitate to derive from that the theory and practice of their enterprises. To be sure, viewed from this angle, Karl May is every bit as experimental as Jack Kerouac. The difference between the two experiments lies in the result, that is, in the number of copies sold. That such experiments possess esthetic relevance may be doubted.) Experiment as bluff does, indeed, flirt with the scientific method and its demands, but has not the least intention of getting seriously involved with it.[6] It is unconditional "pure action"; intentions of any kind are not to be attributed to it. Method, possibility of proof, stringency have no share in it. The farther removed from any sort of experience they are, the more the experiments of the avant-garde are "experimental."

That proves that this concept is nonsensical and unusable. What has yet to be explained is what makes it so popular. That is not hard to say. A biologist who undertakes an experiment on a guinea pig cannot be held accountable for its behavior. He is answerable only for the irreproachable observance of the conditions of the experiment. The result is out of his hands; the experimenter is literally obligated to interfere as little as possible in the process he is observing. The moral immunity he enjoys is precisely what appeals to the avant-garde. Though it is by no means ready to adhere to the methodical demands to which the scientist submits, it does wish to avoid all responsibility, both for its activities and their results. It hopes to achieve this by referring to the "experimental" character of its work. The borrowings from science serve as an excuse. With the designation *experiment*, the avant-garde excuses its results, takes back, as it were, its "actions," and unloads all responsibility on the receiver.

[6] Exception must be made of the experiments Max Bense and his students have conducted by means of electronic computers. These experiments do meet scientific requirements. Concepts derived from combination and probability theories are here put to meaningful use. Whether the "stochastic texts" thus derived can be valid esthetic objects is a question of definition. Cf. *Augenblick* (*Instant*), Vol. IV, No. 1, Siegen: 1959.

Every boldness suits the avant-garde perfectly as long as it itself remains safe. The concept of the experiment is to insure it against the risk of all esthetic production. It serves both as trademark and as camouflage.

What is under investigation here is the aporias of the avant-garde, its concept, its assumptions, and its postures. Such an analysis reveals the claims made in behalf of concrete poetry, the Beat Generation, tachism, and other present-day avant-garde groupings to be untenable, each and all. On the other hand, it can by no means serve the purpose of condemning the productions of such groups as a whole. It does not unmask doctrinaire fraud only to fall prey to it itself. Not a single work can be dismissed by pointing to the fact that its creator has joined up with such-and-such-a-guard, and even the silliest esthetic program does not *ipso facto* vitiate the potency of those who subscribe to it. The person who demolishes the terminological tricks and doctrinal screens with which today's avant-garde tries to shield itself does not thereby save himself the trouble of critically examining its products: he merely makes such a critical examination possible in the first place. Such examination must be insisted upon all the more determinedly the more advanced a work claims to be; and the more assiduously it appeals to a collective, the more it must affirm its individuality. Every popular movie deserves more leniency than an avant-garde that would simultaneously overpower critical judgment and timorously rid itself of the responsibility for its own works.

The aporias that have rent it and delivered it into the hands of charlatans have always been contained in the concept of the avant-garde. They were not first dragged in by hangers-on and stragglers. Already the first futurist manifesto of 1909, one of the earliest documents of an organized "movement," makes *"dynamisme perpétuel"* into an end in itself: "We live," Marinetti writes, "already in the absolute: we have created permanent and omnipresent speed. . . . We extol aggressive motion, feverish sleeplessness, marching on the double, the slap of the palm and the blow of the fist above all things. . . . There is no beauty but that of battle. . . . Only in war can the world recover its health." (The last sentence in the original: "*La guerre seule hygiène du monde.*")[7]

In futurism, the avant-garde organized itself for the first time as a doctrinaire clan, and already then it lauded blind action and open violence. That in 1924 the nucleus of the movement collectively rushed into the fascist camp is no accident. In formal matters, the futurists, exactly as did their descendants, advocated the removal of all "literary, grammatical and syntactic barriers." Even the disconnected slapping together of pseudomathematics and questionable mysticism can already be found among them. The painters of the movement declared in 1912 that they wished to "reinforce the emotions of the viewer according to a law of inner mathematics"; there is talk also of visions and ecstasies. In the futurist texts, mathematical formulas crop up alongside occult incantations and chaotic verbal debris.[8] The catechism of the avant-garde of 1961 contains hardly a sentence that was not formulated fifty years earlier by Marinetti and his circle. Be it mentioned in passing that the few significant authors of the movement left it shortly after the publication of the first manifestoes and that these manifestoes are the only texts futurism has left us.

An extensive survey of the countless avant-gardist collectives of the first half of the twentieth century is neither possible nor called for here. The role of most of them is overestimated. Literary and art historians, who, as is known, enumerate "currents" and isms with passionate fondness because that relieves them of concern with details, have accepted too many such group appellations as gospel truth instead of sticking to the particulars of the given works; indeed, they even, as it were, invented such movements a posteriori. Thus German expressionism became

[7] Reprinted in A. Zervos, *Un Demi-siècle d'art italien* (Paris: 1950).
[8] Cf. *Poeti futuristi*, Filippo Tommaso Marinetti (ed.) (Milan: 1912).

hypostatized into a collective manifestation which, in reality, never existed: many expressionists did not even live to hear the word *expressionism*, introduced into German literature in 1914 by Hermann Bahr. Heym and Trakl died before it came up; as late as 1955, Gottfried Benn declared that he did not know what it was supposed to mean;[9] Brecht and Kafka, Döblin and Jahnn never "joined a movement" that went by that name. Every historian can claim for himself the right to bundle manifestations and lump together the manifold under one heading, but only on the condition of not confusing his auxiliary constructs with reality, whose representation they are meant to subserve.

In contrast to expressionism, surrealism was, from the outset, a collective enterprise that had at its disposal a well-developed doctrine. All previous and subsequent groupings seem, compared to it, impoverished, dilettantish, and inarticulate. Surrealism is the paradigm, the perfect model of all avant-gardist movements: once and for all it thought through to the end all their possibilities and limitations and unfurled all the aporias inherent in such movements.

"Only the word freedom can still fill me with enthusiasm. I consider it suited to keep the old human fanaticism upright for an indefinite length of time yet to come." With these words, André Breton, in the year 1924, opens the first surrealist manifesto.[1] The new doctrine crystallizes, as always, around its yearning for absolute freedom. The word *fanaticism* is already an indication that this freedom can be acquired only at the price of absolute discipline: within a few years, the surrealist guard spins itself into a cocoon of regulations. The tighter the bond to the collective, the blinder the "pure action": "The simplest surrealist deed consists," we read in Breton, "in walking out into the street with guns in the hand and shooting as long as possible

[9] In his introduction to the anthology, *Lyrik des expressionistischen Jahrzehnts (Poetry of the Expressionist Decade)* (Wiesbaden: 1955).
[1] Quoted from *Surrealismus. Texte und Kritik*, Alain Bosquet (ed.) (Berlin: 1950).

blindly into the crowd." A few years were yet to pass before this maxim was realized in Germany. In any case, even before World War II broke out, Salvador Dali reached the conclusion that "Hitler is the greatest surrealist." [2]

Long before the coming to power of this surrealist, inner aporias had split open the movement. Its sociology would deserve more detailed consideration. At the end of the twenties, the intrigues, declarations of apostasy, bickerings, and "purges" within the group reached their high point. Its development into a narrow-minded sect strikes one as both ridiculous and tragic; yet it cannot be stemmed by the energy and self-sacrifice of the members because it follows of necessity from the presuppositions of the movement.[3] Its commander-in-chief assumes more and more the features of a revolutionary pope; he sees himself compelled solemnly to excommunicate his companions-in-arms one after another. Occasionally this turns into show trials that, in retrospect, seem like bloodless parodies of the later Stalinist purges. At the outbreak of World War II, the surrealist movement lost all its best brains without exception: Artaud, Desnos, Soupault, Duchamp, Aragon, Eluard, Char, Queneau, Leiris, and many others turned their backs on it. Since then, the group ekes out a shadowy existence.

The party-line surrealist literature is faded and forgotten; the above-named authors have, with the exception of Breton, produced nothing worth mentioning while submitting to the group's discipline. Surrealism was destined to have an enormous

---

[2] Hannah Arendt comments, in the work cited above, *Origins of Totalitarianism*, and particularly in the chapter on the mob and the elite, on the latent totalitarian strains in avant-garde movements. Of course, the occasional sympathies of the avant-garde with the totalitarian movements were thoroughly one-sided, as the example of the futurists in Italy and Russia demonstrates. Their love was not requited, and modern art, avant-gardist or not, was promptly lumped together and put on the index.

[3] The details of this development are related by Maurice Nadeau in his *Histoire du surréalisme* (Paris: 1948); Amer. ed.: *The History of Surrealism* (New York: 1965).

effect, but it became productive only in those who freed themselves from its doctrine.[4]

We see no reason for gloating over its foundering. Every backward glance at an avant-garde whose future is known has an easy time of it. Everyone today participates in the historical experiences of surrealism. No one has the right to encounter it with condescension to or pleasure in its plight; it is, however, our duty to draw the consequences from its downfall. The law of increasing reflection is inexorable. Whoever tries to dodge it ends up offered for sale at a discount by the consciousness industry. Every avant-garde of today spells repetition, deception, or self-deception. The movement as a doctrinairely conceived collective, as invented fifty or thirty years ago with the purpose of shattering the resistance of a compact society, did not survive the historic conditions that elicited it. Conspiring in the name of the arts is only possible where they are being suppressed. An avant-garde that suffers itself to be furthered by the state has forfeited its rights.

The historic avant-garde perished by its aporias. It was questionable, but it was not craven. Never did it try to play it safe with the excuse that what it was doing was nothing more than an "experiment"; it never cloaked itself in science in order to be absolved of its results. That distinguishes it from the company of limited responsibility that is its successor; therein lies its greatness. In 1942, when, except for him, nobody believed in surrealism any more, Breton raised his voice against "all those who do not know that there is no great departure in art that does not take place in mortal peril, that the road to be taken quite obviously is not protected by a breastwork, and that every artist must set out all alone on the quest for the Golden Fleece."

This is no plea for a "middle way" and no cue for an about-face. The path of the modern arts is not reversible. Let others harbor hopes for the end of modernity, for conversions and "re-

4 Cf. Maurice Blanchot's "Réflexions sur le surréalisme," in *La Part du feu* (Paris: 1949).

integrations." What is to be chalked up against today's avant-garde is not that it has gone too far but that it keeps the back doors open for itself, that it seeks support in doctrines and collectives, and that it does not become aware of its own aporias, long since disposed of by history. It deals in a future that does not belong to it. Its movement is regression. The avant-garde has become its opposite: anachronism. That inconspicuous, limitless risk, of which the artists' future lives—it cannot sustain it.

A. R. AMMONS / *Four Poems*

PEAK

Everything begins at the tip-end, the dying-out,
    of mind:
the dazed eyes set and light
dissolves actual trees:

    the world beyond: tongueless,
unexampled
burns dimension out of shape,
opacity out of stone:

come: though the world ends and cannot
end,
    the apple falls sharp
to the heart starved with time.

PASSAGE

How, through what tube, mechanism,
unreal pass, does
    the past get ahead of us
to become today?

the dead are total mysteries, now:
their radiances,
    unwaxed by flesh, are put out:
disintegrations

occur, the black kingdom separates, loses
way, waters rush,
    gravel pours—
faces loosen, turn, and move:

that fact, that edge to turn around!
senselessly, then,
    celebrant with obscure
causes, unimaginable means, trickles

of possibility, the cull beads
catch centers, round out,
    luminescence stirs,
circulates through dark's depths

and there—all lost still lost—
the wells primed, the springs free,
    tomorrow emerges and
falls back shaped into today: endlessly

SELF-PORTRAIT

In the desert a
clump of rocks
sang with hidden water:

    I broke in &
    water spilled:
    I planted trees:

wild animals from the hills
came at night
to tame water
and stood still:

    the air gathered
    hoverings of birds
    from
    drought's celestial trees:

grass sprouted
and spangled into seed:

    green reaches of
    streams went out:
    the rabbit that
    had visited,
    dwelled:

this was a dream.

ZONE

I spent the day
differentiating
and wound up
with nothing
whole to keep:

tree came apart from tree,
oak from maple, oak
from oak, leaf from leaf,
mesophyll cell
from cell
and toward dark
I got lost between
cytoplasm's grains
and vacuoles:

the next day began
otherwise: tree
became plant, plant
and animal became
life: life & rock,
matter: that
took up most of
the morning: after
noon, matter began
to pulse, shoot, to
vanish in and out of
energy and

energy's invisible
swirls confused, surpassed
me: from that edge
I turned back,
strict with limitation,
to my world's
bitter acorns
and sweet branch water.

MORDECAI RICHLER / *Going to New York* / AN EXCERPT FROM

St. Urbain's Horseman

Every autumn, since childhood, he had watched the birds, the cunning birds, fly south, and this October, at last, Jake was following after. Across the border, to the sources of light. For Jake's uncles, Miami, the Catskills; for his aunts, the wonder doctors of the Mayo Clinic. New York had always been their true capital. Ottawa? Quebec City? Those were bush league towns where you went to pay off a government *goy* for a contract or a building permit. They were the places the regulations came from, not life's joys. New York, New York. There wasn't a cigar store between Park Avenue and the Main that did not carry the essential New York dailies: the *News*, the *Mirror*, and the *Daily Racing Form*. Ed Sullivan, Bugs Baer, Dan Parker. *The Gumps* and *Smilin' Jack*. Dorothy Dix, Hedda Hopper. But, above all, Walter Winchell.

Jake had only been a boy during the war. He could remember signs in Tansky's Cigar & Soda that warned THE WALLS HAVE

EARS and THE ENEMY IS EVERYWHERE. He could recall his father and mother, his uncles and aunts, cracking peanuts on a Friday night and waiting for the United States, for those two unequaled champions of their people, Roosevelt and Walter Winchell, to come off it and get into the war. They admired the British, they were gutsy, but they had more confidence in the United States Marines. They could see the likes of John Wayne, Clark Gable, and Robert Taylor, making mincemeat of the *Panzers*, while Noel Coward, Lawrence Olivier, and others seen in a spate of British war films had looked all too humanly vulnerable. Like you, they could suffer heartburn and disrespectful children. But Winchell, marvelous Walter, was proof against plain people's ailments. Out there in Manhattan, night after night, he was always ready to award orchids for the best, regardless of race, color, or creed. Ever watchful under a broad-brimmed fedora, Walter Winchell cruised in a radio police car, uncovering America Firsters, giving FDR-baiters what for, and smashing Hatemongers in their lairs. Who was there, if not W.W., to tell Mr. and Mrs. America in the evening and all the ships at sea about the Jewish war effort? About Barney Ross. About Irving Berlin and Eddie Cantor, giving so unselfishly of their time and talent. Or that the bombardier in the first airplane to sink a Nip ship was a Jewish boy, good enough to die for his country, not good enough for some country clubs W.W. could name.

New York was quality, top quality. It sent Montreal Jenny Goldstein and Aaron Lebedoff. When *Abie's Irish Rose* finally reached His Majesty's Theatre and uncles and aunts went not once but twice, the signs outside, a veritable guarantee, read DIRECT FROM NEW YORK. From blessed New York, where Bernard Baruch sat on a park bench telling presidents and prime ministers when to buy cheap, when to sell dear. Where Mayor Laguardia could speak a Yiddish word. Where there were second cousins on Delancey Street or in Brownsville. Where the side-splitting Mickey Katz records were made. Where Pierre Van Paassen flew in from, to bring forth sobs and donations as he told an SRO audience about the Haganah fighting off Rommel in the desert, sometimes isolated for days and being driven to drinking their own urine.

"Piss. Is that what he means?"

"Sh."

"Imagine," Jake's mother said, "imagine. What a piece of work is man."

It was where Jake's father went for his best material. For only fifty cents a While-U-Wait headline that read RITA HAYWORTH LEAVES ALY KHAN FOR ISSY HERSH. It was where Jake's father bought his itching powder, metal ink spots, and the business cards which he had handed out at Rifka's wedding.

KELLY'S TOOL WORKS
Does Yours?

America, the *real* America, was a chance for Jake to see the cream of the Montreal Royals (Duke Snider, Carl Furillo, Jackie Robinson, and Roy Campanella) at Ebbet's Field. It was *Partisan Review, PM,* and the *New Republic.* It was the liberating knowledge which struck him one day at university that he was not necessarily a freak. There were others, many more, who read and thought and felt as he did, and these others were mostly in New York. On the streets of Manhattan, where you could see them, real as relations, and maybe even get to touch some, talk to others.

Would *Commentary* take him on as a copy boy, Jake thought, as he packed his suitcases and promised his mother, yes, yes, yes, to write once a week. Or still better, he thought, as he assured his father that this trip he really meant to find a job, he would be chatting up a cashmere-sweatered girl in the bar at the Algonquin when the eavesdropper with the shiny bald head seated next to him would say, "Wow! Have you ever opened these tired old eyes! I wonder if you'd be willing to put that down on paper for us?"

"Us?" Jake says coldly.

"Oh. Sorry. My name's Ed. Ed Wilson." (Or would he say "Bunny"?) "I'd like you to say hello to Dorothy here . . . A.J., he's the one with the Groucho moustache . . . E.B., and Harold."

Or he's having a quick drink at Jack Dempsey's bar and a young Italianate man gives him a shove ("Move over, Hymie"), and Jake flattens him with a punch (the feared Hammer of Hersh, the very whisper of which is enough to turn champions to jelly), upsetting the Italian's middle-aged companion no end. "Rocky, speak to me. MiGod, you've broken his jaw. He was going against Zale in the Garden tomorrow night. Now what am I supposed to do?"

Rising with the birds, the migrating birds, Jake caught the early morning train, thinking, I'm not going away yet again, this time I'm heading for my spiritual home.

Or he's eating *latkas* or cheese cake or whatever it is Lindy's is celebrated for, reading that W.W. has wished him orchids again, ditto Leonard Lyons, when Lauren Bacall drifts over to his table, crossing her legs showily, trying to lure him to her hotel room, anything to get Jacob Hersh to write a screenplay for her. "Sorry," Jake says, "but I couldn't do it to Bogie."

Or even though he went twelve innings in the series opener the day before yesterday, allowing only two cheap hits, Leo looks at the loaded bases and Mantle coming up and their one-run lead, and asks Jake to step in again. Jake says, "On one condition only."

"Name it."

"You've got to tell Branch I want him to give the Negroes a chance in the big leagues."

At ten o'clock, as they were approaching the border, the latest Italian star, even sexier than Lollobrigida, began to shed her clothes in Jake's penthouse. *They've got to stop doing this,* he thought. Zip, zip. Then the fall of silk. (No, a cascade.) Ping goes the garter belt. Snap goes the bra clip . . . And Jake, looking down at the sudden upspringing of a pup tent between his legs, hastily concealed his embarrassment with Norman Vincent Peale's column in *Look,* coughed, and lit a cigarette, as he was startled by a tapping on his shoulder.

"Yes?"

An American immigration officer with a sour purple-veined face, tufts of hair curling high on his cheeks, loomed over him, sucking at a stubborn sliver of meat caught between yellowing teeth, and asked to see his birth certificate. He looked at it, scribbled Jake's name down on a pad, and waddled away, rocking with the train. Fifteen minutes later, just as the Italian star was pleading for help with a troublesome zipper, Jake was tapped on the shoulder yet again with a chewed-out pencil.

"You get off at the next stop, fella."

"*What?*"

"The desirability of your presence in the United States is suspect. The next stop will be St. Albans, Vermont. You get off there so that immigration officers can make a more thorough appraisal of your desirability," the officer said, waddling off again.

Jake sat for a minute, petrified, remembering that he had signed the Stockholm Peace Appeal and a petition asking for clemency for Julius and Ethel Rosenberg. Oh you fool, hadn't you ever heard of Senator McCarthy? Jake, having decided to go forward in search of more information, jumped up, *Look* spilling to the train floor, the pup tent between his legs remembered and prominent. Shit! Mindful of the other passengers, Jake's hands moved swiftly, instinctively, to cover his groin and just as swiftly retreated again with nowhere to go, as he grasped that he was only drawing attention to himself. Jake sunk back into his seat, cheeks burning red. Closing his eyes, concentrating, he lifted *Look* on to his lap again and willed the star back into his penthouse.

"Get your filthy hands off that zipper," she said.

"You've been leading me on. Why did you come here, then?"

"I didn't realize you were so short and funny-faced—"

(The throbbing abated.)

"—so jewy—"

(Good good.)

"—and besides I'm a lesbian—"

(Ahhh . . .)

Relieved, clearing his throat and lighting up again, Jake went forward. He found the immigration officer sitting in an empty coach, working on his teeth with the edge of a bookmatch as he scanned a book full of names the size of a telephone directory.

"Why am I being taken off the train?"

"You will have to make a formal application for admission to the United States at St. Albans. If you pass the examination there, you will be allowed to go to New York tonight, if not, you will be sent back to Montreal."

"What's this all about?"

"We have reason to believe you might be an undesirable person."

"What reason?"

"I can't tell you."

"How long will the trial take?"

"It's not a trial."

"How long will *it* take?"

"As long as it does."

"The only reason why I ask, sir, is today is Friday. I'm, well, Jewish. . . . Our sabbath begins at sundown and then it would be against the articles of my faith to travel."

The immigration officer peered at him with fresh and, Jake dared to hope, benevolent interest. "We arrive in St. Albans in ten minutes," he said. "I'll meet you at the exitway to your coach."

A dense downpour started just as the train was rounding into St. Albans. The immigration officer pointed at a three-story stone building at the top of a hill and started to climb toward it, Jake following after, his two suitcases bouncing off each other and his legs. Jake finally made it to the stone building, panting and drenched. Over the main entrance he recognized the insignia of the U. S. Department of Justice, which he remembered from *T-Men*, with Denis O'Keefe. The immigration officer led Jake to the second floor landing and left him there, dripping on the brown lino, while he conferred with another man. Then they continued to the third floor, where all the corridors, as far as Jake could see, were choked with filing cabinets of the small card variety. The officer asked Jake to step inside a room for a minute, politely holding the door open for him. It looked like a hospital ward. Three neatly made-up double bunks and, off to the left, a bathroom. Jake heard the clang of metal behind him and whirled around to discover that he was imprisoned. The officer had gone.

Rain, rain, rain. A window, the bars greasy, looked out on a grubby inner courtyard. The room was clean but impersonally done in the inevitable civil service colors. Jake lay down, deflated, on a lower bunk. "H.W. was here" and other initials had been cut into the brown metal bed post, and on the underside of the upper bunk another prisoner had scratched out *"baise mon queue, oncle Sam."* Jake reached for his ball point pen and marked a "1" on the wall. For the first day. Then he pressed his ear against the wall, which was pleasurably cold, just in case an urgent message was being tapped out to him. Actually, there was a radio transmitter in the room next to his. It crackled and squawked as the radio operator rasped out messages to border agents. "Watch out for Anafukobropolis, Anafuka—A as in *Able*, N as in—Yeah, he's a Greek. He's expected to try to enter from Montreal in a party of forty roller skaters."

Outside Jake's room, male and female clerks passed again and again, without showing any interest in him. They seemed to be forever opening and kneeing shut metal files. Whirr, pause, clang. Whirr, pause, clang. "Hear this," the radio operator said, "We expect those baby smugglers to make another crossing in two days. So this time let's get with it, eh, fellas?"

At noon the janitor looked in, Jake gave him a dollar, and an hour later he came by with sandwiches and cigarettes. Next the immigration officer returned, unlocked the door, and pointed his chewed-out pencil at Jake's head. "*No chapeau*," he said.

"What?"

"I know about Jews. Read up on them in *Life* magazine once. You're eating without a hat. So you'd travel after sundown too, wouldn't you, fella?"

"You're very observant. I'm sure one day Herbert Hoover will take notice."

The immigration officer led Jake out of the building and across town to a rambling, boxcar brown, clapboard unit that had been set up alongside the tracks. Jake followed the officer's shiny trouser seat up the wooden stairs to an office with four desks and a potbellied stove, where the interrogator sat. Hair parted straight down the middle, dead eyes, almost no lips, and a soiled shirt collar curling at the edges. One heart-sinking glance and Jake knew he was done for. Full name, the round-shoulder interrogator asked? Age?

"Twenty-two."

Father's full name? Place of birth? Religion?

"Jewish."

Employer?

"None."

"Uh-huh. Have you ever belonged to any of the following organizations? I'll read them over slowly. The Young Communist League?"

"I should say not."

Friends of the Spanish Civil War Refugees? The League of Canadian Consumers? Students for Peace?

"I'd like to make a statement."

The interrogator leaned back in his swivel chair, and the immigration officer took off his hat and scratched his head.

"One of my enemies at university used to sign my name to left-wing petitions."

114

"What's his name?"

"It was a joke. He thought it was a funny thing to do."

"I see. The Progressive Book Club?"

"Um, one minute. Let me think . . . I'm not sure. The Progressive Book Club?"

"Yes or no."

"Yes."

Next the interrogator read out a seemingly endless list of newspapers and magazines and asked Jake if he had ever subscribed to any of them. All of Jake's replies were typed out in quintuplet and then he was asked to check his answers for inaccuracies and misspellings before he dated and signed each copy.

"It says here . . . religion 'Hebrew.' I clearly remember saying 'Jewish.'"

"So what?"

"I'm sure you wouldn't want me to sign a false statement."

"He's a fresh guy," the immigration officer said. "I warned you."

"There are higher courts than this," Jake said.

"Christ almighty, but you believe in making things tough for yourself. O.K. I'll write in Jewish over Hebrew. You initial each copy where I've done that."

"Roger," Jake said, winking.

"Now listen here, kid. You cut that out."

Jake signed the copies. Then he was fingerprinted and brought back to the office. "This hearing is now closed," the interrogator said, "because you are considered undesirable to the United States. Your application for admission has been refused, and you are temporarily excluded under the provisions of Section 235(c) of the Immigration and Nationality Act of 1952. You will be returned to Montreal this evening at seven-thirty."

"You still haven't given me a reason."

"We are not authorized to divulge information on which we pass exclusion."

This time Jake was driven back to his place of detention,

where he immediately vomited in the toilet. Oh, God, he thought, this can't be happening to me. I'm imagining it. He fell asleep and wakened two hours later to find that there was a thin middle-aged man with a sunken potbelly perched on the edge of the upper bunk opposite him, spindly legs dangling in mid-air. The man was wearing a natty straw hat and a checked shirt at least two sizes too large for him and split running shoes. He had enormous pop eyes, opened, it seemed, in an attitude of perpetual amazement; and he held a walking stick over his head. "Don't move," he said, shaking the stick at Jake. "Not an inch closer."

"Jesus Christ. Who are you?"

"As if you didn't know."

Jake sat up tentatively. The man, watchful, didn't protest. "I knew they'd send somebody," he said. "Cockroach. Vermin, that's you."

Jake stared, frightened.

"Admit it. Feigelbaum's paying. Or is it Shapiro?"

"Nobody's paying. Nobody sent me here. I'm a prisoner. I'm being sent back to Montreal tonight."

"To keep tabs on me. Well, I'm on to you. Human trash. If you so much as reach into your pocket for a weapon, I'll scream for the guards."

"I'm unarmed."

"Don't make me laugh."

"I'll stand up with arms over my head and you search me."

"Oh no, you don't. No sirree. That's when I get the judo chop."

"Why would I want to kill you?"

"For the money. Five million."

"Dollars?"

"American."

Jake whistled.

"Didn't they tell you *that* much?"

116

"I'm not completely trusted."

"They'd stop at nothing to put me out of the way and you know that. My case is before the Supreme Court in Manhattan right now. Calendar number 33451/1953."

"I wish you luck," Jake said, laughing for the first time.

"It's my father's money. It belongs to me. I know where Feigelbaum is and I've located Shapiro, but I still have to find Czucker and Leon Feigelbaum."

The man's eyes, to Jake's astonishment, appeared to open even wider. They might actually pop, he thought.

"I'm willing to share the money with anyone who helps me recover it and bring the criminals to justice."

"Cigarette?"

"Not one of yours, thank you. Are you crazy?"

"Surely you don't think my cigarettes are poisoned?"

"Last time Feigelbaum tried to murder me it was with supersonic rays. They paralyze and destroy bodily organs. They're not trying to kill me themselves. No sirree. Instead they hire people to try for them. Human excrement like you."

"Honestly, nobody sent me."

"Tell Feigelbaum this. I have witnesses among the paid hirelings who have used these supersonic waves on me and will testify to it in court."

"I'll pass on the message."

Tears welled in the old man's eyes. His hands shook. "I can't do anything. I can't go anywhere. Once a dentist I went to see in New York City injected me with what he called local anasthetic. Sure. It was a drug causing eye illness which leads to blindness. Wherever I live microphones and radar are installed so that everything I write, everything I read, every movement I make can be seen and heard."

"Do you think they can hear us here?" Jake asked. "Now?"

"Don't be childish. Even outside, on the street, every movement I make is spotted on the radar. Someone is always after me. Even when I go into a telephone booth, they pick up my conversation with a microphone in their pocket. They have complete control over every movement I make. This goes for my mail also. They also look through my mail. Nearly all my mail except *registered, certified,* is stolen from my post office box."

Suddenly a metal clipboard was banged against the door and a man peered through the window. "What did you say your mother's maiden name was?" he asked Jake.

"I already told you in quintuplet."

The old man leaped down from the bed and threw himself against the door. "You've got to get me out of here. I'm not like him."

"We want the name again."

"He was put in here to murder me. He's a hired killer."

"The name, please."

"It's on the form. You've got it right there."

"Spell it for me, will you?"

"Belloff. *B-E-L-L.* Off. Like in fuck off."

"You'd better watch it, buddy." But he opened the door for Jake all the same. "You can go now. Train time."

Jake scooped up his suitcases. "What about him?" he asked.

"Don't put me on the same train," the man said, retreating, "please."

"Don't worry, grandpaw. Somebody's coming for you."

Somebody's coming. The man slid to the floor, holding his head in his hands, and began to sob.

"Can't you do anything for him?" Jake asked, exasperated.

"Got any ideas?"

The door was shut behind Jake and he was led downstairs and put in the care of another officer, a young plainclothesman with a clean crisp feel about him and a most disarming smile. The young man immediately stooped to relieve Jake of one of his suitcases. It was a small gesture, but the unfussy kindness of it all touched Jake, and it occurred to him for the first time that he was sweaty and rumpled, and that in the eyes of this young man he must seem a small-time con artist or maybe even a nut, like the man Jake had left behind. After such a long day's seediness the young man looked so wholesome to Jake; he seemed such a good credit risk. As he and Jake stepped outside together into the fresh air he dared to hope that passersby would take them for friends, not a prisoner and his guard, and he was filled with a need to dissociate himself from the day's squalor and make a good impression.

"Pardon my asking," the young man said, "but you're a political, aren't you?"

"Well, yes. I mean that's the charge."

"I don't mind the politicals. They're educated and are really, well, idealistic sort of. It's the drug addicts and homosexuals that I find so degrading. Or do you think of them as . . . sick?"

Jake shrugged.

"What were you going to do in New York?"

"Overthrow the government by force."

"That's rich; that's a good one."

"Me and my little supersonic ray gun."

"You were put in with him, then? Now isn't that man something? A real beaut."

"I'll say."

"Say, I must tell you how much I admire things Canadian. In our house, we always watch CBC-TV. It doesn't insult your intelligence, if you know what I mean? They allow for nonconformists. Like that, um, Professor McAllister who sometimes debates on foreign affairs."

Brian McAllister lectured on economics at Wellington. A tiresome, literal socialist.

"Would you know McAllister? Personally? Coming from Montreal?"

"You with the FBI?"

"Hell, no, nothing like that," the young man said, grinning.

"They said somebody was coming for the old man. Who?"

"Oh, him. Hell, we've had him three times already. Say, did the old boy get to show you the number on his arm?"

The number? "No," Jake said, beginning to feel the nausea rising in him again.

"Cigarette?"

"No, thanks."

"The Dodgers are going with Erskine tomorrow. The ole perfessor's going to put in Whitey Ford."

No answer.

"When the train pulls in you just get on ahead of me. No need to embarrass you, is there?"

"What number? What are you talking about?"

"It was something they did to them during the war. In the concentration camps. Didn't you ever read about it?"

Jake glared at the young man, suppressing an urge to hit him with his suitcase.

"The irony of it is," the young man said, "that now some of those same Germans are back in office in Western Germany. Now what do you say to that?"

"Kiss my Royal Canadian ass."

"Be friendly. Come on."

"Be friendly. Come on. Shit."

"There's nothing personal in this."

"Okay, okay."

He offered Jake a cigarette again and this time Jake took it.

"Off the record," the young man said, "I'd even say there was something to it."

"To what? What are you talking about now? Concentration camps? The world series? Is everybody crazy in this country?"

The young man stopped, his pleasant face aching with high seriousness. "Would you say that?"

"That? This? What are you talking about?"

"Communism. The original idea. Brotherhood. Well, I buy

it. But you can't make it work. It rubs against human nature."

Jake stared at the tracks, trying to will the train into the station.

"I suppose some of your buddies were going to meet you in New York?"

"A parade was planned. A big demonstration."

"Seriously, can I phone anybody for you to explain why you didn't turn up?"

"I'm going to be sick. I've got to sit down."

Jake slumped against a pillar.

"Here she comes. You just get on ahead of me. We don't need to sit together."

The young man settled in five seats behind Jake, and when they reached the border he got up and jumped off the train. Jake caught his eye as he stood on the platform, lighting up. The young man waved, his face broke into an infectious grin. Jake's heart thumped crazily, his head was pounding, and to his own amazement, he spit venomously on the window just as the train lurched backward—vibrated—and jerked forward again. The young man looked after him, shaking his head, appalled. And Jake, consumed with shame, realized that he had done it again. Shown himself one of the oily ones, an off-white. He had done the ugly and childish thing, made a fool of himself, when hitherto all the right had been on his side. So that when he remembered this day and came to talk about it at dinner parties years later, garnishing the truth some, he would recall with stinging freshness his stupid spit on the window, but he would always leave that out of the story, except when he told it to Nancy.

Back in Montreal, Jake made straight for the bar in Central Station. He ordered a double whisky and paid for it with American money.

"Montreal is the Paris of North America," the waiter said. "I trust you will enjoy your stay, sir."

Jake stared at his change. "What's this," he asked, "Monopoly money?"

"It's Canadian."

Jake laughed, pleased.

"Canada's no joke. We're the world's largest producer of uranium. Walter Pidgeon was born in this country."

ROBERT BRUSTEIN / *The New American Playwrights*

Yes yes, the new American playwrights. To ask of them the question they so frequently ask in their plays: Do they exist—or merely appear to exist? Are they a fact or just a figment of a feverish imagination? Reality or dream? From the amount of chitchat they inspire, and the accumulated copy in newspapers and magazines, they would seem to constitute a rich, fertile alluvium. But once past the mirage of press agentry and chic, you find that the oasis has turned into a few desultory palm trees with rather droopy fronds.

Still, there is something there beyond the haze, something that we should probably examine a little closer. For the sheer quantity of young Americans turning out serious plays is impressive, especially at a time when the serious play has almost vanished from the Broadway stage. And compared with the generation that preceded—the generation of William Inge, Paddy Chayefsky, Lorraine Hansberry, and Robert Anderson—this new breed seems adventurous, sophisticated, hip, and advanced. Still, the previous generation hardly set the highest standards of comparison, and the ambitiousness of these youngsters compels more rigorous judgments. Today's revolt against the sentimental realism of the fifties is certainly invigorating, and it is heartening to find some of our serious dramatists finally thinking in noncommercial terms. But the results are spotty—the new American drama has yet to find its own identity or develop it's own integrity.

The experimental substance of these plays makes such failings more obtrusive, for if realism necessarily subordinates imagination to authenticity, antirealism demands a passionate individual style. American playwrights have not yet evolved such a style; they are usually imitating playwrights from abroad. Compared with Beckett, Ionesco, and Genet (who constitute a central inspiration), the Americans look rather pale and wan; their plays have a chronic anemia that comes from too much borrowed blood; and they do not even—like the English—give the sense of a healthy movement which may eventually produce significant results. Who are the country's new dramatists? Are they part of anything more than passing vogues and ephemeral fashions? And is any single writer emerging from the mass as a powerful presence around which others may group?

EDWARD ALBEE

Albee is the logical starting point for any discussion of the new dramatic writing. No young American playwright has collected so many laurels or collected them so quickly. If raw talent were the only criterion, Albee would certainly seem to deserve his astonishing reputation. His instinct for the theater is matched by few contemporaries, and he is unmatched among professional American dramatists—except perhaps by Tennessee Williams—in his control of language. Albee's verbal power is

particularly singular in a medium marked by graceless prose—
O'Neill's notorious difficulties with the language typify the way
our playwrights have been hobbled by literary awkwardness.
Albee, on the other hand, brings to the stage a corrosive wit, a
confident control of idiom, and a vocabulary of invective surpassed only by the Englishman, John Osborne; and though
he lacks the deeper resources of the genuine dramatic poet, he is
frequently able to create stunning theatrical effects, both
through words and striking visual images.

Albee, furthermore, has an unusual knowledge of the medium
in which he works. Unlike past American dramatists—most of
whom were either unlettered or only dimly conscious of other
dramatic traditions—Albee has assimilated a huge number of
plays by other writers and can reproduce their techniques with
little effort. This facility, however, is not entirely a source of
strength. Aside from the brittle corruscating dialogue which is
his trademark, little in Albee's work seems peculiarly his own;
few of his plays can be readily identified as the expression of a
single playwright; and no two works seem to be written in the
same style. Influences on his plays, even in a partial list, reveal
an eclectic range: *Who's Afraid of Virginia Woolf?* is a clever
blend of Strindberg, Pirandello, and O'Neill; *The American
Dream* is a close imitation of Ionesco's *The Bald Soprano; The
Death of Bessie Smith* owes its setting, atmosphere, and one of
its characters to Tennessee Williams; *The Ballad of the Sad
Café* is an adaptation of Carson McCullers' novel, reproduced
very closely, with McCullers' narrative spoken by a presenter;
Tiny Alice, reverberating with echoes of a dozen writers, including Dürrenmatt, Graham Greene, Genet, Strindberg, and Enid
Bagnold, is most deeply dependent on T. S. Eliot's *The Cocktail Party;* and even *The Zoo Story*—Albee's most distinctive
play to date—could hardly have been written in the same way
without the precedent of Jean Genet.

Under certain circumstances, such distinguished models might
provide distinguished drama, but Albee generally exploits the

work of other writers in order to invest his own with an unearned significance. To be blunt about it, Albee has nothing particularly urgent to communicate—though blessed with the artist's technical facility, he does not possess the artist's compelling vision—and lacking the power to penetrate a subject deeply, he creates instead a drama of impersonation, recapitulating the themes and attitudes of other dramatists without first experiencing the inner anguish that originally gave them birth. Thus, Albee will build his plays around such well-worn problems as the conflict between reality and illusion, the inability of human beings to communicate with one another, the emptiness of existence without God, the nightmare vapidity of middle-class family life—but his approach to these problems is extremely glib, and he has yet to convince me that any of them are central to his own artistic being.

What does seem fairly consistent in his plays, though subordinate to other issues, is the author's concern with sexual pathology: each action revolves around a protagonist whose sensual life is paralyzed or perverted. From Jerry, the ecstatic hipster in *The Zoo Story*, who impales himself gratefully upon a knife he forces into a stranger's hand, to the hallucinating lay brother Julian in *Tiny Alice*, who fantasizes about being eaten by lions and bloodied by gladiators, Albee's central characters have an abundant store of Krafft-Ebing characteristics: narcissism, impotency, sado-masochism, and homosexuality, disguised or declared. Like Williams, however, Albee is unwilling to be explicit about the problems afflicting his characters, and smuggles their sexual difficulties inside metaphysical abstractions. Thus his plays conclude, almost invariably, with ambiguous religious affirmations or garbled philosophical generalities. The masochistic love-death which completes *The Zoo Story* is represented as a mystical union with God; the incredible triangle in *The Ballad of the Sad Café*—a triangle composed of a homosexual dwarf, a bisexual convict, and a mannish female giant—is exalted into a generalization about the strangeness of love itself; and even the conclusion of *Who's Afraid of Virginia Woolf?*—a blistering domestic squabble for most of its length—is marred by reality-illusion clichés and some fake Pirandellian mystification about an imaginary child.

By the time of *Tiny Alice*, Albee's weakness for empty profundities has so overcome him that he finally produces a play with no denotative meaning at all: a cloud of obfuscation that evaporates in its own meretriciousness. The vapors choking this pseudo-religious fable are heavy and noisome, but in smaller quantities, they have infiltrated all of Albee's work: the author's worst failing is his passion for pretense. Praised too quickly on the basis of too little, he now runs the danger of dissipating what real talent he has in the pursuit of specious effects, for his gifts, I suspect, are shaped for considerably smaller purposes than he is willing to concede. At any rate, his ambitions, at present, far outreach his capabilities, and his plays, though executed with considerable skill and occasionally dazzling in their pyrotechnical displays, are too often shallow in conception, superficial in design, facile in feeling. Still, if Albee could discover the true limits of his powers, as well as a subject of his own, he might still produce effective dramas, for his talents are genuine, and the excitement he manages to arouse with each play is not entirely unjustified. He is one of the few American playwrights, for all his faults, whom one can contemplate with more than apathy and indifference.

JACK GELBER

Gelber has little of Albee's technical dexterity; as a writer, he is crude, rough, and unschooled. Those who read his plays without seeing them on the stage are inclined to dismiss this playwright out of hand: his prose is colorless, his style careless, his organization vague. Although Gelber can hardly be called a born writer, he nevertheless strikes me as an instinctive dramatist, and his plays have a Spartan honesty which makes one willing to forgive him many faults. The antithesis of Albee, who plays magical tricks with illusion, Gelber has an Ibsenite passion for the truth, accompanied by a cold contempt for hypocrisy and cant. This gives him an aloofness from society and a certain disdain for the theater itself as an illusion-making factory. He is more interested in reality than in literature, and though he has a good deal of sophistication, his secrets are those of the hard-boiled realist rather than of the literary esthete. Gelber, as a matter of fact, likes to pass himself off as an intellectual innocent, largely indifferent to books and plays, more intrigued with the movies. This is partly a pose: Gelber is much more literary than he cares to admit, and *The Connection*, at least, is deeply influenced by previous experiments in the drama. Still, Gelber, as a writer, is less concerned with creating literary masterpieces than in showing an audience "the way it really is" (this refrain runs continually through his first play), and doing this in a striking and original manner.

Even *The Connection*, for all its borrowings from Pirandello and O'Neill, has its own distinctive stamp. For unlike Albee, who uses elements from other plays without transcending them, Gelber is incapable of walking over familiar ground without running through it with his own harrow. Thus the drugged narcotic atmosphere of *The Connection* may remind one of *The Iceman Cometh*, and its ironic assaults on the fourth wall may derive from Pirandello's theater trilogy, but the play's free style, improvisatory technique is Gelber's own, and his use of live jazz as a contrapuntal figure in the action is a wholly original device. Most important, the play takes tired theatrical conventions— the conventions of naturalism—and gives them new life. Without rising to false climaxes, refusing even to tell a story, the play stands as an authentic documentation of the agony and boredom of the junkie, waiting for a fix. First and foremost, *The Connection* is a work of verification which uses reality as a criticism of all phony concepts of reality: namely, the treatment of addiction in previous books and plays.

On the other hand, Gelber often seems immobilized by his very virtues. Reluctant to repeat himself or to fall into commonplace attitudes, he sometimes strikes postures that are over-strained and bizarre. In the two plays that follow *The Connection*, his desire for originality begins to overcome his interest in coherence, and he fails to achieve that penetrating relevance that made his first play such a hopeful stage event. *The Apple* has its amusing passages and is a brave effort to formulate a theatrical parallel to action painting, but it loses itself in crude audience-baiting and inchoate effects, meaningful only to the author. As for Gelber's most recent play, *Square in the Eye*, it seems to lack any structure at all, being flawed by an unfortunate time scheme (the action moves backward and forward simultaneously) and by the absence of any correlation between plot and subplot.

The latter play, however, reveals Gelber developing some talent as a social satirist, for it ridicules—deftly and incisively—the callous incompetence of professional men (doctors, undertakers, rabbis, and so on), the chauvinism of Jewish parents, and the confusions of modern marriage, as well as producing some affecting moments of emotion (rare in Gelber's writing), in the scenes between the husband and his wife. The play, moreover, is interesting as an experiment in the use of stills and movies, introduced at climactic moments as an ironic commentary on the stage events. Artfully employed in the first act, however, this device is almost completely abandoned in the remainder of the play, an example of the careless management of which Gelber is sometimes guilty. The author seems a little too listless at present to give his work a compact form; the goodnatured apathy with which he contemplates society is beginning to infect his art; and he does not yet seem to have committed himself entirely to writing for the stage. Still, Gelber has courage, honesty, and an indifference to failure; he is curious about the drama and eager to explore the flexibility of the medium; and he is discontent with everything that remains unquestioned and assumed. These qualities, while not enough to make him a playwright of the first rank, make him a continually developing writer and an honest man, and there are few American dramatists about whom one can say as much.

JACK RICHARDSON

Richardson probably has a better mind than either Albee or Gelber, but lacks some basic instinct for the stage. In none of his plays, with the possible exception of *Gallows Humor,* has he succeeded in translating his conceptual intelligence into a compelling theatrical statement. His first play, *The Prodigal,* is a very youthful work, written in imitation of the French myth dramatists. A modern adaptation of the *Oresteia,* it converts the heroes and heroines of Greek mythology into the sleek characters of drawing-room comedy, with Orestes as a self-conscious adolescent rebel, mouthing philosophical bromides. Richardson's model here is Giraudoux, who also approaches remote grandeur from a romantic middle-class perspective; but the play lacks Giraudoux's wit, and reads like a verbose translation from another language.

Gallows Humor gives evidence of more maturity and originality. A pair of dark comedies in the modern mode—the first about a condemned man, the second about his executioner—the play possesses the kind of lighthearted mordancy suggested by its title, as well as a carefully worked out structure. But Richardson is too content with the ironies of the contrasted situations, and fails to press any issues to their resolution. In *Lorenzo,* a full-length play produced on Broadway, Richardson turns once again to the past, a rather uncertain area for him, and creates a tired comedy–drama about a troupe of itinerant actors caught up in the midst of a Renaissance war. Although the play features one striking character, an ingratiating monster of a military man, it suffers from comparison with *Mother Courage*, to which it owes its animating idea and its pacifist theme; and although such debts might have been requited by a fertile invention and an epigrammatic style, Richardson can contribute only predictable turns of plot and pseudo-Shavian witticisms. Richardson is a literate writer but also a rather flaccid one: he does not seem aroused enough at present to thrust his imagination beyond what he already knows.

MURRAY SCHISGAL

Schisgal is a sheep in wolf's clothing. Basically an entertainer with an amiable manner, a wry sense of humor, and a firm grasp of stage technique, he might—before the cultural revolution— have been very happy writing light comedies in the vein of S. N. Behrman, Philip Barry, or Neil Simon. But now that commercial dramatists have fallen victim to upward mobility, Schisgal has developed somewhat larger ambitions, modernizing his style to suit the times. What Schisgal produces is a hybrid form: commercial comedies in experimental skins. He exploits the serious drama, and patronizes it at the same time, a quality that has endeared him to the Broadway audiences because it gives them the tribute of the avant-garde without any of the tribulations.

Thus in *The Typists* and *The Tiger*—the two short plays with which he first came to public attention—Schisgal uses the techniques of Ionesco, Beckett, Adamov, and Pinter, but adjusts their themes to conform with middle-class values. *The Typists*, for example, is a poignant little comedy about two office workers with empty lives who age rapidly over the course of the action with no apparent lapse in time. Fundamentally absurdist in its basic technique (the play owes a lot to Ionesco, and especially to

The Chairs), *The Typists* is concerned with the flatness and futility of everyday life, but it also admits a strain of sentimentality into the proceedings which eases and palliates the harshness of its statement.

In *The Tiger*, Schisgal inadvertently exposes his true affinities, which are less with the French avant-garde than with James M. Barrie and William Saroyan: the play is permeated by a rather cloying whimsicality. It concerns a misanthropic postman who, under the influence of Nietzsche, abducts a young Long Island housewife for the express purpose of raping her. Despite his threatening manner, however, and his apparently psychopathic tendencies, the housewife has soon converted him to her own domestic purposes, and by the end of the play they are settling into a snug little love nest. This suburban version of *What Every Woman Knows* is presumably an attempt to satirize the platitudes of nonconformism, but the author unfortunately ends up with a platitude himself.

Much the same difficulties can be found in *Luv*, a full-length comedy produced on Broadway to great acclaim: here again Schisgal deals with an adulterous situation, but becomes so enamored of incongruity that anything meaningful is soon swallowed up in farce and whimsey. The play has been interpreted as a satire on love and marriage, but if so, the author's satiric intention has been very carefully hidden: it is more like a series of vaudeville skits with burlesque boffos and top banana toppers. If amusement were all that were intended, one might feel more well-disposed toward Schisgal, for he has a strong talent for lightweight comedies, as well as a friendly, affectionate sense of humor. But beneath the ersatz experimental manner, there is little in him to distinguish him from a host of journeymen dramatists now working on the commercial stage.

ARTHUR KOPIT

Kopit also borrows avant-garde techniques without adding anything original of his own, but whereas Schisgal wants to entertain the middle classes, Kopit wants to ridicule them: his short pieces are semidisguised acts of aggression against the very domestic values Schisgal celebrates. Kopit's derision, however, is often combined with petulance, and since it is primarily aimed against overprotective mothers and insensitive fathers, it hardly seems very daring or brave. There is something a little juvenile about Kopit's writing; for him, the theater is mainly a medium for pranks, an intention he suggests in his looping, longitudinal titles. In his most notorious work, *Oh Dad, Poor Dad, Mamma's Hung You in the Closet and I'm Feelin' So Sad*, the title is ultimately the most revealing part of the play, since it sums up this author's major characteristics: his Oedipal fixation, his hatred of maternal women, his skittishness, his black humor, and, especially, his nostalgia for childhood. The play itself is an exercise in the absurdist mode which borrows freely from various avant-garde styles, blends in the fruity atmosphere of a Tennessee Williams play, and comes off as a curious mixture of satire, irony, fantasy, and farce. Kopit is most interesting when he is most outrageous—the funniest scene in the play concerns a young boy and girl prevented from making love by a corpse which keeps falling on top of them—but aside from this brief necrophiliac episode and a few other isolated passages, the play fails to rise above a certain brittle archness.

The two short plays that follow this famous sketch are also limited by deficiencies in attitude and feeling. *Sing to Me Through Open Windows* is a fantasy of childhood about a sensitive boy, a cute clown, and a wise old man which is embarrassing in its cloying sentimentality: the sort of thing that appeals to drama coaches in boys' camps and elocution schools. *The Day the Whores Came Out To Play Tennis,* though facile in its satire, is a better work, and its basic notion—that a group of prostitutes should attempt to wreck a country club by hitting tennis balls against it—is wacky enough to promise real amusement. But once again, the author is unable to sustain his action or to find a meaningful target for attack: the crude manners of wealthy country club Jews are hardly a universal subject for satire. Kopit has wit, a good sense of the bizarre, and a developing satirical talent, but he is still impeded by a certain undergraduate peevishness and cuteness.

LEROI JONES

Jones is the wild man of the new American playwrights: for him, a play is a bludgeon to flail his audiences into insensibiilty. This does not promise very subtle drama, and indeed, Jones's talent is extremely crude and unformed; the fame he has achieved is far in excess of his desserts. Actually, Jones has come to prominence coasting on two seperate waves: the Negro revolution and the vogue for violence recently introduced to literature by Norman Mailer. I suspect that he is more interested in expressing his own hostility than in advancing the Negro cause, but he has developed a sure instinct for manipulating a ready masochistic nerve in guilty white audiences. As it stands, his plays are fantasies of uncontrolled revenge, barely dramatized and almost inarticulate with rage.

Despite his recurring harangues against the white power structure, Jones indicates, with each play, that his revenge fantasies are personal rather than representatitive, though for a while he makes some perfunctory effort to vindicate his feelings. *Dutchman,* his first one-acter, is the most coherent of his plays, but it is impaired by gassy dialogue, by pretentious symbolism, by literary thefts (from Albee's *The Zoo Story*), and especially by an intrinsic dishonesty—the action involves an educated Negro who, on a subway, is goaded into violence by a white girl who finally kills him. Jones, in short, tries to exonerate the racist anger of his male protagonist as something forced from a mild victim by a malevolent woman—but the rage obviously belongs to the author and needs no incitement at all.

In the two short plays that follow, Jones makes even less effort to exonerate his angry feelings: their intention is as direct and as uncomplicated as karate blows. *The Toilet*, for example, takes place in the boy's john of an integrated high school, and concerns the mugging of a Puerto Rican homosexual by a gang of Negroes who dump him unceremoniously into a urinal. The play concludes with the return of one of the Negroes—the one to whom the Puerto Rican sent a love letter—who thereupon lovingly cradles the head of his unconscious victim in his lap. In *The Slave*, Jones's aggression explodes into a convulsive fantasy of future war between the races. The protagonist, a Negro poet and leader of the black insurgents, returns to the home of his old professor—now married to the Negro's former wife (a white girl)—to taunt him, to insult his manhood, and finally to shoot him, while leaving the woman and their two children dying under the ruins of their demolished house. Needless to say, none of this is redeemed by the slightest hint of subtlety, complication, or craft. That Jones should be taken with any seriousness today indicates a profound malaise among certain cultural consumers who are more and more coming to confuse acts of violence with expressions of moral heroism.

There are, aside from these six playwrights, a number of younger writers who have aroused legitimate expectations with single works—among them Kenneth H. Brown (*The Brig*), Lewis John Carlino (*Telemachus Clay*), Arnold Weinstein (*The Red Eye of Love*), Charles Nolte (*Do Not Pass Go*), and Charles Dizenzo (*The Drapes Come*). And there are also others (Frank Gilroy, William Hanley, Herbert Lieberman) who command respect from many critics, though their virtues still elude me. None of these, for all the interest they have aroused, can yet be said to display a fully developed talent. It is certainly within the realm of possibility that the new American playwrights will still fulfill our expectations, creating a finished enough technique or significant enough vision to justify the attention they have recently been receiving. Certainly, they have some of the necessary qualifications, sharing as they do a powerful discontent with existing theatrical conditions, a genuine desire for reform, and a real impulse to move in new directions.

But so far, the pickings have been slim. Vacillating between an exhausted realism and an imitative experimentalism, their ears always cocked to the sound of distant trumpets, the new playwrights have yet to create an independent body of work which can be taken with any seriousness. Compared with American writers in other literatures, they seem to be lacking in creative juices—one looks in vain for signs of that fresh renewal that is currently benefiting American poetry and fiction. The drama, to be sure, has always been the victim of cultural lag in this country, and its advances have always come about twenty years late. Still, it is not novelty or sophistication that is missing today so much as vigor, strength, conviction, originality, and the sound of a real voice.

The prospect, however, is not altogether bleak, for nourishment is beginning to enter our drama from an unexpected quarter—American literary men have begun to revive a long latent interest in the stage. The poets Robert Lowell and Kenneth Koch, the novelists Saul Bellow, Philip Roth, Bernard Malamud, and George P. Elliott, the essayist James Baldwin—all are writing or have written plays in addition to their other works. Not all of these, of course, have proved to be contributions to the theater—Baldwin's two plays, *Blues for Mr. Charlie* and *The Amen Corner*, in fact, are bald agitprop works in a thirty-year-old style. But enough of these plays have been sufficiently unique and fascinating to inspire hope. Kenneth Koch's brief costume pageants—*Bertha,* for example, and *George Washington Crossing the Delaware*—are funny iconoclastic attacks on the stiff pieties of historical myths, written in the form of high school tableaux. And Bellow's one-act farces, not to mention his full-length comedy *The Last Analysis,* are witty displays of virtuosity in a Jewish idiom which mine a rich lode of theatrical rhetoric.

The most impressive of all these new writers for the stage is Robert Lowell. In his trilogy *The Old Glory,* he opens up territory never adequately explored before by an American dramatist (though O'Neill was groping toward the same goals in his eleven-play cycle, unfinished at his death). Using Hawthorne sketches and a Melville novella as source material—much as the Greeks used Homer and Shakespeare used Plutarch, Cinthio, and Bandello—Lowell turns back to three periods of American history to create an imaginative chronicle of the American character, showing the development of its violent temperament, its hostility to aristocratic values, its ambiguous attitude toward freedom and slavery. Scorning conventional theatrical rhythms, weaving his themes into a subtle embroidery, creating an undulating, hypnotic pattern of language, Lowell invests his source material with a new authority—*The Old Glory,* like the *Oresteia,* functions at the same time as drama, history, and myth. Thus Lowell has begun to solve one of the most vexing of modern dramatic problems: how to maintain ties with the past while keeping a play contemporary, singular, and relevant. By returning to literary and historical roots, and by making these flower into his own poetic concept, Lowell has initiated an American drama with continuity, thrust, and range.

And this is precisely what has been missing from the plays of our professional dramatists—something that will rescue them from being mere technical displays, routine social commentaries, or myopic personal confessions. Through its parasitical dependence on the style and substance of foreign works, our own drama has been prevented from stagnating entirely, but it has yet to find a purpose of its own beyond the examination of limited social-psychological problems: the imitativeness of current American drama signifies the need for a common well of inspiration from which our playwrights can draw their strength. This well used to be filled by tradition—and later by the rebellion against tradition—but in each case, the drama was able to define itself against some historical identity larger than itself. Because this historical identity has been largely lacking in America, Robert Lowell's effort to create one in dramatic terms deserves our gratitude and admiration—hopefully, his achievement may serve as a pattern for future theatrical development. For without that larger context, American drama will continue to be an event of little reality—an illusion, a phantasm, a waking dream.

STEVEN KATZ / *Two Poems*

A LIP SERVICE TO DEPARTURES

I

The city coughed, and I dropped my wounds
In the Hudson, and took my ex-bridge
By the lower tier, for Ithaca, where I work
At the Cadillac of Universities. They learn
And they learn, and they want to leave.
I want to leave. I tell my wife,
"Africa next." So she cries, and stuffs kids,
The cat, Chuck's collage, my scrap
Bathrobe, my mask, into her jeans.

Pack it up, Louise, we're going somewhere,
Like a brush fire, like the moon,
Like apples dropping we're on our way

Out there. Lately I haven't
Wanted to talk with anyone, except
Bob Rosenthal, if he's still around, that Certified
Public Accountant. All my friends
Have gone to Tanganyika. The schoolyard's
Gone to Tanganyika, and on its way
The Bullets' "B" team in purple and gold
Satin reversibles. It's not the color of the skin
That matters. It's the color of the skin. "What matters
Then?" The color of the skin. Why did Queequeg
Leave his hometown? I can't answer
Every question and still keep going.
She said that and then, Indian style, tied her braids
To the bridge rail, and hung there till her scalp
Ripped, and she hit the gorge with a leather thud.
One more of those and I leave for sure.

II

I came home last night like a felt hat.
"You're my little pincushion," said the wife,
And sunk in me her knitting needles,
The paring knives, her leather-stitching kit.
"I do," I said. "I believe there is a god."
"That something, somehow made the world up."
"Right," she responded, a number-two needle,
Still threaded black, in my softest part.
We need some continuity, or else
We'll miss the train, the boats peeling off.
This time I made the weight limit, my luggage
Full of depth charges, and my blow gun.
The children, at the windows, flap their cotton wings.
The wife winds the jet in plastic wrap;
She wont let anything spoil.
"How?" I ask, looking up at that aforementioned god
Through the perforated soundproofing. "How

Do you manage to get the word any more?
Do you know what's going on down here?"
Eric Herzlich wears his steel-tipped
Gloves, his grenade-pouch full, his flare
Gun. Like an ivory ball the jet spins
In the world's rim, by odds and evens, double zero,
Reds and blacks. "You son of a bitch," I say.
It isn't just one of your everyday games.
Our pilot walks the wing edge, saying his list of names.

WAITING TABLES IS A PROFESSION

A plastic dickey, my black bow tie,
Orders on the cuff, and my tray
With the chicken, with the rare roast beef
In the brown ointment, I work my station,
I make the salad grow, I bake the pumpernickel.

The spoils of Nagasaki keep me feeding.
So many inviting deaths
That Golden Special is running again;
And down the river into Kenya
Watusi flow like boiling onions.

I need to catch a train, I'm
Departing, disordered, an Old-Time Favorite
Unrediscovered, and disordered again
My blind returns. "Wherever ya go
The people's gotta eat." O Lyndon Johnson

Protect me with your rule of thumb
From demeaning niggerhood and the vengeful
Asian stomach. I couldn't be
Lonelier, with my lack of sheer customers.
Something's going bad. The Silent Days again

And Chaplin, they're screening Charlie on me.
He tugs my big bow tie, and I'm ankles
And wrists, I'm shifty-hipped, Yeah,
But I'm not amusing anybody. The piano tuner
Grows mushrooms in the wings. I can walk through walls.

Wade through walls. We said that last time
And triumphed across the oceans.
Them turkeys flew up,
And we froze them. We froze the cobbed
Corn, the pizza pie. We boiled stones.

JASCHA KESSLER / *Perfect Days*

FARCE

Characters / THE WIFE

THE HUSBAND

THE BROTHER

An ultramodern kitchen. On the RIGHT, *the breakfast nook; on the* LEFT, *the spotless stainless steel, chrome, and enameling. The ultimate-seeming appliances are operated, it would appear, from the small panel of controls on the wall at* CENTER REAR. *The whole place is large, comfortable, and utterly silent with power. At the* LEFT REAR, *a door leads to another part of the house. Outside the large window of the breakfast nook nothing at all can be seen: the light is a neutral, pearly, misty light. A red, a green, and an amber light are flashing in a sequence of about three to five seconds' duration, followed by a thin, high bleep* (*at least five times repeated*); *but the control panel re-mains unanswered. The length of time becomes annoying.*

Abruptly the backdoor (*at* RIGHT SIDE) *slides open: there is a great roaring from outside: it is the ceaseless din of traffic— trains, autos, trucks, helicopters, jets, and so on.* THE WIFE *slips through, presses a button that closes the door, shutting off the noise and the lights on the panel. In the silence her breathing is hard. She leans her back against the closed door in relief. Gradu-ally her desperate expression calms; her face grows pensive, then quite blank. In the one hand she carries a folded, thick news-paper. She is young, between 30 and 40. She wears an expensive silk kimono and heeled satin slippers; her hair is covered by a fine gauzy silk kerchief or turban. But she is pale, her eyes ringed by shadows of hypertension; she slits them against the smoke of the cigarette she has drawn from a pack in her pocket and lit in the manner of the heavy smoker. From the control panel now another series of lights comes on: azure, rose, white; they are synchronized with tiny pleasant chimes and buzzes. She hesi-tates, drawing deeply to steady herself, and regards the panel as if in momentary doubt as to the meaning of their pattern. Her free hand feels along the wall and manipulates a pair of switches; over her shoulder, set in an oblique corner of the wall, a very large TV screen lights up and plays. She cocks her eye at it, half annoyed but also half reassured that the world continues, and she smokes a little longer while looking at it. The smoke having cleared her thoughts, she crosses over to the complex of appliances and sets up a tray with a great number of items; then she carries it back to the glossy large table in the nook. She sits upright opposite the trays, draws herself a cup of coffee from the large urn standing on the table, and while sipping, the cigarette burning between her fingers, reads the newspaper, all of it, at arm's length, with terrific speed and total lack of interest. When she is done, she puts it down, crumpled and misfolded, fills an-other cup of coffee, lights another cigarette, and slips into reverie as she gazes out the blank sunny-shady window.*

THE HUSBAND *bounds into the kitchen and heads straight for the table. He is astoundingly rosy, briskly strong, and spic and span in his tailored clothing. He has no ears. Sitting down at his place, he begins dispatching the appetizing courses heaped on his tray. First he downs the juice, then systematically finishes one plate after another from the tray, accompanying his happy breakfasting with much clatter. He is hearty and gay, just like the youthful executive* DADS *of the automobile advertisements.*

HUSBAND: Looks like another perfect day. Doesn't it.

WIFE: (*in reverie, she responds without having heard him*) Yes it does. Doesn't it.

HUSBAND: That makes the twohundredtwentyfirst perfect day. Doesn't it.

WIFE: Yes it does. Doesn't it.

HUSBAND: My, I'm hungry. Perfect days make me so hungry.

WIFE: Yes they do. Don't they.

HUSBAND: (*glancing at his watch*) Got off all right. Didn't they.

WIFE: Yes. Got off all right.

HUSBAND: Of course. Tell them I'd be back Sunday morning?

WIFE: That's when you're back?

HUSBAND: Of course. That's when I'm back. I don't have to *tell* you. Do I. That's when. Of course.

WIFE: I wasn't sure.

HUSBAND: As usual.

WIFE: I wasn't sure. What is it today?

HUSBAND: Monday. Of course. You know I leave Mondays.

WIFE: Of course.

HUSBAND: To work.

WIFE: The work.

HUSBAND: My work.

WIFE: Your work.

HUSBAND: Of course. To work. My work. I'm so hungry on days like this! Perfect. The work. Perfect days. They'll be perfect—um—days like this—um—all week. Through part of next. As well. My, I was hungry! (*He pours himself a great mug of coffee, adds much sugar. He reaches for the newspaper, turns it back to its original state by painstakingly refolding it; then he unfolds it and proceeds to read and drink busily. As he becomes immersed in reading, the wife, lighting another cigarette from the butt of the old one, smokes steadily and speaks tenderly, meditatively, to the window*)

WIFE: How surprised I was to notice, when I happened to look at the world this morning, that the sun moves. No matter what they say, it really moves. Up it came: up and up and up. Nothing could stop it. The black trees grew a silvery green. The misty gray air turned lavender. Slowly the glistening streets became visible, and the gardens glimmering wet, and the houses, and then even the shadowy snow-covered hills—as though it were all just being brought into existence out of the very emptiness. Suddenly a cool breeze passed, opening my eyes and turning the leaves. And then, as I watched, the red edge of the sun came up there, there at the end of the world. It grew and it grew until it was a round rosy platter, oh about the size of our fruit dish. And then it flattened, and it shrank, smaller, smaller, higher and hotter and whiter. Of course it moves. And changes. It is never the same.

HUSBAND: Now we're talking!

WIFE: And there was also the pale moon, stained as an old handkerchief, drifting off to the other side of the world, floating away down into the sea. The robins have returned. The sky was no longer a black and empty place, but blue, pale blue, blue as the veins in my wrist, and very high and very quiet. There will be roses to cut this week. How the dewdrops sparkled on the roses!

HUSBAND: We were coming to this. It was about time too. We've reached it, we've got it now. Admit it! That's what I say! Tell them!

WIFE: Kitty sat watching the robins: only the white tip of her black tail twitched hungrily, just so. It was all so still. And beautiful. And polite.

HUSBAND: Logical too. Of course.

WIFE: And pointless. I lit my first cigarette. Altogether pointless.

HUSBAND: They don't guess half of it!

WIFE: I'd gone for the milk. There it was. Of course. How does it come to be there, fresh and cold? I could assume it's brought by—um—Mister Daly, that man who came to the door when we moved in, three or seven years ago, and asked if we wanted milk. Or was it Adly? Or was it Lady? Yes, I said, Mister—um—Daly, of course. Of course we need milk. He was glad. And polite. No, he didn't smoke, thank you. He only brought milk. But now it could be someone else. Couldn't it. I could suppose that. Couldn't I. Of course.

HUSBAND: Of course! If they knew even half of it! Hah! If they knew—

WIFE: Or somehow automatic. Many things are. Automatic. The techniques. The boxes. Inside the boxes there are motors and wires and gears. On the outside there are buttons and switches and wheels. On, off. Up, down. In, out. Simple. The boxes. Automatic. Either it's off or it's on. Yet even when it's off, it's on. Which is strange but true. Which means it's off only when it's OUT OF ORDER. But that's hardly possible, they say. What with the techniques. So you must never put your finger in. Never. Never. And that —that is how the milk comes to be there every morning. I think.

HUSBAND: Obviously it has to be simplified. Otherwise it would be incomprehensible. To *them*. Otherwise it would be confusing. To *them*. *Over*simplified. Is what it has to be. For *them*.

WIFE: But I'm not sure. I might be mistaken. As when I thought the sky was pale blue. It is not blue, they say. Or that the sun rose up and changed before my very eyes into a bright, white burning ball. It does not move, they say. It has all been simplified. It's bad to make the old mistakes, they say. But it is inevitable. I think. Or why do I make mistakes like that. *They* don't.

HUSBAND: And it's foolproof.

WIFE: They say that if *they* made mistakes everything would be turned off. Definitely OUT OF ORDER. Then what would we do? We would begin to die.

HUSBAND: It's settled for good. Now we know.

WIFE: If everything were definitely OUT OF ORDER . . .

HUSBAND: (*excited enough to speak to her over his paper*) Of course it's old stuff now, but listen to the idea. (*reads impersonally*) Instantaneous release of ten × ten solar units . . . vehicles utilize random path trajectories . . . invulnerable . . . delivery in three minutes . . . obliterates one million cubic megameters . . . forever. Once and for all. Forever and ever! And ever and ever. What do you think! Of that!

WIFE: Sounds somehow automatic.

HUSBAND: It is, it is! To prevent mistakes, they say.

WIFE: Oh. Of course. I see. (*Lighting another cigarette, she directs her attention now from the window to the TV screen. She presses a remote-control button, makes the round of channels, and returns to the original station. Gazing at it absorbed, she speaks, however, to him*) . . . Well, what do you think?

HUSBAND: (*He is reading again, and answers her queries from a distant part of his attention*) What do I think?

WIFE: About last night.

HUSBAND: Oh. Yes. Of course.

WIFE: How did you like it?

HUSBAND: All right. Actually. Yes. Novel approach. Interesting development. Sort of a—um—reverse twist in there. It was all right. Almost ready to go. Good you thought of it like that. Yes. I was surprised. Really.

WIFE: What shall we call it?

HUSBAND: Call it? I don't know. What shall we call it?

WIFE: What about—oh—"Operation"—um—"Reverse Twist"?

HUSBAND: Reverse Twist is all right. I think.

WIFE: I wonder why it took so long to find it. Because when you have it, it seems obvious. Doesn't it. So unexpected, yet . . . so simple. So . . . natural, I think. How could we have overlooked it all this time? Where were we? What were we doing? Oh how stupid it makes me feel! But I am not stupid, am I?

HUSBAND: (*still reading and marking his paper industriously with his red pencil*) Those things take time. Sometimes years. They say.

WIFE: Is that what they say?

HUSBAND: Um. Years. Sometimes.

WIFE: But it's *been* years. Don't forget that. *Years!*

HUSBAND: (*reading*) I'll make a note of it.

WIFE: Years. I was that sick of your old Double Jumper Routine. Only a routine, it seemed. Automatic.

HUSBAND: Um.

WIFE: Didn't it seem somehow automatic?

HUSBAND: Um.

WIFE: And what was it before that old Double Jumper Routine? I forget. What was that again? Remember? What it was? I can't. Now why should I forget . . .

HUSBAND: (*reading*) Boom Town. How could you forget Boom Town? Where would we be today without Boom Town?

WIFE: Boom Town? *Boom* Town? What was that? Boom Town?

HUSBAND: Yes. Boom Town. You always used to say, "There's just so much I can stand!"

WIFE: (*laughs abruptly, a gay barking laughter, her eyes glowing for a moment with the memory*) Ah, oh! *Boom*

Town! Oh. Oh. Oh. Yes, I'd forgotten Boom Town. (*quite expressionless again, and still watching the TV screen*) Now why is that? Whatever happened with that?

HUSBAND: With that? We quit wildcatting. Settled down. Roots. Built home. Renewed land. Found community. There were the children to consider. Older. Experienced. Attitudes change, they say. As you get older. Experienced. Moreover, experienced.

WIFE: Oh. Attitudes.

HUSBAND: Yes. They change. Attitudes. That's why you forgot. Life changes. Moreover. Changes. Life.

WIFE: Attitudes. I suppose they do. Life changes. How curious. I never noticed. First one thing. Then another. That's why I forgot. Changes. You forget pleasure. You forget pain. You forget everything. So that's why I forgot Boom Town. Forgot that I used to say, "There's just *so* much I can stand!" It must have been long ago. How strange . . . (*somber*) We haven't much time now.

HUSBAND: Yes. I'll make a note. Operation . . . Reverse . . . Twist. Technique. Model. Patents? Research? So forth. And, um, yes: Not . . . much . . . time.

WIFE: That way you'll remember. (*He reads his paper and doesn't notice her taunt*)

HUSBAND: Um. That way I'll remember.

WIFE: That way you won't make a mistake.

HUSBAND: Um. That way you *can't* make mistakes, they say.

WIFE: That's why you've been so successful.

HUSBAND: That's why I've been so successful.

WIFE: Um. (*She is gazing out the window, her voice neutral.*

He explains, looking over the top of his paper at the TV)

HUSBAND: That's why I've been so successful. Yes. Because the techniques demand it. A record. Everything. That way you remember.

WIFE: Um.

HUSBAND: Yes. Because if you have no record you don't know what happened. If you don't know what happened you can't hope to grasp what's happening. And if you can't understand what's happening you don't know how to prepare for what is going to happen. (*His tone is didactic: he has expounded these principles countless times, and patiently does so again*)

WIFE: (*startled, looking out the window, which is bright and blank*) For what is going to happen?

HUSBAND: Um. As I've said, I think. Haven't I? Yes. Always said.

WIFE: (*neutral again*) Um.

HUSBAND: The future. We're going on. Into the future. Somehow. We should be prepared. It's simple. If you know what you're doing. Example: weren't we prepared when the waters were used? Suppose we hadn't been prepared! But we were. We were. All right.

WIFE: Um.

HUSBAND: If you can remember—can you remember? That was merely the first of our—um—difficulties. You've forgotten. Since then there have been so many— Doesn't matter. Um. Anyway it's simple. If you know what you are doing.

WIFE: *If.* But what happened to your grandfather? He knew what he was doing. They say.

HUSBAND: Um.

WIFE: Didn't he. Well, did he?

HUSBAND: Um. He knew. Yes. But. It was just beginning then. Actually. Primitive. No method. Crude techniques. Unsystematic. He never knew what happened, they say. That's what happened to my grandfather. I think.

WIFE: He wasn't unlucky?

HUSBAND: No. No no no. Unlucky! No such thing. How absurd you are. How can there be any such thing? Unlucky! Didn't he live a long time? Didn't he finally have his son? My father. I wouldn't call that unlucky. Would you?

WIFE: Um.

HUSBAND: And my father lived a long time too. And he knew what had happened. Moreover, did he do well or didn't he do well? And why did he do well? Technique! He knew what was happening. He recorded. Clarified. Diversified. Consolidated. Would you call that unlucky?

WIFE: Well . . .

HUSBAND: And then my father had his son. Me. Moreover, I've done—um—pretty well. Despite everything I'm doing well. Even better.

WIFE: Well . . .

HUSBAND: And despite everything I'm prepared for what is going to happen. In fact, in fact—I'm so well prepared that, that—

WIFE: Well . . .

HUSBAND: (looking actually at her for the first time. And she at him. They are expressionless) Well, what?

WIFE: I—

HUSBAND: Well, what? You know there isn't any time to lose. There's so much to do. We're on our way. Things are happening. Things will be happening. Inexorably. We're on the move. We must keep moving. On. Moving. Why just the techniques alone—

WIFE: Do you want to know?

HUSBAND: Um. Of course.

WIFE: Do you really want to know?

HUSBAND: Of course. I do. Um. You never know, I think.

WIFE: Do you?

HUSBAND: I should. I need to. Moreover everything may come to depend on it. Inevitably does, they say. Have I forgotten anything? *Could* I have forgotten anything?

WIFE: Your brother.

HUSBAND: (*somewhat puzzled, if not surprised*) My brother? Why do you mention my brother?

WIFE: *You* never do.

HUSBAND: *I* never do? Why should I? It's been twenty years. We've drifted apart. I have no brother. No idea what's happened to him. Who knows where *he* is? What *he's* doing? He doesn't matter. He's out of it. My brother. Don't know why you should mention him.

WIFE: Why I should mention him. Just wondering. (*Her eyes drift back to the TV screen. She lights another cigarette, stifles a yawn; she is ready to let the subject drop. His eyes drift outside the window*) He came into my mind, I think. You would say it's about time. Wouldn't you say it's about time?

HUSBAND: What does that mean? Nothing at all, does it! No, I would *not* say it's about time. About time. Doesn't mean anything. At all. Can't. About time. (*He rises abruptly, brushes himself, rolls up his napkin, puts away his marking pencil, folds the paper neatly and tosses it neatly into a basket. He goes round the table to her, and stands behind her chair, holding her head tenderly against him and looking absently out the window, through which is seen the luminous fog that has been there from the beginning*) At all. What were you thinking? About my brother.

WIFE: (*watching the TV*) I?

HUSBAND: (*squeezing her throat*) You . . . were . . . thinking. . . .

WIFE: I . . . don't . . . know . . . what . . .

HUSBAND: (*throttling her*) You were thinking: *It's about time.* (*harder*) What . . . is . . . about . . . time?

WIFE: (*She has not noticed anything*) I . . . don't . . . know. Your brother.

HUSBAND: But why? (*rapidly*) Why?

WIFE: I . . . don't . . . know. He just came, I think.

HUSBAND: (*murderously shaking her*) When? Where?

WIFE: Into my mind. (*He relaxes his grip instantly, holds her head tenderly once more. She has noticed nothing at all*)

HUSBAND: Um.

WIFE: Tell me about him.

HUSBAND: (*stroking her cheek absently. Now he watches the TV screen, and she is not listening to him at all*) They say Mother favored him. He'd be the lucky one. She thought luck was everything. Luck! Father believed in me. They say. Because I'd keep things moving. Develop things. Organize things. Right from the start there was that difference. But not enough was known. Picture not clear yet. I think it is now. Clear. Getting clearer. (*longish silence as they stare into their respective focal points*) . . . If it isn't really clear yet . . . Mother was like you. She'd have notions. She guessed things. Not that she *knew*. She'd come in upset one fine morning. No reason at all. She would say to Father, You see! You see! (*The wife starts, looks up at him, as he looks tenderly at her*) There was nothing there. At all.

WIFE: There was nothing there. Although—

HUSBAND: Said she saw things happening. Which is impossible.

WIFE: Impossible. Impossible?

HUSBAND: Or at least unreliable. You *think* you see things happen. Merely *think* you do. At best, you're only remembering them a little while afterwards. At best.

WIFE: (*tristfully*) Like Operation Reverse Twist.

HUSBAND: (*taken quite off stride*) Um. What?

WIFE: Like the Reverse Twist.

HUSBAND: Oh. Ah. Um. Yes. Which is why you must note things. Records. History. Everything is in the past. In a sense. Even discoveries have already happened. In a sense. All we can do is make notes. That's the basis of the techniques. You see, don't you? You understand, don't you?

WIFE: Yes. Um. But—

HUSBAND: Take, for example, your Reverse Twist. Assume it was possible. Of course. Even assume it was probable. Of course. But now it has happened. Last night. Now it is today. So that, um, Operation Reverse Twist was *already* in the past. In a sense. You see? You *do* see?

WIFE: Yes. No. I'm not sure. (*After a silence, she cries out very loudly in anguish—though not to him—and she is not in the least aware of her cry*) Oh darling!

HUSBAND: Anyway, my brother. Lacked my concentration. Like my grandfather, actually, in a way. As a boy he was wild. Wild as a boy. He'd always be a boy. Even if he is older than me. My brother.

WIFE: Older than you? I thought—

HUSBAND: Well, we're really the same age. I think.

WIFE: Twins?

HUSBAND: Um. Actually. Yes. No. I'm not sure.

WIFE: I don't understand.

HUSBAND: Brothers. Twins. Same thing. Somehow got turned round, they said. He. I. Um. Us. Doesn't matter now, does it. Which was which. We're not at all alike, I think. You wouldn't know him.

WIFE: (*as though begging for reassurance*) I wouldn't know him?

HUSBAND: Never.

WIFE: You would.

HUSBAND: Of course. I'd know him. Because. An old story. (*He is vague, rather distressed*) They say.

WIFE: I wonder if . . .

HUSBAND: Don't. Doesn't matter. We're different. Always have been. And then . . . because . . . moreover . . . there are certain details. Details within details. Pointless. One of those things.

WIFE: One of which things?

HUSBAND: Natural. (*He is irritated*)

WIFE: Natural?

HUSBAND: Unimportant, I mean. A coincidence. Irregular. Pointless. Unfair.

WIFE: Oh.

HUSBAND: A mistake. Unfair. Incongruous. Odd. Unusual.

WIFE: Oh.

HUSBAND: Accidental. Abnormal. Erratic. Unfair.

WIFE: Oh.

HUSBAND: Unfair. Doesn't matter anyway.

WIFE: (*her voice rising in a crescendo of sheer agony that he doesn't notice in the least*) Are you sure? Are you convinced? Are you perfectly certain? Are you? Are you?

HUSBAND: I hope you got me packed.

WIFE: (*Her voice is quite ordinary*) Yes, you're packed. Yes. Are you ready? (*She is up and leaving the kitchen*)

HUSBAND: (*looking at his watch, shaking his head in annoyance*) I'm late. I shouldn't be late. It's risky.

WIFE: (*returning with two elegant, terribly heavy suitcases and an attaché case: they seem to weigh a hundred pounds each*) Before you go—

HUSBAND: (*to himself*) If I skipped Honolulu, I could pick up some time.

WIFE: —I wanted to ask you, Would you call me? No. I know you're not allowed. But if *I* called, could I reach you? No. I'm not allowed. But— (*Her eyes are drawn to the window*) —just in case?

HUSBAND: (*Involved with his watch and calculations, he is matter-of-fact*) Everything's taken care of. We're prepared for anything.

WIFE: As usual.

HUSBAND: Of course. For this week. And most of next week. I think. Perfect days.

WIFE: But just in case?

HUSBAND: Can't. Rules.

WIFE: (*She sits on a suitcase*) Just in case?

HUSBAND: You know there's no such thing as "just in case." Not allowed. Techniques.

WIFE: Um.

HUSBAND: (*Surprised by her doubt, and grasping its significance, he finally speaks directly to her, and with growing exasperation*) What is the matter with you? Why are you like this today? You know it's not allowed. You know the situation is absolutely delicate. How can you be so irresponsible?

WIFE: Um.

HUSBAND: Sometimes I think you're not with me! Do you realize what you're doing when you ask something like this? No, you don't grasp it at all. Do you. Try to comprehend now: *you are introducing a novel variable!* At this moment. In history. Think of that. You want to do something like that at this enormous moment in history? Do you understand what a mistake a novel variable might be?

(*He is even a little angry*) Under the circumstances? For all of us? A terrible mistake. Think of that. A terrible, terrible mistake.

WIFE: Um.

HUSBAND: (*longish silence. Now he is petulant, even pleading*) You should know I would tell you. You should know this is part of something much bigger, and much more important than—I can't risk introducing a novel variable. Not now. Everything's set up. Rules are . . . Old mistakes . . . They say that . . . (*glancing at his watch again, baffled, worried. Speaks to himself*) . . . I'll have to skip Madrid. Can't be helped. What will they say in Nairobi? (*Turns on her in full rage*) You're my wife. Have you forgotten that, too? You can't do this to me now. Not *now*. My wife! Why if I'd known you would be the kind to lose your nerve, I would never have married—

WIFE: (*responding suddenly with equal vehemence, pounding frail fists against his unfeeling chest*) You're my husband! Don't forget that! I can't go on. As I have. What has happened to us? I have the right to know! What is happening to us! Why, if I had known you would think only of the techniques, I would never have married—

HUSBAND: (*speaking sweetly to her, as though their voices had never been raised*) You've never been like this, I think. What's the matter? You know nothing's happened to us. You know nothing's happening to us. You know nothing can happen to us. Tell me.

WIFE: (*She places her cheek tenderly against his breast. She keeps one eye on the TV, however*) It's nothing. Really. Just a little frightened. Haven't you ever been frightened?

HUSAND: That's a mistake. It isn't something that—it can't be something that—

WIFE: Don't you know what it is to be frightened?

HUSBAND: You should have told me sooner. Why didn't you tell me? (*Over her shoulder, while patting her, he looks at his watch*)   It's late. Now. I don't think there will be time to—

WIFE: I did.

HUSBAND: (*to himself*)   Have to cut out Saskatoon as well. Too bad. Risky. Tch. Risky.

WIFE: (*in a low dreamy whisper: she is absorbed in the TV*)   I did. I did tell you. I did.

HUSBAND: (*to himself, thinking about his schedule*)   The past cannot be helped. What's happened has happened. Too bad. Gone. Can't be adjusted. We'll have to change patterns for next week is all. Which, of course, involves the week after. And so forth. For good. Um. Risky risky risky. Where's my margin? I've got to have *some* margin! But no variables!   (*He is both determined and panicky*)

WIFE: Last year, I think. I think I told you last year.

HUSBAND: (*rapidly, nervously, thinking out loud*)   Must alert the analytical boys. They'll team up with the factors to re-synthesize the flow. That's more staff. Overtime. Dammit. Office crowded now! Dammit. Yes . . . But . . . And . . . Very risky.

WIFE: Or the year before. You made a note. You promised you'd remember. Now you've forgotten. Aha! You see! You see!

HUSBAND: (*coming back to her line of conversation without transition*)   No. Not at all. How could I?   (*Explains patiently*)   Part of the record. You've forgotten. Why we made this place. You don't remember. You wanted something. I gave it to you. Extended the complexes. Don't you remember? We installed ourselves.

WIFE: (*sighing contentedly, whispering softly, eyes glued to the TV*) Yes. Yes yes. Yes.

HUSBAND: (*hasn't heard her: enumerates features with satisfaction*) Safe, now. Whole thing's automatic. Doors. Keys. Perpetual lights. Permanent pressurizer. Stabilizer. Conditioner. Electronic exterminator. Self-renewing garden. Synchronized, miniaturized, and directed by the self-encasing units: the boxes. Automatic. Plugged in from A to Z. Nothing can happen now. System engages itself.

WIFE: (*cries out in her dream of TV, as though in terror*) Oh darling! Oh darling!

HUSBAND: Except, of course, for an error.

WIFE: (*lamenting piteously, twisting his lapels in supplication*) Oh please! Please! Please, darling, oh please, please!

HUSBAND: Just set the switch. It takes care of the rest.

WIFE: (*in utter desperation*) Oh darling! Please! I'm frightened. Frightened, frightened, frightened! (*last exclamation moaned*)

HUSBAND: Don't worry. Nothing to surprise you. It's automatic. You *do* understand?

WIFE: (*quietly watching TV again, as though she'd made no outburst*) Yes. I needn't worry. Of course.

HUSBAND: (*pats her head, lifts his suitcases as if they were empty*) I'm off. I must go. Understand?

WIFE: (*Looking coyly at him, she tries once more with a wee wheedling voice that knows it will get its way*) But . . . just . . . in case?

HUSBAND: I think I'll be sorry for this. But, um, all right: just
in case . . .   (*He consults his watch as he gives his itin-
erary. She has returned to the TV and doesn't listen. She
lights a new cigarette, pours herself a cup of coffee, gets
involved with whatever is showing or turns channels for
amusement. As he matter-of-factly reviews his schedule,
there may be a sequence of changes in lighting to corres-
pond with the passing days. His speech is not delivered
monotonously but with variations and self-dramatization,
to render it interesting. TV may weaken and fade in coun-
terpoint with lights*)   . . . running behind badly . . . um
. . . I should be leaving Buffalo at ten-thirty: only a brief
reconstruction conference. Four to six-thirty, Buenos Aires:
they're having hydrostatic-ramp difficulties there, as well as
local recalcitrance—probably will require reportioning of
the malleable districts. Hope they won't be stubborn. Odd
traditions surviving down there: they like friction for its
own sake! Then the native dinner at the Tenochtitlan
Hostal, where we'll cover social aspects of geobiological
refabrication, regarding particularly the introduction of the
prolific configurations. Leaving Mexico before coffee—have
to apologize for that, can't help it now—and pick up four
hours enroute to Manila. Assignment complete by midnight: merely recoding the hypothetical transducers for
omnivoltage capacity and highload transference along the
polar magnetic ducts. Then Tokyo, for the microscopic
air-bearings. Also looksee in at Kyoto: they seem to be concerned about my schedule for those superorbital disciplines.
Um. Maybe we could reactivate our planetary calendars
without using subtemporal circuits? Say, how about that!
Um. Hate to cut close corners like that: sets a bad example.
Well, we'll see. Melbourne by eight in the morning. Pack-
aging. Lunch. Wednesday: Munich. For pneumatics, dy-
namics and stress-sensors. Best people in the world there
for that. Their psychology, I think. Nothing special in-

volved, but it's important to have it all molecularly identical, because unless it is . . . you can just imagine what . . . oh boy! Trust them in Munich for the hydraulic barriers! So . . . let's see, I was . . . Um. By three, Roma. Napoli at four. Squeeze hard and get Palermo in by five. (*muttering, vexed*) Can't understand what could be causing the hitch in that hyperplastic transshipment. They promised me that . . . they should know that . . . Karachi for dinner; that would be eight-fifteen. I bet that committee will solve those synoptic variations in solar torques with that new tensor they've evolved. Personally, I don't care for their Oriental approach. Too spooky for me. But if it works, it will change even the most reliable basis for the techniques we have ever had. Won't they be thrown for a loop in Edinburgh! Heh heh! I *told* them to drop those Manchester–Cambridge empirics, I *told* them! Well, Stockholm at midnight, for alloyed rotors. Which brings us, I think, to Thursday A.M.: Houston. Collocation of reports. Must watch out for them there: there are deals within deals. They say. Let 'em just try! Then, on to Caracas: four-forty. Inspect hyperhydraulic presses for proper phasing at macrovelocities. We'll get up into the mountains for some evening air. Say, weren't we giving them a Totalization Festival that night? I think I could sit in on that. Can't harm. Might be interesting. To consider, I mean. Posttransference side of things. Ultimates and all. The ultimates, the ultimates . . . I like Caracas. Change of pace. Why miss the chance? So then. It's now Friday noon: Singapore—check out designs and test rigs for reactor gear. New mockups. It will be a remarkable demonstration of advanced universal projection. Well ahead of schedule, too. Really fascinating the way time doesn't affect them. Chinese. So Chinese. . . . Only they could think of it. Friday night is open. No. Ah, yes. The Bamboo Shrine Moon Motel in Hong Kong. Dinner. Casual. Some people

I must see, even if they're not ready to see me. (ANGRY) Some people don't know what they want! What they *think* they want. As if we'd leave it to *them* to do the wanting! Or thinking. Dammit. Oh, I'll hear what they have to say for themselves. Show them we care. See them, talk to them. In person. Personal relations. Heh heh. (*dark now: small, hot spot on the top of his head, as he speaks to himself sinisterly*) They'll know . . . what . . . to think . . . then. Um. Saturday morning bright and early, very busy: Vladivostok. Then Leningrad at two-thirty. Stuff of theirs is still formative. But promising. Very. *If* it can stand adaptation. The cycle there, as I see it (*greenish-tinted light perhaps*), seems to be *not only* polyphasic and hypermutational but *also* regenerative. They've come up with rather unusual self-deducing control servos. Nifty. Have to give them credit for their initiative. I always had a soft spot for the right thing in control servos. . . . Built-in, too. . . . At five o'clock top directorate of Aesop meets: Paris. Formality. I'll insist on it, though. Formal dinner in Monte Carlo. A bore. I'll insist on it, though. And then . . . (*lavenderish light*) . . . for a nightcap. Tangiers. And the recapitulation of our *finality sequences*. The ultimates again. Have to look at the results. Every week. I don't like to see the damned results. Need a drink for that. Techniques demand it. Ultimates and all. Then, Sunday morning—and I'm back again! If something tricky doesn't happen. Somehow. Expect me. Have I forgotten anything? No. How could I? After all. Well, then. All right? All right. (*He doesn't wait for her response, which is not forthcoming in any event, but brushes his lips over the top of her head, mechanically, and slips out the door, which has opened at his approach, and remains open. The din of traffic enters like Niagara as the door slides open, but it is as nothing beneath the incredible decibels of an extraordinarily powerful motor that starts up and moves away, rapidly shaking the very house with its power. The door slips to.*)

There is the silence, machine silence, of the kitchen again.
The wife looking at the TV, assents, somnambulistically)

WIFE: All right? All right.   (*She stretches, yawns luxuriously
as though waking for the first time that day*)   All . . .
right . . .   (*She emits a burst of laughter*)   All right!
(*She smiles at the TV; she doesn't really see it any more*)
All right.   (*She switches it off*)   All right.   (*She has answered an unheard voice*)   All right.   (*She looks about the
room contemptuously, as if she were a complete stranger*)
All right.   (*She goes to the window, hisses at it*)   All right.
(*She turns round, lights a cigarette, seems to be making up
her mind about something*)   All right!   (*She goes out the
other door with brisk steps, returns with a large make-up
box, seats herself—facing us, or back to us—and by the garish light emitted from the box, makes up her face, muttering
to herself in mounting anger*)   All right . . . all right . . .
all right . . . all right . . . allrightallrightallright . . . etc.*

*She stops in mid-phrase as she becomes conscious of a faint, low
sensuous drumming that is neither in the house nor outside it—
may be done by an electronic pulse. It will steadily grow louder.
At a parallel rate the light will diminish. As though hypnotized,
she rises, closing the box—her make-up completed—glides lan-
guorously backward to the CENTER FRONT, her hips moving inside
her kimono in the suggestion of the dance that might accompany
this beat. Then she glides, still dancing from the waist down,
backward to the RIGHT STAGE, where she comes to rest with her
back against the door, as the drumming is loudest. By now it is
very dark: the drumming ceases with the appearance of a man in
the door at LEFT. He is tall, well-dressed: indeed he wears the
same clothing as her husband had worn, though it is rumpled
and used hard. In fact, were it not that he has ears, he might
seem to be her husband himself. He wears dark glasses. He carries luggage identical with her husband's except that it is worn*

and seems to be very heavy for him. He puts it down and steps forward a pace into the kitchen, which is lit only by the more luminous control knobs at rear, and perhaps the grayish TV. [Here, the walls may disappear, or recede, if desired.] His face is calm, in repose. When she speaks her voice will be passionate but poised and luxurious: a much richer voice than she had used. Perhaps a spot grows on her, very slowly, from overhead.

WIFE: Is it you? At last?

BROTHER: (*nearly inaudible*)   Um.

WIFE: I've waited for you. So long. I've waited for you so very long.

BROTHER: (*nearly inaudible*)   Um.

WIFE: Now you're here. (*Takes off her kerchief. Her hair is set perfectly for evening. There is actually a diamond pin sparkling in it. She whispers*)   Well?

BROTHER: (*quiet, noncommittal*)   All right.

WIFE: (*She drops her kimono. She wears a long luxurious nightgown or peignoir*)   Well?

BROTHER: All right.

WIFE: (*feverishly*) Wait. Wait. (*Unhooking her nightgown, she lets it fall to the floor, revealing a glamorous, backless, and low-cut evening gown. Spotlight may sparkle on her. There is enough light from a spot on his head now to reveal a trace of a smile on his impassive face*)   Now. Well?

BROTHER: (*softly*)   Yes. All right.

WIFE: (*holding out her arms*)   At last. At last. At last. It must be you. At last.   (*crooned*)

BROTHER: (*reassuringly*)   All right. Yes.

WIFE: But you do want me? You will take me? At last?

BROTHER: If there is time. (*He steps forward a pace. His hands seem to open a little toward her. The spot on his head grows and fades almost imperceptibly: this "pulsing" is not strong enough to be disturbing but merely happens, slowly and rhythmically. His head is bowed and contemplative*)

WIFE: Free me? Save me?

BROTHER: If there is time.

WIFE: I have been alone. Too long. Always. Now you've come.

BROTHER: Um.

WIFE: Oh you don't have to answer. You don't have to promise. Wait. If there is time.

BROTHER: If there is time.

WIFE: (*She moves toward him almost imperceptibly. He waits, unaware of her approach. Finally, she will be in his arms [at the point noted below]*) Last night, somewhere between sleeping and waking, you came. I don't sleep much. I seem to have lost the habit. Though it is not really necessary, they say. Sleep. Because it is a delusion. A disappointment. Sleep. Moreover it is dangerous, they say. They say that sleep is very dangerous. Because that is the way we are approached, that is the only way now that we can be approached, they say, and reached, they say, by . . . by . . .

BROTHER: A novel variable?

WIFE: Yes. That. Last night—if it was last night—I can't remember—in the dark of that room, in the silence, in the utter isolation of that room, lying on our bed, alone, together, I thought of you.

BROTHER: And you were thirsty.

WIFE: Very thirsty. How long had it been? I was parched. How long since I had been touched, since I had been opened, since I had been filled? I was in darkness, in the silence. Was that my breathing I heard? I was not sure. It was cold. I was naked. I was sinking into the cold. My ears ached. My head ached. I was growing heavy.

BROTHER: Heavy. Heavy.

WIFE: Heavy. So heavy. I was a piece of scrap. Broken metal. Sinking through the coldness of the stone of the earth. And as I sank, slowly, into the deeper cold, I could feel my knees, my belly, my breasts. (*She does so with her jeweled hands*) And they were no longer a part of me. They belonged to a cold body, someone else's cold body. The hands that touched them were another's hands. Sinking. Where was I? How long had I been falling? After the third day—

BROTHER: You were no longer thirsty. After the fifth day—

WIFE: —I wanted to die. To kill myself. Die. Yet I'd grown used to this darkness. Time. There was no such thing as time.

BROTHER: You were hungry.

WIFE: I wanted to pick the cherries. There were cherry trees near by, all around me. I could smell the ripe cherries. An orchard. I was in an orchard. And then I thought of you. At that moment.

BROTHER: You were lonely.

WIFE: So lonely. All those years, how long had it been? Following him, from one life to another. And I had never thought of you. Though you were there all the time, I had never thought of you. Don't you find that strange?

BROTHER: Is it strange?

WIFE: Very strange. Nothing else I have thought of is so strange as that. I was on the bottom. I had sunk down and down—through the transparent darkness, the cold darkness that pressed upon me, heavier and heavier, until now I was on the bottom, under the stone. Nothing but the burning cold and the thick silence of a hundred hundred miles of frozen stone. I was on the bottom, among a few scattered, broken shells and stars. I was not afraid any more. I was on the bottom. And then I thought of you. For the first time. (*She laughs a short, gay laugh*) And I worried about you. Someone I had never known or even heard of! Worried! Don't you find that very strange? (*She has reached him. She looks up into his impassive face*)

BROTHER: Is it?

WIFE: Anything might have happened to you! Our world has changed over and over again. Yet we have gone on. Until now, when it seemed . . .

BROTHER: That you thought of me.

WIFE: (*She caresses his face, his head, shoulders, arms, while speaking*) How, how I have *needed* you. How I have needed *you*. You must have starved. While he lunched. Alone and aching and cold while he rested. You might even have died, while he was contracting the future. Anything was possible!

BROTHER: Anything.

WIFE: (*Embracing him hungrily. He is impassive*) How did I know it was you? I can't remember my childhood. My girlhood. My men, my marriages, my children. Yet—when you came into my mind I recognized you!

BROTHER: That is very strange.

WIFE: (*She kisses him, kisses him passionately about the face, speaking all the while*) And then, I wondered—how would I ever find you? Could I live until I found you? Would I be able to speak to you? Would you hear me? And if I cried out to you in that emptiness, "Come! Come to me!" Would you come? Now I've found you. Where have you been?

BROTHER: (*Stage has grown fairly light by now. It grows slowly, steadily, inexorably brighter—until the light is unbearable*) Here.

WIFE: Here?

BROTHER: Here. Somewhere near. Always. (*He seems to be searching vaguely from behind his dark glasses*) (*Silence: he is baffled by what he fails to recognize*) . . . He went away. One night. A long time ago. Alone. Empty-handed. Never returned. Never will. I stayed. Here. It was my home. Hard to remember, but somewhere here. . . .

WIFE: He went away?

BROTHER: Ran. If he hadn't . . .

WIFE: Ran away?

BROTHER: Disappeared. Vanished. Into the hills. Gone. Had to. I would have—

WIFE: (*Clutches him*) Killed him?

BROTHER: Killed him. If he'd stayed here. If he'd had the courage. If he weren't such a thief, such a swindler, such a coward. I'd have—

WIFE: (*incredulous*) Killed him?

BROTHER: Got away by luck. Sheer luck. He always had it. Luck.

WIFE: Killed him? (*She laughs*)

BROTHER: (*angry*) Killed him! Yes! Cut him down and chopped him up and thrown away the pieces! (*calmly*) Family matter. (*distant, ruminative*) You never heard about it? He has a way of talking. Oh, there is nothing he wouldn't say or do to . . . you were never told?

WIFE: No. Yes. I'm not sure. (*Faintly, far-off there is a sonic boom*) I was just wondering . . .

BROTHER: Don't. Doesn't matter. Anyhow. It's over. Done with. Forgotten. But if he came back . . . here . . .

WIFE: (*She whispers loudly at his ear*) He always does.

BROTHER: If he ever tried . . .

WIFE: He will. Sunday morning.

BROTHER: Although it happened so long ago . . . It really doesn't matter—

WIFE: (*another sonic boom, somewhat stronger*) That's his. He's passing.

BROTHER: It's been so long since . . . No one remembers. Anymore. World changes. People change. No one cares. I don't either . . .

WIFE: (*She has released him. She begins to drift away, backward, almost imperceptibly. By the end of the action, she will be once more pressed back against the door at right [if walls have gone, she is pressed against the invisible barrier that limits room]*) We have so little time now. This is our enormous moment.

BROTHER: (*quietly, to himself*) Though I've thought about it so long, it doesn't matter, in the end. What matters is now. I'm ready. Finally. To begin. Never mind what happened. It's gone. We're moving ahead now, into the future.

WIFE: (*She is exuberant: she begins in full joyous voice—yet*

her enthusiasm diminishes as his voice grows stentorian)
So much to discover! Our selves! (*another sonic boom, stronger*) That's his. (*to herself with relief*) He's passed. (*aloud*) We have our lives. And so little time. We must begin. But where?

BROTHER: (*starting low and rather indecisively, but gathering momentum and power and exaltation, gradually, until the very end*) Because, now that I'm here . . . Where I've always been . . . In a sense . . . We are going to start. Again. From here. Where I have always been. Here, somewhere.

WIFE: Yes. That is what I meant. That is what I have always wished, always. Do you see my tender little toes?

BROTHER: Never mind what is happening. I am going to do it my own way. All right.

WIFE: Yes. That is what I mean. Do you see my feet, my pretty feet, with their fine ankles?

BROTHER: Never mind what they say is going to happen.

WIFE: And my round calves? So cool to the touch . . .

BROTHER: Never mind them, the others who have failed in their miserable blind purposes and ways. Never mind the rules, the clubs, the societies, the companies and committees, the judges, the juries, the banks, soldiers and sailors and syndicates of space, the politicians of the world and their police, the philosophers, psychologists and professors and priests and prophets and poets and prostitutes and people of the professions in general, the people, the people and people and people. . . . It is my way that matters now. My way only. From here.

WIFE: Yes. That is what it will mean. And my legs, my long, strong legs . . . ?

BROTHER: From the ground up. And up. To choose a site, if such there be, that has truly natural advantages—

WIFE: —my knees that are so smooth and round . . .

BROTHER: —something solid amidst the ancient swamps and sands and marshes where I've always struggled, where I have been lost again and again, yet going on step by step, hand over hand, a place exposed to the skies, yet sheltered from the changing winds of the inevitable and prolonged bitter seasons, a site dry and warm yet abundantly watered, where the roads shall meet—

WIFE: —and these firm and straight thighs that are like polished marble, my full and lovely legs?

BROTHER: —meet, meet, yet will not cross or tangle, where there is light and quiet and safety (*sonic boom, louder yet*), and the air is free and fresh, the food tasty and tender and newly grown in neat gardens visited by bees and watched over by song birds, where we shall walk and ride and swim and run, dance and sit in places conveniently planned and commodiously arranged, where the materials are cheap and lightweight and strong and adaptable, easy to use and keep clean, where there are centers for shopping and temples for prayer and meditation, for exercise and games, information and entertainment, for working and playing—

WIFE: —and here is my deep belly, complete and round and yielding, a secret fountain framed by my wild and slender sides. And here, here are my breasts: like soft birds. Do you see my body, my desirable body?

BROTHER: —for eating and meeting, for judging and speaking,

JASCHA KESSLER / 175

and squares for hospitals and schools and cemeteries, prisons and libraries and factories and theaters and offices and prisons and parades and parks and gardens and prisons and—

WIFE: Or my shoulders of old ivory, my arms like alabaster vines, warm and strong and light as feathers on your heart, and my neck like a milky column of—

BROTHER: —and all of it full of my invented healthy families, spreading over the great green and tree-lined boulevards, spotlessly broad, branching across the lands, across the world, bridging the seas, diving below the seas, above the valleys and over the earth and beyond, beyond, growing beyond, spreading— (*another sonic boom, louder yet and closer. Fills the stage*)

WIFE: —and, and my head, do you see my head? Like a blossom, a flower of the morning, and my lips soft and covered with honey, my eyes like coral grottoes through which the deep-sea waves drift with changing lights, my hair like a delicate and living thing? Do you see? For you. All. For you. Now. But now. While there is time. (*She sways in supplication*) Do you see? My body, my beautiful body? (*Stage is very bright now*)

BROTHER: —spreading and growing, everywhere the same, everywhere equal and everywhere together, the many as one, now and forever, united, like, like—

WIFE: My simple, my spontaneous, musical and utterly original body? My beautiful human body? (*very loud sonic boom indeed*)

BROTHER: —and it is one, like one vast radiant incorporation (*his tone exalted and thrilling*), a scintillating body, a city golden, ruby and emerald, an organism, jeweled and sparkling and glowing with the brightness of many suns, and governed by one and only one law, governed I say—

WIFE: (*whispering piteously, desperately, for the last time*) It is all I have. It is all there is for me to give. It is all there ever was for you . . . For you . . . For me . . . My life . . .

BROTHER: (*triumphantly*) —governed, I say, with the same indivisible justice and meaning and mercy for all, from here, from now on, for ever . . . and forever, and ever and ever and everand foreverand everand ever andeverandever- foreverandeverandeverandev— (*With a flourish, he removes his dark glasses as he ecstatically pronounces his last "andevers":* he has no eyes.)

A sonic boom rocks the audience. A blaze of blinding light.

Silence.

Darkness

JANE COOPER / *Practicing for Death*

I

Monarch and fritillary, swallowtail—
Great butterflies red-brown or glossy black,
Spotted or striped or plain,
Each glistening with down—
I chased you through my earliest fields and back
Along a tangled track
To where the woods grew secret, dark and tall.

There you would disappear with a last hover,
Scurry or zigzag purposeless to the eye,
Witless and teasing, yet
Always beyond my net,
Beyond my fluttering hand that could not fly.
Brave alter-mystery,
Always you found some shadow for your cover.

Or I would watch you trembling on a branch
Open and close with pure control your wings,
As if a steady hand
Slowly could wind, unwind
The coil that steeled those frail yet tensile springs,
As if unhurried breathings
Had drifted you aloft, out of my reach.

Lost beyond reach—yet still I tried to follow
Down your close paths and into the sun again,
For what except to yield
All pleasures of the field
Into a single, gold and gathered grain?
To force the flash of vision
Under my grasp to fill that pulsing hollow?

And what if I garnered death, the fix of art,
Instead of the moving spark I chose to race?
When winter found my hoard
Pinned to a naked board,
Was it my own long-legged, sidelong grace
I had betrayed, the space
Of instant correspondence in the heart?

II

For there were times, after a daylong spent
In meadows smelling hot and dry of noon,
Where every grass would stir
Shagged over with blue aster,
I would surprise you, dozing, fumbling drone.
Quickly my sliding prison
Would muffle you in clouds of blinding lint.

And I would pinch my net around that weed
You hung from until, beating up and out
In strong, bewildered strivings,
You battered with your wings
And head against the deep net's lightstruck throat,
Or, loosening your feet,
Crawled up the folded shadows of its side.

Then carrying you as hopefully as an egg
Cradled in cotton, I would poise, advance
On cautious legs until
I begged someone to kill
The body I had pinioned in its dance—
Small, ignorant, intense
And homely engine of the whirligig.

Still in odd dreams I wonder, was it strength
Never to bear the final act of prey?
What native cowardice
Clamped me as in a vise
Before the oozing promise of decay?
Veined, irradiant beauty,
I found no stillness in your labyrinth.

Even the fields that beckoned then seemed wild,
Shimmering with sun traps and cloud plays.
Some lingering violence
Threatened each waiting sense—
How could I trust? When shall I learn to praise,
Tracing you down dark ways
Again, live butterflies? ablaze, scared child!

MAURICE CRANSTON / *The Later Thought of Jean-Paul Sartre*

André Gide used to say of himself, on the strength of having one Protestant and one Catholic parent, that he was a child touched by "conflicting extremes." Sartre might with greater reason make this claim, for his father was a French Catholic and his mother came from a family of German-speaking Alsatian Protestants. At any rate, in Sartre's thought the extremes of French and German culture meet. His existentialism was an answer to the disappointment of a French Cartesian yearning for a universe of rational order, and that answer was a German one, for *Existenz-philosophie* (which Sartre studied in Berlin) was itself a reaction of the German romantic mind against the rationalism of Hegel. But Sartre, who had no grudge of his own against Hegel, came increasingly to feed on that source against which German existentialism rebelled, so that his kind of existentialism is as much Hegelian as it is anti-Hegelian.

Sartre himself, however, claims to have become something

more than Hegelian. He says he has become a Marxist. In his autobiography, a short, brilliant, very French book, published in Paris in 1963 with the title *Les Mots*, Sartre declared that he had derived his metaphysical yearnings from the upbringing he had had, in his bookish grandfather's world of words, and that he had been cured of his idealistic hankerings, not by existentialism, but by the impact of Marxism. Elsewhere he claimed to have been converted to Marxism by the late Maurice Merleau-Ponty at the time of the Occupation, though Merleau-Ponty's Marxism was always, to say the least, peculiar. Sartre's sympathy for the Communist Party, on purely political grounds, has certainly been more steadfast than was Merleau-Ponty's. But does that sympathy go together with any real adhesion to Marxist philosophy? How far is Sartre, as he claims to be, a Marxist?

To answer this question we must turn to Sartre's most substantial contribution to social theory, the *Critique de la raison dialectique*, published in 1960. This is one of Sartre's Germanic works, long, diffuse, replete with technical language and jargon. Moreover, for all its 755 closely printed pages and numerous footnotes, it is only one volume of a longer projected work. No one has as yet ventured to translate it into English.[1] Some critics have proclaimed it unreadable. I myself find it fatiguing but rewarding; and since we know from the memoirs of Simone de Beauvoir that the author had to keep himself going with drugs to finish it, he might reasonably expect some comparable effort on the part of the reader. Sartre might well say with Rousseau: "*Je ne sais pas l'art d'être clair pour qui ne veut pas être attentif.*"

The *Critique de la raison dialectique* has an ambitious title, if only because of the obvious reference to Kant's *Kritik der reinen Vernunft*. And indeed Sartre sees himself as doing some-

---

1 The preliminary essay of the *Critique* has been translated by Hazel Barnes and published as *Search for a Method*. Excerpts from the *Critique* have been translated and published in *The Philosophy of Jean-Paul Sartre*, edited and introduced by Robert Denoon Cumming (New York: Random House, 1965). Reprinted by permission of Alfred A. Knopf, Inc.

thing analogous to Kant; where Kant, as Sartre supposes, was making a synthesis of empiricism and rationalism, Sartre is attempting to make a synthesis of existentialism and Marxism. In a prefatory essay, *Question de méthode*, Sartre explains that he has set out to revitalize and modernize Marxism by giving it a new method. In the main body of the *Critique* he shows how this modernized, or existentialized Marxism unfolds itself in a new *anthropologie* (in Kant's sense of that word), that is to say, in a philosophical theory of man and society.

Sartre's approach to the subject is not, as he explains, purely academic. His *Question de méthode* appeared originally in a Polish journal in 1957, when "destalinization" first became the order of the day, and the theory is consciously put forward as a destalinized philosophy for bewildered Communist intellectuals, and as a basis for reunion between such intellectuals and those of the Left who remain outside the Party: that is to say, as something to fill minds left painfully empty by Moscow's repudiation of Stalin's teaching, and as a theoretical foundation for a new United Front against the bourgeoisie. This public-spirited purpose in no way detracts from the academic interest of the *Critique*; many of the best political theorists have had some such further motive; the philosopher and the polemicist are often the same man.

Sartre begins by paying the most lavish tributes to Marxism and making the most modest claims for existentialism. Indeed he says that whereas Marxism is one of the main philosophies of the modern world, existentialism is not even a genuine philosophy at all. Existentialism is merely an "ideology." But he does not use the word *ideology* in Marx's sense. He provides his own Sartrian definition both of that word and of the word *philosophy*. Philosophies, according to Sartre, are the great creative systems of thought which dominate certain "moments" or periods of history, systems which cannot be gotten beyond (*dépassé*) until history itself has moved on to another stage. Thus in the seventeenth century, the philosophical "moment" was that of

Descartes and Locke; at the end of the eighteenth and the beginning of the nineteenth century, it was the "moment" of Kant and Hegel; our own age is that of Marx. No philosophy could go beyond Descartes and Locke in their time, or Kant and Hegel in theirs; and no philosophy can go beyond Marx today. We are compelled, Sartre says, to think in Marxist terms.

Not content with thus exalting Marxism, Sartre is at pains to diminish existentialism, the mere ideology. Ideologies, in this Sartrian sense, are little systems which live on the edge of the great systems of thought, and which "exploit the domain" of the genuine philosophies. Since the present century falls within the Marxist epoch, existentialism "exploits the domain of Marxism." Existentialism, then, is "a parasitic system which lives on the margin of a Knowledge to which it was at first opposed, but into which it seeks now to integrate itself." [2]

This is a decidedly original perspective. There is also something audacious about the proposal that existentialism should "integrate itself" into Marxism, for no two systems of thought could be more dissimilar. Two things, at least, would seem to offer insuperable obstacles to any fusion. First, existentialists believe in free will, libertarianism, indeterminism; and Sartre in particular has always put great emphasis on this. No theme is more marked and recurrent in all his work than that man is "condemned to be free." Marx, on the other hand, belongs to that tradition of philosophy which would banish the free will problem altogether. Freedom, for Marx, is, in Hegel's words, "recognition of necessity." Marx holds first that all history is shaped and determined by the relations of production which spring from the inexorable laws of matter, and secondly, that men can master their destiny in so far as they understand those laws and consciously direct their action in accordance with them. Thus Marx thinks he is entitled to believe equally in both freedom and determinism. For Sartre, on the other hand, determinism is not only false, it is a form of *mauvaise foi*, or

[2] Sartre's *Critique de la raison dialectique*, p. 18.

culpable self-deception, by means of which certain people evade their moral responsibility.

Next, there is the matter of individualism. Existentialists lay great stress on the isolation, the solitude, the "abandonment" of the individual; and no existentialist writer has stressed this more than Sartre, from his earliest novel *La Nausée* to his latest play *Les Séquestrés d'Altona*. But Marxism regards individualism as a "delusion of theory" and holds that man's true nature is a social one.

Sartre does not shirk these contradictions. He believes they can be resolved. He suggests that the trouble lies in the fact that Marxism—orthodox Marxism—has become out-of-date, hidebound, dogmatic; it has lost its touch with humanity. This is where existentialism can help to renovate it—by "humanizing" Marxism. Sartre goes on to make this curious prediction:[3]

> From the day that Marxist research takes on a human dimension (that is to say, the existential project), as the basis of its sociological knowledge, existentialism will no longer have a reason for being—absorbed, transcended and conserved by the totalizing movement of philosophy, it will cease to be one particular enquiry, and become the basis of all enquiry.

Sartre insists that his quarrel is with the Marxists and not with Marx; indeed he gives an interpretation of Marx's essay on the "Eighteenth Brumaire" which suggests that Marx himself, in his most inspired moments, was an existentialist without realizing it. Sartre's complaint about the Marxists is that they are lazy. Sometimes they are too metaphysical and sometimes too positivistic. Their thinking is old-fashioned, and often it is not thinking at all, but blind assent to authority.

Many of Sartre's criticisms of the orthodox Marxists hit the nail on the head. He shows, for example, how shallow is the judgment of those Marxist literary critics who dismiss Valéry as a "petty bourgeois intellectual." Sartre agrees: Valéry *is* a petty

[3] *Ibid.*, p. 111.

bourgeois intellectual, but the important point is that "not every petty bourgeois intellectual is a Valéry." Sartre also demonstrates the absurdity of the Marxist critical habit of bundling together such diverse writers as Proust, Joyce, Bergson, and Gide as "subjective"; he shows that this category of the subjective is not empirically viable; it is not drawn from experience; it is not based on the study and observation of real men.

"Lazy Marxists," Sartre says, reveal their laziness not only in their unreflective use of categories but in their tendency to constitute the real a priori. Just as Communist Party politicians use these methods to prove that what has happened had to happen, so Marxist intellectuals use it to prove that everything is what it was bound to be. And this, Sartre shrewdly observes, is merely a method of "exposition" from which one learns nothing. It is tautologous; it cannot teach us anything, because it knows in advance what it is going to find out. Hence the need for giving Marxism a new method.

Sartre describes this method which existentialism offers Marxism as "heuristic"; that is to say, it is a method serving to discover truth; it is also "dialectic." Sartre asserts that whereas the lazy Marxist when confronted with any problem immediately refers to abstract principles, his own new method works by no other means than that of "cross reference" (the *va-et-vient*) within the flux and movement of the real world. For example, Sartre's method would seek to explain the biography of individuals like Flaubert or Robespierre by an equally deep study of the epoch which shapes the individual and of the individual who shapes the epoch. He calls it the Progressive–Regressive method. It is progressive because it seeks part of the explanation in the aims of conscious beings; and it is regressive because it looks at the conditions in which each conscious being pursues his objectives. People have to be understood both in terms of their own aims and in the light of the circumstances in which they formulate and seek to realize their aims.

Sartre gives an interesting example of what he has in mind in discussing the case of Flaubert. Sartre is as quick as any lazy Marxist to classify and castigate Flaubert as a petty bourgeois. But this is only the beginning. The important thing about Flaubert, for Sartre, is not that his class was petty bourgeois but what he did to rise above that condition. Flaubert, in Sartre's words, "threw himself across the several fields of possibility toward the alienated objectivation of himself, creating himself ineluctably and indissolubly as the author of *Madame Bovary* and as the petty bourgeois that he refused to be." [4]

Flaubert's career is thus seen as instance of the project (*le projet*). This is a characteristically existentialist concept and one of which Sartre has often made use. It figures prominently in the most substantive work of his earlier years, and still perhaps his masterpiece, *L'Etre et le Néant* (1943), where the project is defined as the way in which a person chooses his mode of life and creates himself in action. The design according to which we make ourselves is our project. Of Flaubert's project, creating himself as an objective being in the shape of an author, or more precisely as *the* author of *Madame Bovary* and other novels, Sartre writes:[5]

> This project has a *meaning*. It is not a simple negativity, the flight (from the petty bourgeois predicament); but rather through it, the man aims at the production of himself in the world as a certain objective totality. It is not the pure and simple abstract choice to write that makes the nature of Flaubert, but the choice to write in a certain fashion so as to manifest himself in the world in a certain way—in a word, it is the particular meaning that he gives (in the framework of contemporary ideology) to literature as the negation of his original condition, and as the objective resolution of his contradictions.

A man "defines himself" by his project. We make ourselves what we are by what we do. Sartre has had something to say

4 *Ibid.*, p. 93.
5 *Ibid.*

about this in several of his earlier books. For example, in his play, *Huis Clos* (1943), the male protagonist, Garcin, tries to maintain that he has a noble and courageous nature in spite of the fact that he has done cowardly deeds, and the *farouche*, plain-speaking Lesbian, Inès, tells Garcin that a man has no nature apart from his actions; his actions define him, so that a man whose behavior is cowardly *is* a coward. We *are* what we *do*. Sartre is equally emphatic in saying that what we do is what we choose to do. We are totally responsible for our actions; since as beings "condemned to be free" we could, if we had chosen differently, have acted differently. Garcin, in *Huis Clos*, could have done better deeds and died a hero; and Flaubert, in the real world, could have made a worse choice, and lived in idleness as a *rentier*, and then he would not have been *the* Flaubert we know, the author of *Madame Bovary*.

In *L'Etre et le Néant*, the notion of the project is bound up with existence; and here again, in the *Critique*, Sartre speaks of the project as a kind of "uprooting of oneself toward existence"; and by existence, he adds, "we do not understand a stable substance, which abides in itself, but a perpetual disequilibrium, an uprooting of the whole body. And this drive toward objectivation takes different forms in different individuals as each projects himself forward through a field of possibilities—of which one realizes some to the exclusion of others. We existentialists call this Choice, or Liberty." [6]

I think it is clear from this quotation, and from what I have so far summarized, that Sartre has retained the libertarian principle of existentialism and by no means assimilated the Marxist theory of necessity. So in spite of all that Sartre said at the beginning about Marxism being the true philosophy and existentialism being a mere ideology, it is obvious that an essential part of the so-called integration between the two will have to be the surrender by the Marxist, and not by the existentialist, of one

[6] *Ibid.*, p. 95.

fundamental belief. To modify the shock of this demand, Sartre invokes the aid of the Marxist concept of *Praxis*. This word is often used by Marx and his followers, though not always in the same sense. At different places in Marxist writings, *Praxis* appears to mean (1) the common sense that stands opposed to speculation, (2) the process of acting, as opposed to meditation, by which understanding is acquired, (3) empirical, scientific, or industrial work. Now Sartre, with some adroitness, has taken this ambiguous and rather rough-and-ready Marxist notion of *Praxis* and made it more or less identical with the existentialist notion of the project. In other words, Sartre uses this idea of *Praxis* as a means of injecting his own notion of project into Marxism. The notion of project, as we have seen from the quotation above, is a libertarian one. Therefore if the notion of *Praxis* could be interpreted as meaning what "project" means, and the Marxist admits to believing in *Praxis*, then the Marxist might be shown to be a libertarian without knowing it.

Sartre, however, can hardly expect to have this ploy pass unchallenged. The project is by definition something that can be undertaken only by men who have free will, whereas *Praxis*, however loosely the word may be used in Marxist writings, is always represented there as something undertaken in full consciousness of the laws of necessity. Hence if the concepts of project and *Praxis* are to be united, it is the Marxist, and not the existentialist, who is going to have to make a radical revision of his categories.

Let us next consider the other subject on which existentialism and Marxism are notoriously at variance: individualism. Existentialism as it is commonly understood, and certainly as it is expounded by Sartre, entails an extreme form of individualism, whereas Marxism has no more conspicuous feature than its rejection of individualism—its belief that man must be seen in terms of the social whole or common humanity. Sartre has attempted to resolve this antithesis by putting forward in his *Cri-*

tique a theory of society which he claims to be both Marxist and existentialist. How far can he be said to have succeeded?

Once again Sartre makes free use of the kind of technical language which is favored by Marxists. First, he invokes the notion of alienation. But Sartre, as we shall see, has a different theory of alienation from that of Marx. Whereas Marx saw alienation as the result of the exploitation of one man by another, Sartre sees alienation as an unalterable feature of the human predicament. Indeed Sartre's notion of alienation cannot be understood in purely Marxist terms. The words Sartre shares with Marx are words they have both rifled from Hegel. Sartre's theory of alienation is an existentialized Hegelian concept, not an existentialized Marxist concept. His alienation, already explained in *L'Etre et le Néant*, is *metaphysical*. Nevertheless he does not forget that his subject here is *l'anthropologie* as opposed to *l'ontologie*; and that a fresh, and so to speak, specifically sociological reason has to be given for what he has always regarded as the fundamental characteristic of human relations—mutual antagonism.

This theory is developed in the most striking, if also the most intricate and tortuous, sections of the *Critique*. The principle Sartre introduces at this point is that of shortage, or *scarcity*. Sartre says that all human history—at any rate, all human history hitherto—has been a history of shortage and of a bitter struggle against shortage. There is not enough in this world to go around, and there never has been. And it is this *scarcity*, according to the *Critique*, which makes human relationships intelligible. Scarcity is the key to understanding the attitude of men to one another and to understanding the social structures men have built up during their life on earth. Scarcity, says Sartre, both unites and divides us. It unites us because it is only by united efforts that we are able to struggle at all successfully against scarcity; it divides us because each one of us knows that it is only the existence of others which prevents there being abundance for oneself.

Scarcity then is "the motor of history." Men cannot eliminate scarcity altogether. In this sense, men are powerless or impotent. The best that any man can do is to try to overcome scarcity by collaboration with others. But such collaboration is itself paradoxical, for each of the collaborators knows that it is the existence of the world of others that makes scarcity. I am a rival to you, and you are a rival to me. When I work together with others to struggle against scarcity, I am working with those whose existence makes that work necessary; and by my work I nourish my competitors and rivals. Scarcity, then, not only shapes our attitude to the natural world but shapes our attitude to our neighbors. Scarcity makes us all rivals, yet compels us to collaborate with our rivals; for being impotent alone, we can only struggle effectively against scarcity by the division of labor and other such joint endeavors.

Nature, however, is "inert" and indifferent to human welfare. The world we inhabit is in part the world of nature and in part the world that has been made by our forebears in the course of their long struggle against scarcity. Sartre calls it the world of the *Practico-Inert*. The world is the world of *Praxis* in so far as it is a world shaped by the work and projects of its past and present inhabitants. This is the world to the extent that it is manmade. But the world is also the passive, or inert, world of nature on which man has had to work. Ironically, many of the things that men have done with the aim of making the world more bearable, with the aim of diminishing scarcity, have had the effect not of improving but of worsening the world. Sartre gives the example of Chinese peasants cutting down wood to make fires and to build houses, and doing this on so large a scale, that they effectively deforest their land, and so expose themselves to the hazards and disasters of constant floods. Men are tormented by their own inventions in the world of the Practico-Inert.

Thus, in a hostile universe, defined by scarcity, man becomes the enemy of man. In a typically Sartrian phrase, man becomes antiman, *le contre-homme*. And in a paragraph which is dramatic enough to be a speech in one of his plays, Sartre writes:[7]

> Nothing indeed—neither wild beasts nor microbes—could be more terrible for man than this intelligent, flesh-eating, cruel species, which knows how to follow and outwit the human intelligence and of which the aim is precisely the destruction of man. This species is manifestly our own, as each of us sees it, in the Other, in the context of scarcity.

The conflicts—or relationships of antagonism—between man and man are thus given an *economic* explanation in the *Critique*. We come next to a piece of "dialectic." Antagonism is negative reciprocity; but that negation is itself negated in the collaboration between neighbors which is necessary to overcome scarcity. This is Sartre's "dialectical" theory of the origin of society.

He distinguishes two forms of social structure: one he calls the *series*, the other the *group*. The two are significantly different. A series is a collection of people who are united only by external proximity. It does not exist as a whole "inside" any of its members. The example Sartre gives of a series is a line at a bus stop. This is a collection or gathering of people that can be observed. You can look at it, count the number of people in it. Everyone is there for the "same" purpose; but they do not have a *common* or collective purpose. No one is interested in the others. Indeed, each member of the line is a rival of the others. Because of the scarcity of seats in the bus, each wishes the others were not there. Each is superfluous, each is one too many. But because everyone *knows* that he also is one too many to the others, just as each of the others is one too many to him, all agree to take it in turn to get on the bus when the bus comes. They form an orderly series to avoid a fight or war on the platform of the bus. The forming of an orderly series like a line

[7] *Ibid.*, p. 208.

192

waiting for a bus is thus a negative reciprocal relationship which is the negation of antagonism; it is the negation of itself.

The people in the line form a plurality of solitudes. And Sartre maintains that the whole social life of mankind is permeated by series of this kind. A city is a series of series. The bourgeoisie is a series of series, each member respecting the solitude of the others. But in human society, there is another kind of collection or gathering which Sartre recognizes; and this is what he calls the *group*. A group is a collection of people who, unlike those in a series, *do* have a common objective or end. A football team is the example he gives. The difference between a group and series is inward. From the outside you cannot tell the difference. What makes a group is the fact that each member has committed himself to act as a member of that group. The group is held together, and therefore constituted, by commitment. Each member, as Sartre puts it, has converted his own individual *Praxis* to a common or social *Praxis*. The working class becomes a group when its members commit themselves to socialism. A group can get things done, whereas a series is impotent, since each member pursues only his own *Praxis*. And indeed it is precisely *because* the series is impotent that the group is constituted in the first place. The origin of the group, Sartre suggests, can be summed up in the discovery that "we must either live by working together, or die by fighting each other."

Scarcity again is the driving force, since it is scarcity, and scarcity alone, which makes men work together for a common end. Scarcity is thus seen as the origin of the group. And in developing this thought, Sartre introduces three colorful notions: the pledge (*le serment*), violence, and Terror. Sartre explains that the group comes into being when each individual gives his pledge to become a member of the group and not to defect from or betray the group. A group is thus defined as a *pledged* group. But the pledge must be enforced, and the members must be assured that it will be enforced. This is where violence and Terror come in. It is fear which drives men to form groups in the first place, and it is fear that must keep them in these groups. The fear which keeps men in their groups is Terror. Indeed the pledge itself, says Sartre, is an invitation for violence to be used against oneself if one breaks one's own word; and the existence of Terror is an assurance that violence will be used against any other member of the group who tries to break his pledge.

All groups, says Sartre, are in constant danger of dissolving into seriality. Everyone is conscious of the threat of dispersion in himself and in others. Hence Sartre can say that "Terror is the statutory guarantee, freely called for, that none shall fall back into seriality." Terror indeed is more than this: it is "mortal solicitude," for it is thanks to Terror that man becomes a social being, created such by himself and by others. Terror is the violence that negates violence. Terror indeed is farternity. For Terror is the guarantee that my neighbor will stay my brother; it binds my neighbor to me by the threat of the violence it will use against him if he dares to be "unbrotherly."

The most important example of a group which Sartre gives is the state. The state, he says, "is a group which reconstitutes itself incessantly, and modifies its composition by a partial renewal—discontinuous or continuous—of its members." [8] Sartre argues that the group in fusion throws up leaders; later the group perpetuates itself by founding institutions. This is the basis of sovereignty. Authority is connected with Terror in the sense that the sovereign is the man who is authorized to exercise Terror. In a serial society, I obey because I have to obey. But in a state I obey myself because it is I, by my pledge, who have merged myself in the group and authorized the sovereign to command. Sartre does not, of course, fancy that every member of a state has actually given his pledge personally; he has been pledged *by proxy*; but the pledge is no less a pledge.

Now, Terror is not only fraternity; it is also liberty. For I

[8] *Ibid.*, p. 610.

194

freely merge my individual project in the common project when I pledge myself (or am pledged by proxy) to the state; and when the sovereign, fortified by Terror, commands me on behalf of the state, he is giving me back my freedom.

Such, in summary terms, is Sartre's theory of social structures. How far can it be considered a Marxist theory? There is not much doubt that it is a thoroughly *Sartrian* theory, one which harmonizes completely with the theory of human relationships put forward in *L'Etre et le Néant*, and summed up by a character in his play *Huis Clos* with the remark "hell is other people." This theory is, briefly, the following: If I speak, I objectify myself in words. Those words, once uttered and heard by other people, become *things* in the external world. Other people can hear them, think about them, talk about them. My words are part of the furniture of *their* world. Once I have spoken them they are no longer, strictly speaking, mine. I can no longer control them. This is what leads Sartre to say that in communicating with other people, or indeed even in being seen and heard by other people, I lose part of my self to other People. I cease to be a Self to myself and become an Other to another. At the same time, you become an Other to me. It is the Other Person, the Witness, who makes each of us an object in the universe— and to that extent robs each of us of our complete freedom. The word Sartre uses for this otherness is *alterity (alterité)*.

This theory of alterity (which owes much to Hegel) Sartre developed fairly fully in his earlier exposition of existentialism, *L'Etre et le Néant*, where he argued that relations between people are inevitably subject to mutual tensions because each individual, acting toward others as an objectifying Other, robs others of their liberty. This is what leads Sartre in *L'Etre et le Néant* to say that all relations between men are forms of metaphysical conflict, each individual trying to outtranscend the other, each robbing the other of the other's freedom by objectifying him as a *thing* in the world, and each trying to defend his own freedom from being thus objectified. Sartre's conclusion in

L'Etre et le Néant is that the only possible relations between people are those which tend toward the sadistic and those which tend toward the masochistic. Togetherness, harmony, love, the *Mitsein* is impossible; all relationships between men are relationships of conflict.

In the *Critique*, Sartre gives a new reason for this conflict; but the conclusion is the same. He still maintains that each individual is at war with all the others; and though social groups are formed, these groups are held together only by the pledge and Terror; they are in constant danger of relapsing in the individualistic condition of the series. Just as love, togetherness, friendship is rejected in *L'Etre et le Néant*, so here is any Aristotelian notion of man being social by nature.

Now, precisely because this social and political theory of Sartre is so close to his own earlier teaching, it is all the further removed from Marxism. First, Marxism, though ambiguous in many ways, is unambiguous in its rejection of the picture of mankind as divided into individualistic and competing atoms. Marxism believes in community or social unity as the natural condition of man, and regards class antagonisms as the product of exploitation. Therefore all this talk about pledges and political societies being held together by pledges is the antithesis of Marxism. Secondly, Sartre's theory of scarcity has nothing in common with Marxist economics, which is, indeed, directly opposed to the scarcity theory as put forward by Malthus and other economists of the classical school who followed Hume. Marx says that men lived originally together in a state of primitive communism; then with the invention of things like iron tools and machinery, some men learned to exploit others. Expropriation reduced the dispossessed to a condition of penurious slavery; the exploiters stole from the slaves the difference between what they produced and what was needed to keep the slaves alive. And this, as Marx said, is a theory of *surplus*, not a theory of scarcity. The scarcity is the result of exploitation, not a characteristic of nature.

So Sartre's aim of producing a modernized Marxism can hardly be said to have been achieved. Indeed one has the impression, as one gets deeper and deeper into the thick of this thick book, that Sartre himself has forgotten his original intention. His early talk about Marxism being the great philosophy and existentialism being the mere ideology gives way to increasingly bold assertions about the metaphysical status of his own system. Already by page 153, Sartre says he is going "to establish a priori (and not as the Marxists think of doing, a posteriori) the heuristic value of the dialectic method." He goes on to explain that starting with the discovery of the existential validity of the dialectical reason, he proposes to show that "the dialectical method will be efficacious as a method in so far as it will become permanently *necessary* as a law of intelligibility and as the rational structure of *being*." [9]

Sartre is thus making for his theory higher claims than Marx makes for his; Sartre is out, as he puts it, "to establish an order of certitudes." And this is something more than Sartre allowed in his preliminary essay, *Question de méthode,* to Descartes, Locke, Kant, Hegel, *or* Marx; all these "great philosophies" had validity only within the context of their historical periods and as expressions of the aspiration of the rising class of the time. Sartre's own system, however, is going to be *necessarily* true, a law of the rational structure of *being*. So much for existentialism as a "mere ideology."

Sartre's "restatement" of Marxism is certainly more sophisticated than the original thing, but how far can it be considered a "modernization"? One striking feature of the theory is that it moves from nineteenth-century philosophy not forward to that of the twentieth, but back to that of the eighteenth and even seventeenth centuries. This is not only a question of language, although Sartre's talk of "Liberty" as "Terror" and "Terror" as "Fraternity" might come straight from a speech by Robespierre. It is the basic elements of the theory which belong to pre-Hege-

[9] *Ibid.,* p. 128.

lian thought. For Sartre is putting forward a doctrine of social covenant which is identical with that of the seventeenth-century English philosopher Thomas Hobbes. Sartre then adds to Hobbes's doctrine something which comes directly from one of Hobbes's critics, namely the theory of scarcity put forward by the eighteenth-century Scotsman David Hume.

Hobbes's word is not *Violence*, it is *War*; he does not speak of a "Pledge," but a "Covenant"; he does not speak of "Terror," but of a sovereign who keeps peace between men by "holding them all in *awe*." The words are slightly different, but the theory is uncannily the same. Neither Hobbes nor Sartre offers what is, strictly speaking, a social contract theory of the kind one finds in Locke or Rousseau, but both Hobbes and Sartre hold promise-and-force theories. And although Sartre's theory of sovereignty is a little more elaborate, perhaps, than Hobbes', Sartre says exactly what Hobbes says about fear being the basis of political society and about the sovereign being *authorized* by the people to do whatever he decides to do, and so giving them back their freedom when he commands them to act as he wills. And just as Hobbes is haunted by fear of political society relapsing into the intolerable condition of the state of nature where no man is safe, Sartre goes on and on about the danger of the group's relapsing into an intolerable condition of seriality. Sartre writes:[1]

> The group is not a metaphysical reality, but a certain practical relationship between men toward a shared objective and among themselves. If certain circumstances of the struggle lead to a disbanding, and if this is not followed by a regroupment, the group is dead, the contagious panic reestablishes the dominion of the Practico-Inert—*voilà tout*.

Voilà everything indeed—and how extraordinarily Hobbesian everything looks. And what does not look Hobbesian looks Humian. The theory that scarcity lies at the origin of society

[1] *Ibid.*, p. 427n.

(though anticipated in some of the unpublished work of Locke) was first elaborated by Hume in the Third Book of his *Treatise of Human Nature*, in this memorable passage:[2]

> Of all the animals with which this globe is peopled, there is none towards whom nature seems, at first sight, to have exercised more cruelty than towards man, in the numberless wants and necessities with which she has loaded him, and in the slender means which she affords to the relieving of these necessities. . . . It is by society alone he is able to supply his defects, and raise himself up to an equality with his fellow-creatures and even acquire a superiority above them. . . . When every individual person labours apart and only for himself, his force is too small to execute any considerable work; his labour being employed in supplying all his different necessities, he never attains a perfection in any particular art; and as his force and success are not at all times equal, the least failure in either of these particulars must be attended with inevitable ruin and misery. Society provides a remedy for these *three* inconveniences.

Hume argues that society which comes into being because of scarcity entails what he calls a "convention" being entered into by all its members, but he denies that this convention is "of the nature of a promise"; society arises only "from a general sense of the common interest." Hume was attacking, among other sorts of promise, the Hobbesian notion of the "covenant"; but Sartre, though he takes the Humian notion of scarcity, has to restore the Hobbesian notion of promise because, like Hobbes, Sartre puts great emphasis on the idea of *war* between men as part of their natural condition; in the world of the Practico-Inert for Sartre, as in the state of nature for Hobbes, there is no "general sense of the common interest," for all men are enemies and rivals.

Are we to conclude that there are no elements of Marxism in Sartre's theory? That, I think, would be an unjustified conclu-

[2] David Hume, *Treatise*, Book III, Part II, Section 2.

sion. But the Marxist elements are all peripheral; and one is much more conscious of them in Sartre's literary and journalistic writings than in the pages of the *Critique*. In these other writings, three points about Sartre's political views may be noted. The first is his antipathy to the bourgeoisie and his yearning for socialism. The second is his belief that "dirty hands" are necessary in radical politics. This view is developed in the play significantly named *Les Mains sales*, in a later play, *Le Diable et le Bon Dieu*, and a film script, *L'Engrenage*. The theme of all these dramatic works is the same—namely that humanistic, socialistic, radical, or progressive policies will not succeed if those who struggle for them shrink (on humane, liberal, or Christian grounds) from using violence. This indeed is Marxism in its purest, most orthodox, and most antirevisionist form. The third key political belief of Sartre's is his belief that socialism can be realized only in some sort of alliance with the Communist Party.

In the light of these political attitudes, Sartre's *anthropologie* as expounded in the *Critique* may be seen to have a personal utility for the author, however unacceptable it may be to others. For this new theory enables Sartre to defend the superiority of socialist over bourgeois societies in terms of the superiority of the group over the series. It also enables him to defend the Terror exercised by such institutions as the Stalinist state as a violence that is *authorized* by those who are pledged and as a violence that is needed to prevent the dissolution of the group into seriality. Thus Sartre has an elaborate theoretical device to justify his seeming inconsistency in defending (as he did) Stalin's Terror while Stalin was alive and attacking Stalin as soon as Stalin was dead and discredited. His theory would not allow him to repudiate any Soviet government actually in power; it allows, at most, the kind of anguished and tortuous protest which Sartre uttered at the time of the Russian intervention in Hungary in 1956.

There is one conspicuous difference between Sartre's approach to politics and that of Hobbes. Although Hobbes saw violence at the heart of political society, he did not like violence. Hobbes was a sort of pacifist. Better tyranny than war and anarchy for him. But Sartre, like Marx, is partial to a certain amount of well-directed violence. Sartre, like Marx, is discontented with things as they are; more so, he positively detests the bourgeoisie and everything to do with it. So far as socialist regimes are concerned, Sartre says what Hobbes says—bad government gives no grounds for rebellion. But where bourgeois societies are concerned, Sartre itches for change; he is impatient for the revolutionary fusion of the series into the socialistic group.

In an interview in January, 1962, Sartre said, "For me, the essential problem is to reject the theory according to which the Left ought not to answer violence with violence." [3] Note that he says the *essential* problem. Hobbes would never have said this. But Marx might well have done so.

[3] *France-Observateur*, February 1, 1962, p. 8.

IRVIN FAUST / *Weissburg of Arabia*

On the third day of the Cuban business, as tankers streamed for destroyers, Associate Professor Harold (Hesh) Weissburg, who had never been west of the Hudson River, said thehellwithitall, dug out his Diners' card and caught the 7 A.M. plane to Vegas. To his mild surprise and vast delight, instead of praying he whispered to himself gogogo man as the jets flattened him and then flung him into the sky. (Beside him, a minister was praying for both of them.) He didn't even reach for his antacid tablets or buffered aspirin. Instead, as soon as he was buckled out and in charge of clouds, horizon and land mass (and still thehellwithitalling) he looked confidently around for the stewardesses, reviewed each one and just as confidently settled on a tall, arching Ava Gardner type, which would, of course, be fine basic training for Vegas. She was aloof, light-makeup, windblown aloof, and he had three ringadingding hours to pierce the aloof. He did not push; little Mendy and Hesh never pushed in the long evening discussions, or the evenings they spied on the operators at Plum Beach. No push was a lesson learned from the big boys—Frank, Johnny G., Errol, Gary, Jimmy C. and the Hump—everyone different but with the one success ingredient, no early push, a lesson which the second string never learned. She swayed past; he looked slowly away and down and studied the terrain. In the window he pulled in her hips, the terrain and the minister working over Noah and destruction. He blocked out the minister and the aloof and concentrated on the relief map below. Did it look like that to the crew of the Enola Gay? He shivered. . . . A door opened forward and he glimpsed the captain and copilot and their Thunderbird dashboard. Not a joy stick in sight. No seat-of-the-pants. No faulty deicers. Hell, no wonder Eatherly got so bugged. He looked down, straight down at the approach to Hiro, studied the crosshairs, felt the load beneath the Gay begging for defecation. You're trained by Jimmy, Van Johnson and Dennis Morgan you don't hesitate.

CHOONG.

On to Nagasaki.

He smiled at the minister who was praying his way through an air pocket. Oi that collar, tight like Mendy's, who always buttoned the top button even in summer; you could choke.

"Feel all right, Father?" he said.

The minister smiled weakly. "I'm not a Father," he said, "I'm a Reverend."

"Oh I'm sorry. Can I get you something?"

"No thank you. I'll be all right."

"Nonsense." Unstrapping, he walked forward, brushing the stewardess lightly, drew some water and returned. The pocket smoothed and the minister sighed, cleared his throat and closed his Bible.

"You're very kind. I do so admire people with stomachs of iron."

"It's all in the mind, Reverend."

"Ah yes. My mind has not yet learned. I wait fatalistically for the missiles, yet I pray when we're in danger. Ah yes. I'm Reverend Ernest Baroldi. I'm from Rochester."

Weissburg flew the direct line from Enola to G8 and Falcons of France—"*Jesuschrist Hesh the whole goddam nex war is gonna be in the air . . .*"

"I'm Georges Guynemer, Jr. I'm from Paris. That is, my father was from Paris."

"Somehow that's a familiar name. Have I met you before? I have been to Paris."

Weissburg lit a cigarette and shook his head. "Mmmm I doubt it. But you may have heard of my father." He blew a smoke ring around Mendy as they traded Ace cards.

(A *Richthofen for Guynemer, Mend . . .*" "*Fuck you, Hesh . . .*" "*Richthofen, Immelman, Goering and Fonck . . .*" "*It's a deal.*" The card flashed like a second grade reading drill: "Georges Guynemer, French Ace, credited with fifty-two German planes. One evening in 1916 he flew off toward Paris and was never heard of again . . .")

"My father," he said, studying the card for the five hundredth time, "was, or could have been, the greatest ace of the First World War. Bigger than Fonck, who of course relied on the air cannon. One evening dad flew off toward Paris and was never heard of again." He smiled. "Actually, he crashed near Chateau Thierry and was rescued by an American nurse named Ann Montgomery who was on Edith Cavell's staff. She had a child by him. Father died in her arms in 1929, just after he married her and gave me his name. He knew he was about to go, I think. In a way he chose it. He would have had to live through the destruction of all he loved and believed in. You see after '29 France was no longer France, nor was the world his world. There were no more René Lacostes, or Clemenceaus, Lafayette Escadrilles or Georges Carpentiers. It all became dirt and cowardice. Even Pétain, whom father worshiped. . . . He bagged eight Boches over Verdun, you know. . . ." He sank back and slitted his eyes. "Father taught me to fly when I was nine.

Spads. Nothing but Spads. When I see these monstrosities
. . ." he shrugged. "I've been looking for the real thing ever
since I left Chateau Thierry. After Dunkirk we settled in London. The Poles in exile . . . the Free French . . . the Flying
Tigers with Chennault, who had a sense of the glorious, Indo.
But I fly nothing but Spads. It's always in my contract. You'd be
amazed at how many Spads there are. . . . I'm on my way to
the coast to consult on a remake of *Hell's Angels* . . . they
want me for the Ben Lyon part. Frankly I couldn't see it. I don't
think Dad would have approved; I always try to see things
through his eyes. . . ." He took a deep breath and settled back
while the reverend quivered. Below them Nagasaki was billow-
ing upward. Poor Eatherly, a Spad would have saved him. . . .

"Do you still fly, Monsieur Guynemer?"

"Oh yes. I'll be off to Vietnam after the picture. Then the
Congo. I just can't keep my nose out of things. You might say
I'm chasing the holy grail."

In front of him the stewardess was plumping a pillow. She
turned and smiled, one click down the aloof scale.

"Can I get you anything?" she said. He blew a ring around
her head.

"You look very much like a young, angry Ava Gardner. When
she first broke in and she had that unconquerable thing."

"I just love Spads," she said, sucking a breath.

He leaned forward. "Do you *really?*"

"Yes. And Nieuports, even Fokkers. It was like knighthood in
the air. Are you really going to Hollywood?"

"Excuse me, Reverend," he said, rising and nodding. Push
push PUSH. He walked down the aisle with her. "I'll be in
Vegas for a while," he said confidentially. "At the Sands. Maybe
I can do something for you. Perhaps talk to the people at
Metro . . ."

"Oh Mr. Guynemer."

"Georges."

Vegas. *Oceans Eleven.* Sinatra. Judy. Thirty thousand a week. Sun. Desert. Red neon. One-armed bandits. Action. *Faîtes vos jeux. Les jeux sont faîtes.* Nothing Monaco. Nothing Miami. Nothing Reno. Pools. Tanfastic. Bikinis. Action. Vegas.

He checked into the Sands and hit three bandits (and lost) on the way to his room, hit four more bandits (and lost) on the way down, ate breakfast, walked into the hotel shop and bought a half dozen Madras shirts, three pairs of shorts, three slacks, red dinner jacket, a pair of sandals, a pair of wraparound sunglasses and charged it all to Diners', walked out and hit three more bandits, tapped out of quarters, went back to his room, changed, strolled downstairs in green Madras, red shorts, sandals and sun glasses, loaded up on quarters, stretched out beside the pool and went to sleep.

The sun awoke him at noon. He ordered lunch and a V. O. Collins, propped up on the webbed chaise and checked out the action: A diaper bulging blonde, stomach prone for the sun, bra unhooked for the all-over down-to-the-gluteus tan; a lotion-smearing redhead, carefully caressing every inch; and three cling-ing secretaries, adjusting to the greatest (and possibly last) week of their lives. A few hungover, huge-bellied, long-weekend busi-nessmen, sipping tomato juice and squinting in agony at the sun and the pink and brown flesh. A long way from Plum Beach and the Hudsons and Terraplanes and Packards and the cramped front seat and damn floor shift that stuck in the belly. He drank. A long way for Mendy and Hesh, crouching in the cattails, stak-ing out their favorite blonde and redhead and following her Terraplaned career through the rugged winters and the busy summers, from Plum to Rockaway to the Hotel St. George pool, all eyes and elbow nudges, identifying the interchangeable blonde, the interchangeable red.

MENDY: *"Mine is Joan Blondell."*

HESH: *"Mine is Winifred Shaw."*

He studied the pink red and the bulging Joan and closed his eyes. *I'm sorry, Mend, but I got to take care of both of them.*

"Hot shit," Mendy squealing, *"a sangwich."*

He laughed out loud, and Joan and Wini stopped bulging and smearing and looked up. Snap. The tiniest opening. One hundred and ninety-eight times, exactly, he had missed it. He picked up his drink and walked into the snap and sat down between them.

"Mind if I join you?" A heaving belly closed his eyes in disappointment and ducked under an umbrella. Goodbye, Packard.

"Why not," said Joan. Wini continued to smear; Wini never jumped too soon. Class, Mendy.

"I just flew in this morning from Chicago," he said, "My arms are awfully tired." Wini wrinkled her nose. Joan giggled. Mendy rolled over and gasped for breath. "Pretty bad," said Weissburg, including all of them in his smile.

"Pretty bad," said Wini, slowing the caress to a long, circular stroke.

"Well, it's early and I'm not wearing my Witty Brothers suit."

"Pretty fair," said Wini, without missing a beat. Joan looked confused. *Fuckin wise guy, said Mendy.*

"I'm Georges Guynemer. I'm here with Frank."

Joan's bra bounced once and Wini stopped stroking, then started again.

"Frank Polansky?" she said innocently.

"Touché," he smiled.

"Oh Marcy," breathed Joan, "there's only *one* Frank."

"Well, there's Frank Roosevelt," said Wini.

"Junior," said Weissburg.

"Touché," said Red. "I'm Marcy McGraw."

"I tolya she's a shik," screamed Mendy. *"She screws like a mink."*

"You look like an actress named Winifred Shaw," he said, shaking Mendy off. "She never made it big, except with me. She sang 'The Lady in Red.' "

"Who the boys are all crazy for," she said. "Very good. This is

Holly Addison. She reminds you of Mamie Van Doren, who was married to Ray Anthony, who reminds me of Cary Grant."

"Very good. But wrong. Joan Blondell. Not TV Joan. That's wrong, too. Somebody wrong with the right name. I mean Gold Diggers Joan."

"Dick Powell's ex."

"Hey there. A history major."

"Smith. 1960. Holly, say hello to the smart man."

"Hello, Mr. Guynemer."

"Hello, Holly Joan. Why does your friend hate me?"

"Silly. That's her way. She don't hate you. In fact, it's really just the opposite." (That's right, Mendy. Look at the hard time Colbert gave Gable and Russell gave MacMurray. When they go it's the greatest bang in history. . . .)

"Now just knock it off, Holly," said Wini. "Can't you see Mr. Guynemer is the most dangerous kind of operator." (Listen Mendy, listen) "Slot 3B, corner pocket, prime two. A thinker. No grabber he."

Weissburg held up his glass. "Truce. Interregnum. *Pace. Shalom.* What," he said, "is a girl like you doing? Here."

Wini Marcy Smith 1960 rolled over on her back and pushed her tremendous chest skyward. She twisted her head slowly toward him while Mendy croaked in his ear, *cock tease, Hesh, cock tease* . . . "I resemble that remark, Mr. Guynemer," she said. "Next question?"

"What are you two broads drinking?" he smiled, holding up his glass in salute.

She smiled back. "A Cherry Heering. Holly will have a whiskey sour. Now what about Frank?"

He flagged the waiter and ordered and sat back and said, "Well we're relaxing between pictures." The drinks came and they sipped while he reviewed twenty years of Variety. "We've got some really interesting properties," he said. "Actually, Frank's on a classical kick, you know, the *Sergeants Three-Gunga Din* kind of thing." He lay back and flipped his sunglasses down like he was about to catch a high fly to the outfield. (Mendy, Mendy, you should have stuck in there. Plum Beach wasn't so impossible. Or, goddam purist, did you want it shouldn't be possible?) . . . We're thinking," he said, "about *Pride and Prejudice* in a plush east side setting. Fancy pad, Frank swinging easy, one of those personal, relaxed kinds of things."

"Just Frank, Dean and Janey Austen."

"Yes, that's it. What do you think, Holly Joan?"

"It sounds *terribly* excitin."

"Well, *we* think so. Look, why don't the three of us get together tonight. We can have a few laughs and maybe talk about it. Frank is always looking for new personalities. How about? Ten in the lounge?"

"*Pride and Prejudice*, Mr. Guynemer?" said Wini.

"Uh huh. What do you think, history major?"

She turned over again and stared at him. Snap snap snap snap. "Why not," she smiled. "After all, stix nix hix pix."

His table was halfway down and dead center, exact strategic position at the Paramount on hookey days for B.G., Glenn, T.D. and Frank. Ten dollars held the place instead of Mendy, who, arising after a sleepless night was downtown at 5 A.M. He sipped V.O. and soda while Hesh and Mendy crammed down Oh Henry's and Milky's (from nine to four). A low, buzzing impatience ran through the audience while the comedian filled in time and the leggy tap dancers (he was making out with them too?) smiled through a Busby Berkely-Rockette routine. Then the lights dimmed and the rustling stopped. Hesh and Mendy stopped crunching. Weissburg stopped relaxing. Silence. Craning forward. OhJesusChrist . . . From the depths of the Paramount rose the stage, like a great, open elevator, while the drummer brushed softly and the horns muted "Night and Day." And there he was, leaning backward like he was about to fall on his head, eyes closed, belting out "Who Cares?" carelessly, easily, while all the *mishugenahs* came in their pants. They were together, again, Hesh, Mend and Frank, running from "Black Magic" to "Sweet Lorraine," tapping every worthwhile broad in the Paramount, in Thomas Jefferson, or even out in the street. From the little blonde with her lunch bag in the first row to Rose the redhead walking to the bus each morning. Or any broad whose prim eyes strayed for an instant, whose hips winked as they were trailed for eight blocks, any broad who gave Hesh and Mend the secret message, decoded only by the central intelligence of Frank's secret decoder: "I am untouchable and aloof and practically impossible, but for you swing-easies, you head-back casuals, for you takeitorleaveits, I am stuff. . . ." He tilted his chair far back and balanced . . . So who needed smooth foreheads, shoulders bigger than bellies? Five feet ten vertical inches? Drop dead, that's who! For Frank had disclosed the greatest secret since Seven Up: if you're a skinny, pimply, falling-over-backward, *singing* little isosceles triangle, *this* will make them cream! He swung with Frank through the Riobamba and the Hit Parade, slugged Mark Zilli for hinting Frank couldn't sing "Three Little Fishes," and worked tirelessly on the act down the cellar with Mendy—for if one Frank was a creamer, multiply by two and you hit the *entire* stuff market.

"O.K. Mend, *now take the harmony. Close your eyes and lean way back.*"

"*How come you always get the melody?*"

"*Because you're flat. You're a natural harmonizer.*"

"*Balls. You sing like shit.*"

"*But I got an ear. I got intonation.*"

"*Balls. Miss McGurk don't even let you sing.*"

"*Well, she doesn't know popular music. Listen Mendy, we put this act together and then we sing for her after school. 'I'll Never Smile Again.' I bet she comes down to the boiler room with us.*"

"*Ma-rone.*"

210

"*Whatayouthink she studies Beethoven all day? Come on. She looked at me the other day. You know, the Look.*

"*Yeah?*"

"*Yes. And you know when the bell rings and everybody runs up and crowds around her? Well, yesterday I had my wrist on her ass for five minutes while she was explaining fugues to Meyers.*"

"*OhChrist, you think she knew?*"

"*Shit, don't they all? Mendy, she wears Suspants.*"

"*Ma-ronamerica.*"

"*O.K. Now do the harmony. And forcrissake next time you get a haircut, tell him to leave the top alone, willya?*"

. . . Six encores and Frankie sank into the boiler room of the Paramount, there to take care of Miss McGurk. The lights came up and he blinked and had another V.O. . . . Ah but the night was still young for Mendy and Hesh and their renewed Frankie-boy confidence. They walked bouncy out of the theater, checked in for the Nedick's frank and orange, then began their rounds. First the Astor, a few doors away, where they leaned easily against a post while all the primeyes waited for their pickups. The little (familiar) look of joy and promise as he walked up and they hurried off into the night. There would follow (they knew) dinner at the Stork, the hansom through the park, the dance floor of the Cafe Rouge, the whisper in the ear, the shiver and back like sixty to the Astor and up to his room. Twelve pickups later they checked out of the Astor and moved on. To the New Yorker, where they worked the lobby outside the Terrace Room, studying the crossed, magnificently flashing legs as the prim, aloof eyes sank back on the sofas. All waiting, untapped and in Suspants, for a Hesh or even a Mend, swinging in with heads thrown back. Poor cherry bastards. Missing a lifetime of excitement and don't even know what these two postleaners can do for them. . . . Don't they read the headlines in the do-it-yourself newspapers on 42nd?

So now east to the Commodore, the terminal for the thousands of starry-eyed prims pouring out of Grand Central from points west, gathering for the harvest, for the New York sharpies who lounge around lobbies. *"How about the suitcases, Hesh, whatayou think?"* A careful, slow study, a high-level conference. *"See the one with the headlights? Her satchel is loaded with panties and brassieres and slips and Kotex. I tell you something else, Mend, with these out-of-town dames, they carry their own protection, a couple gross, just in case."* Mendy nodding. *"Jeez all the bags and Kotex there must be in this hotel. All the action. Digest this, think on it. Think of all of it in the city, Mend. On the average, I figure two million intercourses a night."* Mendy shaking the head, Ma-roning. Then uptown to the Savoy with a stop at the Plaza fountain and some history. *"You were still pissing in your crib when Fitzgerald and his wife went swimming here. Zelda. Wild, oi she was wild. Full of zetz."* Then inside with the carriage trade. *"Right here they dated up and then all of them hopped in cars and raced out to these estates on the Island, like Sands Point, and had orgies and drank champagne. I read it all in* The Great Gatsby.*"* They counted the couples scooting up to Harlem, to the Cotton Club, and then out to the Point for the wild three days and nights. *"Shit,"* Mendy commenting, *"the guys are a little funny ain't they?"* *"Well, maybe. See Fitzgerald was before the crash and he just couldn't be a prick. It wasn't in them in those days. Everybody was a nice guy. They were all a little funny, I guess he set the style."* This Mendy could buy. *"You gotta be a prick. They love it. Look at Cagney and Raft. They kick the shit outa them and they love it, ain't that right, Hesh?"* *"Right."* Scott F.'s basic mistake, to live through the crash and not be prick enough, a lesson for all time. Hesh and Mend studied the dinnerjacketed nice guys and the long dresses that craved Raft and Cagney and settled for orgies. Hell. A few knowing, lopsided Frankie grins and then on to the big one, west, to the Hotel Pennsylvania. To the Cafe Rouge. The Red Cafe, Mendy baby. Stand in the lobby crowd, crane for a glimpse of the prick guys working their points on the dance floor with the prim Commodore girls who were blushing and saying yes. Yes. Yes, Jimmy, belt me with that grapefruit. Yes, George, slap my aloof face. Yes, Hesh, you may give it to me whenever *you* like. . . . I tellya Mend, they love it when you're Joe Prick. . . . So watch the operators and perhaps grab a shot of Tommy slushing the horn and looking wise, or Jimmy noodling away and knowing the score. And maybe on a real perfect night catch a slice of Jo Stafford, Marian Hutton or (perfect perfect) Helen O'Connell, who had a little mean herself in "Tangerine," but deep down was the primmest of the prim and looking for the one *understanding* grapefruit squirter, the one who *knew*. . . . Then the band was breaking for ten, strolling through the lobby, sitting down with the flashing legs or cornering them against the wall and setting up the two o'clock date. So easy. So mean, wiseguy singeasy! How about the night Helen walked through and gave him the *Look*. Hah? How about, Mendy? You saw, you got the message. Maybe I'll send her a note. Maybe, maybe . . . and home on the IRT to a sleepless night that reviewed a day of confidence, an evening of wild promise and a rocklike resolve to say hello there to Rose Pensky in biology in the morning . . .

"Hello, George."

He looked up at the young, angry, unconquerable airline stewardess. She was smiling down at him, her prim Hotel Commodore eyes focused on his red jacket and long hair. Next to her, a familiar, embarrassed face, a gabardine suit.

"Hello there," Weissburg said, rising. "Won't you and your friend join me?"

She looked grateful, as if she were afraid a red jacket might choose to ignore her. Her friend extended his hand. "Hello, Mr. Guynemer. Remember me?"

Weissburg shook the hand and felt it tremble with Noah and destruction. "Reverend Baroldi," he said. "You're out of uniform."

The reverend looked around. "Yes," he said. "I . . . I decided this was my last chance. I . . . well . . . had to know . . . if . . ."

"Say no more, Ernie. Let's call it therapeutic. O.K.? Hell, you've got to take care of yourself. Ministers have more nervous breakdowns than anybody."

The stewardess gave him the Cafe Rouge snuggle blush and Baroldi looked down. "You're so direct, Mr. Guynemer . . ."

"Georges."

"Georges. So direct. I admire that."

"I learned it from Frank. We grew up together in Hasbrouck Heights. The rough part of town."

"I thought you were from Paris."

"Well yes, but after my father died, my mother came back to her people in New Jersey. Say, I'm on my way to the lounge to join some friends. Won't you and Ava . . ."

"Luann Johnstone."

"Won't you and Luann join me for a little monte or a spin of the wheel? This is Vegas, men. And with this Cuban business, who knows . . ."

The reverend cleared his throat. A Mendy sound. "Yes," he said. "Yes, I'd rather enjoy that." A Mendy.

"I would too," said Luann, linking both their arms. "Come on you two, I'm on duty tomorrow."

So he casualed them through the lobbies of the Astor and the New Yorker, the Commodore, through the Cafe Rouge and out to the Pennbar where Holly and Marcy were waiting with their prim, carefully averted eyes. Expertly he tossed off the introductions. Buddy, he called the bartender, Buddy. He bought a round of drinks, leaned far back and flopped his head and laughed and looked at each girl just long enough to make contact, then slid away. He monologued for five minutes and gave in gracefully when Ernie Baroldi insisted on buying. Then he walked them into the action. With Marcy looking on coolly and Holly and Luann squealing and Ernie slapping his back, he worked them through the dice, the stud game and the wheel, winding up eighty dollars behind, head back, tie open, eyes slitted, three broads leaning over and pressing their headlights into his swingeasy back, Ernie hustling chips and only too happy to T.L. a little.

Ringadingdingding.

They moved from the Sands to the Desert Inn and then down the street to the Flamingo and into the Tropicana (where Ernie hit for ten), in and out of dance floors with little combos, a quick nuzzle, a yak, a rhumba break and back to the action. At the Dunes Ernie took off his jacket and at the Iveria dropped it and at the Sands after the full circuit he kissed Luann on the neck as she bent over the table. Then the laughter, the heat, the action added up and told him it was time to take the hansom through the park in the dark or drive like hell out to the Point. He ordered a car at the desk and they piled in. He swung the top down and squealed down the highway out toward the desert and the handle of the Big Dipper. They sang "America" and "Onward Christian Soldiers" and "Don't Fence Me In" and "Baby It's Cold Outside" and "Three Little Fishes," and he said to Mendy in his square, white little room, baby, Plum Beach is *bupkess*, *believe* me. And Terraplanes. And Hudsons. You and me, Mend. Georges Guynemer, Ace of goddam Aces, whipping his Spad through the cattails, through the Dipper and Cassiopeia on to the Great American Desert. Stick with me, Mend.

They got out when the wheels began to labor. They took their shoes off and sank down on the sand. A million constellations, identifiable by Star Scouts Heshie, Ernie and Mendy, pasted on the ceiling of the Savoy, provided the backdrop. Shooting Ernie back to palmier days.

"I AM VALENTINO. I AM THE SHEIK," Ernie yelled as he galloped up and down in front of them, whacking his behind.

"Ooooh do not molest me, you cur, sir," said Luann. Picking up her dress she began to run away. Ernie whacked his rump harder and roared, ran after her and dived. They rolled over and over in the sand, her legs and panties flashing in the starlight.

"Go go, Rudy," Weissburg yelled. Marcy and Holly screamed. A hard crack split the screaming and Ernie rolled away. Weissburg heard the sobs jerk into the sand, pictured Mendy's spittle watering the beach at Coney. He felt his eyes tear. Poor losing bastards, in a million years, not enough prick.

"Come on, girls," he said, rising. "Let's go for a walk."

They got up silently and took his arm. Across the whiteness he walked them, into the open through the flatlands of Canarsie. (Two little rib-nudgers behind that sand dune?) A plane droned high against the Big Dipper. The only sound besides Ernie's sobs. He looked up and considered. Poor Eatherly, still flapping around up there, the eternal Dutchman, trying to suck it all back, like a reversed movie, or perhaps (could it be?) drop the equalizer, get even. "Jesus," he said with a shiver, "but all this . . . nothing . . . reminds me of Hiro."

"You were in *Hirah*shima." Marcy. Smith. 1960.

"OOOH," Holly said.

"Yeah. I was in Hiroshima. Right after. First battalion in." Corporal Iceberg, alone and agonizing through the rubble, while the outfit necked with survivors. In the rubble . . . He stopped and sat down in the sand. The two girls dropped beside him, respectfully quiet.

"Yes," he said. "I was there." He saw the plane winking overhead. Come off it, Icey, you wanted some Jap ass, even in the rubble. . . . "Yes," he said. "I mean right after. Christ, you think about these people at work, going about the business of living, and then there's a plane overhead and they look up. Like that one . . ." Prick. Marcy squeezed against him. He felt Holly's leg against his. He rubbed back, gently. Then Marcy's head was on his shoulder. Holly was pulling harder. Now Marcy. And then they were rolling over and over, like a tumbling act, punching, biting, grunting, cursing, sand in their mouths, his hand ripping at a dress, their hands tearing at him. Until they lay exhausted, gasping for air.

Marcy began to cry, short sucking sobs. "Dammit," she said and got up and walked away. He could see her beside the car, head cradled in her arms. He felt a spurt of weakness, but jammed it down. Carefulll . . . not now, not when Guynemer is on the enemy's tail. If she can't take the heat, she has no right operating on the great American desert with an ace of aces. Roger? Wilco. He swung back and into an Immelman turn. Holly was beside him, barely touching, breathing deeply, the familiar Plum Beach, Rockaway, boiler room breathing. He bided his time, lining up the Vickers guns, swinging oh so deadly easy. He gazed off into the Big Dipper.

"Georges," she said finally.

"Ummm."

"Do you think they can use me?"

"What?"

"Do you think they have something for me?"

He looked away from the Dipper. She was on her back, her dress up to her waist. Christ, Mendy, she was taking off her stockings. Casually, he reached down and helped. She rubbed his hand against the length of her leg (naturally) and then pulled him down. He dropped slowly and zeroed in to the great, open, Blondell mouth.

"Do you?" she said.

"What? What?"

She moved her head ever so slightly. "Do you think they *have* something for me?"

He moved her head gently back into position and studied the gleam and the closed eyes and the moment before the moment.

"Yes I think so," he smiled.

She opened her eyes. "When?"

"With this crisis thing, who can say?" He shrugged. His casual hands were gently forcing her legs apart.

"Well Georgie, we can't *count* on it, can we? We got to go on like nothing will happen." Her legs stiffened.

"Yes and no. Hell, let's face it. One finger. One button. CHOONG."

"Oh choong you. When Georges?"

"Well. Tomorrow. Come on baby, open up." O.K., Jimmy, bring up the grapefruit, turn on the Joe Prick. "Cut out the crap, you little bitch."

Her lips nibbled his ear and nipped; her legs locked together like a two-way clamp. "No crap, sweetie. First *you* come across. Tomorrow. O.K. choong sweetie?"

He sat up and looked at her. Her legs were crossed at the ankles and her great, open mouth was closed. Oi, Mendy, cued, screwed, blued and tattooed. Again. He thought he might cry, but he heard Marcy's sobs and Ernie's and knew at a time like this Frank wouldn't cry. Or Guynemer. So he threw back his head and laughed. Easily. Gallantly. He felt her hand patting his laughing face.

"O.K. Georgie? Tomorrow?"

"Sure, baby, sure. Tomorrow."

"That's sweet. And I'll be sweet. Tit for tat, Georgie."

"Hell, it's on the house. The hell with the tit."

"Oh no, Georgie, I wouldn't dream of it. It's like a deal. Now you run along like a good boy and be nice to Marcy."

Exit laughing, shrugging, tipping his wings in salute. Stiff-backed. You crash, you go right up.

He trudged casually through the sand, ankle deep, to the girl who needed *help*. She was still sitting, head in hands, tapering the sobs into long sighs. He dropped down beside her. He let the jammed-down weakness and Holly's ice turn into pity. God, she *did* need help, this one. Whatinhell was a nice college kid doing out here in the desert with a Frankietrained Ace anyway? The pity turned into protection and he put his arm around her shoulder. She sighed and rested her head against him. Hell, this was no Wini Shaw, this was Ann Rutherford, the nice kid at the next desk. He took out his handkerchief and wiped her face. She blew her nose into the handkerchief, a real Ann Rutherford response. He felt the urge to lecture her, or at least throw himself across her body in case the bomb fell, but he heard her say, "You didn't make it, did you, operator?"

"Well no." He stroked her hair.

"You operators always screw up in the clutch."

"Come on now. You don't feel so good. . . ."

"I feel fine."

"You're a funny kid, you know that? A real funny kid."

"Yeah. *She'll* be a big star some day."

He looked at the disappearing plane. "Well," he said, "maybe if we make it through. Who knows . . ."

"Nuts," the funny kid said. "She'll make it through. She'll be big on Mars."

Somehow that sounded sad as hell. And a little desperate. Ann could do that, the laugh and the desperate.

"And you?" he said.

"Ah operator, don't you know the action when you see it?"

Yeah, Ann was a funny kid, a funny desperate kid.

"Well . . ."

"The Lady in Red."

"Oh that was a gag. Hell, but you're a funny one."

"Cut out the shit, Guynemer." He felt himself pulled sharply and then he was on top of her. Her hands were snaking his through zippers and hooks. Jesus, Mendy, no *girdle*.

"All right," she muttered, guiding him. "That's it, operator. That's it. No here. Here, goddammit."

My God, Mendy, *this* was Ann? This was the prim-eyes? MA-RONE.

"It's falling now," she growled. "Isn't it? Isn't it?"

"Yeah. CHOONG."

"CHOONG. Oh baby," she said.

"Yes, yes."

"Say it."

"Well, maybe there is a spot in *Pride and Prejudice*."

"The hell with *Pride and Prejudice*. Say it."

"Oh. I love you, Ann."

"No, say it."

"I love you, Winifred."

"Say it, goddammit."

"Say what?"

"Say *it*."

"What it?"

"Say I, Lawrence, am taking you, Marcy."

"I, Lawrence . . . Who's Lawrence?"

"Hush. Lawrence of Arabia. Say it all."

"Well, I, Lawrence of Arabia . . . Geez . . ."

"Am taking you, Marcy. The whole thing, goddammit."

"I, Lawrence of Arabia, am taking you, Marcy."

"Say I, El Aurens, am taking you, Marcy."

"I, El Aurens, am taking you, Marcy."

"Say, Marcy, you are the only one, I, El Aurens, have ever touched. You have made me whole."

"Christ."

"Say, say."

"Marcy, you are the only one I have ever touched . . ."

"Go on, go on."

"You have made me whole."

"Made who whole?"

"Jesus. I, Lawrence of Arabia, am taking you, Marcy. You are the only one I have ever touched. You, Marcy, have made me, El Aurens, whole."

"Aaaaaaaah."

Holy shit, Mendy. Holy holy. Rest, Mendy, rest. We could have been the greatest in history. The top of the Cafe Rouge. Oh, if only we had *known*.

MA-RONAMERICA.

HAROLD SCHIMMEL /
Two Poems

GAN CHAYIM[1] / *The Company Assembles for*
Drinks Before Dinner

FOR ARIE

"The shack" in shadow with
early afternoon, the two meters'
bramble-roof an ab-
original brown—as of the eye manipulating
down shades of shaley earth-crevice.
   The house, from the pool, supported
as much by a multi-
mythic stand of pine, as by the
two-inch pipe, shipped across wine-dark
seas (let me make
myself clear! placing "wine" as modifier

[1] Literally, "garden of life, the alive and living."

of adjective) to Haifa.
Spruce, cypress, common pine, but absent
here, the sheer-sheathed
(North American, or Virgilian) elm,
visible through the screened
upper of the Dutch front door, limit to an iced-
green vista of lawn—
minuscule, clipped blades rushed
each into each by eye-angle, and the domestic
magic of homely sight
achieving its din from the dining room window.
    The curdled purr (accuracy would substitute
"c" for "p"; rolling, of course, the "rr's") of local
turtledoves, tintintitter of broad-branched
finch-family, humorous hoopoe (his name
in Hebrew—DOO-CHEE-PHAT—hinting his colors) and higher
skreek of nameless birds,
biblical all, habiting groves
of Jaffa-orange, grape-
fruit and lemon, fields of hermaphrodite
artichoke—spiked
leaf on spiked leaf shadowing
                            (womblike) plumage of heart.

ALL ON A SATURDAY AFTERNOON

Boston's Backbay, 1961

"A"—
embroidered like a crown
above my pubic hair. Even here
I was deceived.
My hands rolled down
her tangerine knit-pants from Florence.
Like A. & Nicolette
(I thought) bodily
I carried with love-lust to my
oversized re-renovated
Chinese spring & mattress Tom
bargained for & bore
from Goodwill's basement store.
Four inches from the floor it stood, a telephone at its head
(even the walls' white
they painted).

The smallness, the coldness, the pathos
of her buttocks
'neath 5 & dime spun-cotton
children's pants. Our souls attached like fam-
bily—(o love-lust!)
By the root she took
& put me in, I worked to see
her 12-year freckle-face
blossom. Wonder!
Still innocent I said it proved,
this blossoming. Who'd-
've known that faces bloom
with wombs???

St. Valentine's
I brought the ring. The Boston steam-
ship ticket read Mr. & Mrs.,
to Venice.
Reeling in lung-smoke each of us,
Tom chauffeured, looked
from far. At their bulky
Goodwill office desk
he read with underlines
The Critique of Pure Reason.
He said,
"Marriages are holy."

STEPHEN DONADIO / *Some Younger Poets in America*

About five years ago the younger poets in America seemed to organize themselves like iron filings at two poles: two poetry anthologies then in circulation appeared able to contain them all, if only by implication. The first, published by Meridian in 1957, was called *The New Poets of England and America*; introduced by Robert Frost, it was compiled by three professor-poets: Donald Hall, Robert Pack, and Louis Simpson. In his introduction, called "Maturity No Object," Frost observed that "school and poetry come so near being one thing. . . . In fact the poet and the scholar have so much in common and live together so naturally that it is easy to make too much of a mystery about where they part company." If there was ever an anthology out to refute this notion it was the second, edited by Donald M. Allen for Grove Press and provocatively named *The New American Poetry, 1945–1960*. Explaining his selections, Allen confidently asserted that the mixed bag of work produced by "the true continuers of the modern movement in American poetry" (presumably included to a man in his anthology) showed "one common characteristic: a total rejection of all those qualities typical of academic verse."

The two collections did not overlap. Whatever the intentions of the editors, they were successful in establishing a popular division (eagerly promoted by slick news weeklies as part of the spellbinding drama of American ideas) between Beat and Academic poetry, schoolroom and poolroom verse. That these epithets did not adequately cover the opposed poets—anthologized or otherwise identified—gave no one pause, though surely no one remains who would still find it useful to call Denise Levertov a Beat poet or classify James Wright as Academic.

The difference was, in Robert Lowell's phrase, between cooked poetry and raw—the ideal being, one would imagine, a kind of poetic tossed salad in which the formal dressing does not compromise the existential ingredients. Insofar as the argument was literary, it revolved around the relation of form to experience, each of which makes demands of fidelity (though only in the rarest poems do those demands coincide). Seen simply, in the Academic view, the Beats all lived unshaven in some mental basement and produced a poetry as messy as their lives, ill-bred and pointless. So far as the Beats could see, the Academics comprehended their experience as mere formality, rendering it wholly according to literary considerations rather than the dictates of feeling and relying on traditional patterns of verbal and emotional organization. The ideal Academic would be wry and noncommittal, paralyzed by his awareness of all ambiguities, bound up with witty tensions, gagged with irony. The primary emotion present in his verse was a deep queasiness. A logical extension of Prufrock, he was a casualty of sensibility whose affective relation to society had become so highly wrought as to be irremediably artificial. The sentimental excess of the Beats was a response, in part surely deserved, to the long-suffering solemnity of certain "younger" poets growing old before their time:

> Where are the young poets in America, they
>   are trembling in publishing houses and universities,
> Above all they are trembling in universities, they
>   are bathing the library steps with their spit,
> They are gargling out inocuous (to whom?) poems
>   about maple trees and their children,
> Sometimes they brave a subject like the Villa d'Este
>   or a lighthouse in Rhode Island,
> Oh what worms they are! they wish to perfect their form.

These lines are from "Fresh Air," a poem written in 1955 by Kenneth Koch, a Columbia professor who, because he found his way into Allen's anthology, might be mistakenly identified with some nonliterary views there is no reason to suppose he held. As an antipathetic insider, Koch sums up the *literary* case against the Academics very well:

> My first lesson. "Look around you. What do you think and feel?" *Uhhh* . . . "Quickly!" *This Connecticut landscape would have pleased Vermeer.* Wham! A-Plus. "Congratulations!" I am promoted.

"Is there no one," he asks ultimately, "who feels like a pair of pants?" In short, some poets, like Koch, by refusing to take form for granted and requiring a felt motive for each step taken, merely wished to disassociate themselves from a view of poetry as an institution which demanded likeness rather than unlikeness of its members, consequently inspiring mediocrity. For them, the forms possible were to be determined by personal verification, not consensus.

But there was a more important and essentially nonliterary focus of conflict. The Beats were not simply marching to Whitmania, nor were the Academics really clutching Eliot and Empson and the New Critics to their rickety bosoms. Gods were not being overthrown, replaced, or overhauled: the Beats were becoming their own gods, and so their argument took on a moral dimension. Kerouac, according to Ginsberg, was the "new Buddha of American prose," and his books, among others, were "published in Heaven." Presumably the reviews there would be more favorable: it is no accident that Ginsberg, who had learned his Blake by heart, equated Hell with contemporary America. Such an equation is not without nonliterary implications. Ginsberg's "mysticism," it would seem, was the result of an attempt to be political without quite knowing how.

Indeed, the "Statements on Poetics" appended to Allen's collection, as garbled and pious as they usually are, are a good indication that what was being sought was not A New Aesthetic. The Beats had lost all patience with aesthetics; what seriousness they could muster (those who could) lay in inchoate social protest. Their writings were often no more than occasions for harangues. While in their view their enemies, with growing nervousness and virtuosity, did finger exercises with their transmuted experience, the Beats were taking their clothes off; they exercised their lungs in coffee shops and college auditoriums, where their eruptions signified the end of a condition for which Eisenhower, in speech and appearance, had become the most familiar emblem.

As notoriously apolitical as the Beats were supposed to have been, again and again they urged that writers in particular realize that they were not living in Yeats's Byzantium but in an ugly and extremely troubled culture, a culture with which they had grown somewhat less than intimate. It ought to be remembered that even a writer as apparently frivolous as Lawrence Ferlinghetti felt obliged to distinguish his position, in whatever crude terms, from what was expected of him:

> . . . I am put down by Beat natives who say I cannot be beat and "committed" at the same time, like in this poem ("Tentative Description of a Dinner to Promote the Impeachment of President Eisenhower"), man. True, true, William Seward

Burroughs said, "Only the dead and the junkie don't care—they are inscrutable." I'm neither. Man. And this is where all the tall droopy corn about the Beat Generation and its being "existentialist" is as phoney as a four-dollar piece of lettuce. Because Jean-Paul Sartre cares and has always hollered that the writer especially should be committed. *Engagement* is one of his favorite dirty words. He would give the horse laugh to the idea of Disengagement and the Art of the Beat Generation. Me too. And that Abominable Snowman of modern poetry, Allen Ginsberg, would probably say the same. Only the dead are disengaged. And the wiggy nihilism of the Beat hipster, if carried to its natural conclusion, actually means the death of the creative artist himself.

Times have changed. In the community at large, and in the intellectual community in particular, an implacable and growing visceral awareness of human conditions and events has made it unnecessary, if not downright quaint, for a man to explain his "commitment." We have been through five years of foreign crisis, an assassination, and a troubling presidential election; we are currently at war. The effects of the civil rights movement, which has implicated everyone, have been remarkably far-reaching, extending now into intense concern with foreign as well as domestic policy. Steam generated in the intellectual tea-pot has been drawn off into action and, in consequence, the character of the Academy has been transformed.

This is not to say, of course, that all our poetry has suddenly turned social: merely that the poet, as a moral being, has been placed in an uneasy and direct relation to American society no longer mediated by a reassuring vision of himself as a bona fide member of a school which guarantees his value and success. In short, he has been given the freedom to be himself, and that freedom makes the demands of a necessity. For while Camp and Pop Art assert themselves as forms of a grotesque commitment to the mindless superficialities of our society, our younger poets, whether they like it or not, must bear the burden of preserving a sense of its inwardness.

So far as readers are concerned, the distinction between Beat and Academic poetry has wholly vanished, and with it a prefabricated audience for prefabricated poems. As Donald Hall's recent and highly politic Penguin selection indicates, there is more ticket-splitting nowadays. Poets are read, when they are read, not so much to fulfill our expectations as to form them. When everything threatens to simplify or kill it, they have been charged with the task of keeping alive in us a sense of the intimacy of experience. Whether or not they have all accomplished that task by evolving an idiom at once accessible and individual, the younger poets considered below are those whose presence seems most clearly felt and most persuasive at the moment.

Although we have been prepared to expect the worst of Allen Ginsberg (b. 1926), it is only recently that we have been able to read him as a poet and not just a social symptom. Despite the grating shrillness which he often passes off as ecstasy, the frequent posturing, self-righteousness, and maudlin plunges of his verse, a genuine if muddled concern for human values struggles to survive there, and the chronicle of conflict thus engendered is remarkable both for its truthfulness and for the passion with which it has been invested. Ginsberg's strain of exhibitionism notwithstanding, no poet to emerge in the past decade has been so successful in projecting the sense of wild irony and useless nagging terror which distinguished a mind trapped in America in the fifties.

The definitive work on this subject would appear to be John Berryman's *77 Dream Songs*, a book more brilliant and more beautiful than anything Ginsberg has done so far but one which, inasmuch as it is an attempt to exorcise ambivalence, defines a closed range of possibilities. Berryman adopts the logic of dreams and baby talk to recreate himself in a vaudevillian world more innocent and merciful than present circumstances will allow. His diction has an odd, disquieting finality: once established, it can go no further and tends to close in upon itself, forcing the poet to comprehend experience at the same level, always the same way, and thus to relive in effect the same experience.

Similarly, endeavoring to overpower his consciousness, Ginsberg becomes both the exploiter and the victim of his subject. Unlike Berryman, however, failing to find values which would allow him to make sense of his experience in nonartistic terms, he will not tolerate an artistic resolution of internal conflict. Consequently, from the outset he has had to piece together poems that are, like Pound's, "Fragmenta Monumenti":

> It was to have a structure, it
> was going to tell a story;
> it was to be a mass of images
> moving on a page, with
> a hollow voice at the center

To find that "hollow voice" which he associates with truth and objectivity (but also death) beyond "the roar of memory," Ginsberg must work through the "literary cackle" in his head. His makeshift style, which he describes as "Hebraic–Melvillian," embodies most notably echoes of Whitman and the rhetoric of transcendentalism, Hart Crane, Blake, Yeats, and Rimbaud; it allows him virtually every license and enables him to delimit his diction and therefore its range of relevant concerns. This is important, for what Philip Rahv refers to as the tendency toward "manic verbalization" is both the technique and chief subject of Ginsberg's verse. His is a poetry which is a plea for self-obliteration, an attempt to purge oneself of all experience by telling all, to make of the ego an "Empty Mirror." In this regard he sees himself among "the best minds of [his] generation":

> who talked continuously seventy hours from park to
>   pad to bar to Bellevue to museum to the Brooklyn Bridge,
> a lost battalion of platonic conversationalists jumping
>   down the stoops off fire escapes off windowsills off
>   Empire State out of the moon,

> yacketayakking screaming vomiting whispering facts and
>   memories and anecdotes . . . ,
> whole intellects disgorged in total recall for seven
>   days and nights with brilliant eyes . . .

One may observe that the condition sought for in such a world is silence, and silence, for Ginsberg, is equal to death: "This is the end, the redemption from Wilderness, way for the Wonderer, House sought for All." It is also important to note that in attempting to talk everything out, to rid himself of an experience with which he cannot live because it seems without value and therefore monstrous, Ginsberg can at last identify himself with his country: "It occurs to me that I am America. / I am talking to myself again."

Unlike the poets with whom he is usually associated—Corso, Ferlinghetti, even Kerouac (whose published poetic output consists of one dull book of "blues")—Ginsberg has not seemed to be taking advantage of a lamentable situation simply for the sake of self-promotion, and while their work has evaporated, his has not. In addition to matters of intellect and literary sense, the difference rests in the quality of Ginsberg's comic sense, which goes beyond hip elbowing to locate true horror in the details of routine existence:

> It was the racks, I realized, sitting myself on top of them
>   now as is my wont at lunchtime to rest my tired foot,
> it was the racks, great wooden shelves and stanchions posts
>   and beams assembled floor to roof jumbled with baggage,
> —the Japanese white metal postwar trunk gaudily flowered
>   & headed for Fort Bragg,
> one Mexican green paper package in purple rope adorned
>   with names for Nogales,
> hundreds of radiators all at once for Eureka,
> crates of Hawaiian underwear,
> rolls of posters scattered all over the Peninsula, nuts
>   to Sacramento,
> one human eye for Napa,

an aluminum box of human blood for Stockton
and a little red package of teeth for Calistoga—

Such catalogues are an indication of Ginsberg's chief intention: in his longer poems, which are in general his best, he attempts a poetry of sheer comprehensiveness and living weight. Quoting Thomas Hardy as the title for an early poem ("The road to a true philosophy of life seems to lie in humbly recording diverse readings of its phenomena"), he notes:

> I attempted to concentrate
> the total sun's rays in
> each poem as through a glass,
> but such magnification
> did not set the page afire.

This is an example of the kind of poem Ginsberg does not want to write, in part because he rejects the false purity which may often be achieved in an attractive arrangement of small-scale observations: such a procedure may magnify the trivial out of all proportion to the varying perspectives which an ongoing pursuit of meanings must imply.

Nevertheless, this kind of poem is extremely fashionable these days, and its foremost practitioner is Robert Creeley (b. 1926). Creeley, in all likelihood, is the most overrated poet of his generation. He is the leading exponent of what Leslie Fiedler has shrewdly described as the "diet-slim" poem, a poem which is in effect no more than an artistic reinforcement of the society's most banal aspirations, and in which the fetish for weight-watching has become no less than an aesthetic principle, indeed a mode of composition. By relying on a tone of conspiratorial coolness, Creeley's poetry eliminates the struggle with live experience and the risk of commitment to a necessary vision; it affects a detachment which is never courageous. As the collection of his work published in 1962 (*For Love*) makes plain, his is a sense of the poem as the ultimate wisecrack.

Creeley first emerged as one of several poets who wrote on each other and who dropped each other's names whenever possible; included among the others were Charles Olson and Robert Duncan. Olson, the author of a neglected but interesting book on Melville (*Call Me Ishmael*), is an older poet whose essay on "Projective Verse" has had some influence in some circles: precisely what kind is not easy to imagine, since after boiling down the jargon one is left with little more than commonplaces about the dual sensual and intellectual appeal of poetry and the need for "organic form." What he called "composition by field" ("energy transferred from where the poet got it . . . to the reader") was to be accomplished through the application of a formula defining the relation between breathing and poetic measure:

the HEAD, by way of the EAR, to the SYLLABLE
the HEART, by way of the BREATH, to the LINE

The consequences of this obscure Body English are to be seen in his *Maximus Poems*. In these poems, which are heavily derived from Pound's *Cantos* and Williams' *Paterson*, the poetic intelligence seems nearly mesmerized by muscle-bound rhythm. Similarly, in Duncan's verse, which is ridden by many of the same obsessions, the poetic "field" begins to resemble nothing so much as a fruit cake. Both poets have cultivated an elaborate diction incorporating elements of Poundiana (ampersands, abbreviations, snatches of quotations) and archaic spellings.

Creeley shares with them a precious prosiness, although he has been more cautious in adapting it to a smooth verse of littler ambitions. Skillfully manipulating a short-winded line, he has been able to write the same poem innumerable times. Visible primarily at close range, it is short on images and very neat. This is "Like They Say":

Underneath the tree on some
soft grass I sat, I

        watched two happy
        woodpeckers be dis-

        turbed by my presence. And
        why not, I thought to

        myself, why
        not.

We may have grown accustomed to a poetry of "no ideas but in things," but at least in Williams there is some vivid presence one may grasp: the poet has deliberately subordinated himself to his material to get the reader closer to it. Here, in contrast, the style not only precedes the experience but trivializes it, continually drawing our attention to the poet's insistence on his own unruffled *savoir-faire*. The manufacture of such poems on an industrial scale may be attributed either to the poet's healthy sense of his own limitations or to an overwhelming smugness. Judging by the tone of these poems, which is one of coy concealment, the second interpretation seems more likely.

Creeley's opposite in many ways is James Dickey (b. 1923), a poet who takes chances and trusts to his luck. Born in Atlanta, he was a fighter pilot in two wars and until recently a businessman. His first book, *Into the Stone*, came out in 1960 in the Scribners Poets of Today series (VII); *Drowning with Others* was published in 1962, *Helmets* in 1964, *Buckdancer's Choice* in 1965 (these last three volumes in the Wesleyan series). In addition, he has published *The Suspect in Poetry* (The Sixties Press), a collection of extremely sensible reviews of some of his contemporaries.

Dickey is an unexpected poet, one who has entrusted himself, for better or worse, to his own imagination. At its best, there is an unselfconscious ease and recklessness about his verse. There is a strangeness, too, for his poems are governed by fantasy, con-

236

ceived by yielding to impulse. They move in relentless pursuit of otherness. Dickey is preoccupied with death and metamorphosis, with the varieties of transfiguration; his poems trace the states of passage between the animal and the angelic, treading regions of sense extending beyond the human. Dreaming himself to "the cycle's center," by providing luminous accounts of the journey he convinces us that he sees "as the owl king sees, / By going in deeper than darkness." In his poems men and animals may dream each other into life and for one ecstatic moment fuse, until they must separate and the self be reassembled:

> I shall crawl to my human bed
> And lie there smiling at sunrise,
> With the scent of the fox
>
> Burning my brain like an incense,
> Floating out of the night wood,
> Coming home to my wife and my sons
> From the dream of an animal,
> Assembling the self I must wake to,
> Sleeping to grow back my legs.

He continually transcends himself, pursuing yearnings beyond reason into fantasies in which the living and the dead change places, all is possible, and he is watchful:

> The wind changes round, and I stir
> Within another's life. Whose life?
> Who is dead? Whose presence is living?
> When may I fall strangely to earth,
>
> Who am nailed to this branch by a spirit?
> Can two bodies make up a third?
> To sing, must I feel the world's light?
> My green, graceful bones fill the air
> With sleeping birds. Alone, alone
> And with them I move gently.
> I move at the heart of the world.

An admirable essay on his work appeared in 1963 in the latest issue of *The Sixties*. Written by "Crunk," their anonymous critic, it was generally sympathetic but took issue, justifiably, with Dickey's occasional weakness for "ghastly rhetoric," observing that "the danger of the rhetorical machinery is that it may drive Mr. Dickey to go over the same ground, becoming each time more ornate and long-winded." This criticism applies to a number of the poems in *Helmets*; it is unavoidable when it comes to *Buckdancer's Choice*. Poems like "The Fiend," for instance, go on too long and too loosely to retain our interest. The language exhibits a certain laziness; it flows too easily and does not grip us.

The *Sixties* essay closes with an irresistible image which captures Mr. Dickey nicely: "He is like a big moose adapted somehow to living beneath the water in some calm inland lake. The moose is constantly rising to the surface and breaking water so he can see his own huge horns in the sunlight, and giving a fixed and strange smile to the bourgeoisie out fishing." Dickey's poems are those of a man at one with his deepest aspirations and impulses; whatever their defects, they must be praised for the taste of imaginative freedom they allow us.

In contrast, the work of James Wright (b. 1927), a poet also associated with *The Sixties*, has grown progressively more tense and sullen. Published in the Yale series in 1957, his first book, *The Green Wall*, was undeniably accomplished, though in a way that one acknowledges and usually forgets. It was a skillful book, efficient if not compelling, which made good use of a variety of marketable styles.

With *Saint Judas* (1959), Wright seemed to be coming closer to himself, though as the title indicates he was still easily distracted by the modish ("When I went out to kill myself, I caught / A pack of hoodlums beating up a man"). The poems here were more suggestive and morose, and Wright was still attempting to conceive a diction which would not confine him to the merely decorous. His work has always been highly self-conscious; when it fails, it fails with a certain fastidiousness, by finding the appropriate (all-too-appropriate but uninspired) word. Here are two stanzas from "At the Slackening of the Tide":

> The cold simplicity of evening falls
> Dead on my mind,
> And underneath the piles the water
> Leaps up, leaps up, and sags down slowly, farther
> Than seagulls disembodied in the drag
> Of oil and foam. . . .
>
> Abstract with terror of the shell, I stared
> Over the waters where
> God brooded for the living all one day.
> Lonely for weeping, starved for a sound of mourning,
> I bowed my head, and heard the sea far off
> Washing its hands.

The major problem here is that the reader must be dragged through dreary wastes of language before he can reach the chilling vision of the final line. There are too many words like *dead, sags, drag, stared, brooded, starved, mourning, bowed*: the verbs simply repeat the adjectives and nouns, and the result is a broad effect of weariness which lacks imaginative precision. The inexact language, forced to be subjective, only generalizes the experience and makes it appear commonplace. No doubt Wright became aware of this, and in a poem titled "The Morality of Poetry" proposed a new direction for his style: "Before you let a single word escape, / starve it in darkness." Bad advice, for what was needed in his verse was an increase of energy and abandon, a kind of emotional luxuriance; it had begun to suffer from the onset of a dull earnestness and lack of nerve.

The Branch Will Not Break (1963), his latest book, came as a disappointment. Wright had worked his way into a corner; still unable to work out a diction which would imaginatively fuse his emotions and observations, he began to separate them in an attempt to evade the problem. Lavishing uncommon words on his descriptions, he reduced subjective content almost to banality, employing common words which were supposed to indicate sincerity. As a result, lines like "I am growing old" and "I stand, waiting / For dark" began to recur and deaden everything. The most widely circulated poem from this book bears the title "Lying in a Hammock at William Duffy's Farm in Pine Island, Minnesota"; it is quoted here in its entirety:

> Over my head, I see the bronze butterfly,
> Asleep on the black trunk,
> Blowing like a leaf in green shadow.
> Down the ravine behind the empty house,
> The cowbells follow one another
> Into the distances of the afternoon.
> To my right,
> In a field of sunlight between two pines,
> The droppings of last year's horses
> Blaze into golden stones.
> I lean back, as the evening darkens and comes on.
> A chicken-hawk floats over, looking for home.
> I have wasted my life.

The last line is an unpleasant surprise. The poem has not earned the effect it attempts; it short-changes the reader in an effort to snatch up his sympathies, but once the surprise has worn off, he knows he has been cheated.

Robert Bly (b. 1926), the editor of *The Sixties* and author of a book of poems called *Silence in the Snowy Fields* (1963), while also inclined to state his emotions directly, does so with an exuberant simplicity which makes them convincing and artistically relevant. In his work, such statements function as part of the general diction and not in opposition to it. His emotions and perceptions feed each other:

> Oh, on an early morning I think I shall live forever!
> I am wrapped in my joyful flesh,
> As the grass is wrapped in its clouds of green. . . .

> Rising from a bed, where I dreamt
> Of long rides past castles and hot coals,
> The sun lies happily on my knees;
> I have suffered and survived the night,
> Bathed in dark water, like any blade of grass.

In addition, Bly's frequent use of themes and events drawn from American history has allowed him a reasonance which Wright has denied himself, and made it easier for him to escape the limitations which the continual treatment of the subject of his personality might otherwise impose.

Another group of poets, once referred to as the New York School, includes John Ashbery, Kenneth Koch, and Frank O'Hara. These poets, two of whom have been connected with *Art News,* have more often drawn their inspiration from contemporary painting than from poetry (in which, in any case, they tend to emulate the French). This is not to say that they have abandoned meaning in favor of verbal color but that, in attempting to write a poetry which is not limited by the current American alternatives, they have made use of techniques and perspectives afforded by other arts. This practice has allowed them the independence they required for experiment as well as the possibility of achieving a poetic expression contemporaneous, but not simply continuous, with that of their peers; in short, it has provided an escape from provinciality.

John Ashbery (b. 1927) appears to be the most successful poet in this group, although both Koch and O'Hara have their moments. (Koch especially is a writer of remarkable talent, but too often his work has the effect of raising the question of his seriousness. His mock epic, for example, *Ko, or a Season on Earth,* was too long to stay funny and appeared a wasteful enterprise in any case. There were some lovely poems, or passages of poems, collected in *Thank You,* but too many suffered from a kind of poutiness and helpless unconcern, a compulsion to be witty, often pointlessly.) Ashbery's first book, *Some Trees*, was published in the Yale series in 1956. It was a fine collection, though apparently not as distinctive as he wanted it to be; he wished to go further to find a new means of expression unmistakably his own.

The poems collected in *The Tennis Court Oath* (1962) are a good deal more difficult and more exploratory. Speaking of this book, Ashbery said: "I attempt to use words abstractly, as an abstract painter would use paint. (I have perhaps been more influenced by modern painting and music than by poetry.) This has nothing to do with 'Imagism' or using words because of their sound—words are inseparable from their meaning and cannot be said to exist apart from it. My aim is to give the meaning free play and the fullest possible range. As with the abstract painters, my abstraction is an attempt to get a greater, more complete kind of realism." These poems must be closely read and carefully experienced; at their best, they are conceived as direct but premeditated responses to a world which bears heavily upon the inner life, suggesting alternatives to a worldly organization which is at the same time completely reasonable and murderous: "And of the other things death is a new office building filled with modern furniture, / A wise thing, but which has no purpose for us."

True wisdom, for Ashbery, must allow us to live beyond our needs. His chief subject is disappointment, and his poems attempt to recognize and satisfy "the hungers / That must be stirred before disappointment can begin." He moves toward a realism which, taking account of the fact that one has "lost the beautiful dreams / That enlisted on waking," remains powerful enough to wrest perfection from experience. Consequently, his work records a continual struggle to overcome the hungers of necessity, to make imagination possible and able to sustain life:

> The body's products become
> Fatal to it. Our spit

Would kill us, but we
Die of our heat.
Though I say the things I wish to say
They are needless, their own flame conceives it.
So I am cheated of perfection.

Working with a diction by turns urbane, lyrical, and slangy, Ashbery is able to control a startling range of tonal variations. From the point of view of structure, he has remained consistently inventive, never satisfied to redo something he has done successfully before. As a result, he is continually driven into regions of unforeseen possibility, and he continually comes back with something new.

The most exciting younger poet writing in America is A. R. Ammons (b. 1926). Like James Dickey, he was born in the south (Whiteville, North Carolina) and was, for many years, a business executive. His first book of poems, *Ommateum*, was published in 1955, and has long been unavailable. *Expressions of Sea-Level* appeared in 1964 and attracted some admiring attention. This year, Cornell published two of his books: *Tape for the Turn of the Year*, a long poem originally composed as a journal on a roll of adding machine tape, and a new collection, entitled *Corsons Inlet*, which is of considerably more interest.

Ammons is cagey, quick, and unpredictable. Possessed of an almost uncanny instinct for timing the line, he achieves a poetic structure incorporating silences which have the weight of words:

> . . . rush into the domes
>
> these wordy arches shape: hear
>
> me
>
> when I am
>
> silent: gather the boundaried vacancies.

Just as silence completes speech, so in these poems the self is a scavenger which can only complete itself by assuming the world: it exists in continual assimilation, in "seizures" of reality in which "I could not think but / vanished into the beauty / of anything I saw / and loved." As a result, experience does not solidify: it gathers. Ammons's shifty rhythms keep it moving, changeable, alive, so that one has the impression that the capacity for new experience has suddenly grown limitless.

These poems never struggle: they are in possession of themselves and of the reader. Marvelously poised, they reach a sureness of expression which appears as effortless as flight:

> The sparrowhawk
> flies hard to
>
> stand in the
> air: something
>
> about direction
> lets us loose
>
> into ease
> and slow grace

What is most remarkable about Ammons is the abundance of his vision. He is a poet of many moods and inclinations; within the limits of a diction simultaneously rich and nervy, he can move from the gentleness of the lament for "Nelly Myers" to the ruthless brilliance of "Coon Song":

> . . . I am no slave that I
> should entertain you, say what you want
> to hear, let you wallow in
> your silt: one two three four five:
> one two three four five six seven eight nine ten:
> (all this time I've been
> counting spaces
> while you were thinking of something else)

                    mess in your own sloppy silt:
                        the hounds disappeared
            yelping (the way you would at extinction)
                        into—the order
                        breaks up here—immortality . . .

At a time when many of our best poets threaten to starve themselves by living on self-consciousness, Ammons attempts a
poetry which will "release us from mental / prisons into the
actual . . ." It is a poetry in which perception comes as an
awakening of energy. Rejecting "finality of vision," these poems
seem to come into being endlessly, and Ammons can enjoy "the
freedom that . . . I have perceived nothing completely." Beyond terror and joy, reality remains perpetually available, a
source of renewal and change; it is a habitable place. Perhaps
the best statement of Ammons's intention is a poem included in
Corsons Inlet; it is titled "Dunes":

        Taking root in windy sand
                is not an easy
        way
        to go about
                finding a place to stay.

        A ditchbank or wood's edge
                has firmer ground.

        In a loose world though
                something can be started—
        a root touch water,
                a tip break sand—

        Mounds from that can rise
                on held mounds,
        a gesture of building, keeping,
                a trapping
        into shape.

        Firm ground is not available ground.

As an affirmation of the inexhaustibility of experience, Ammons's poetry finds value in the very act of living in a perishable world. By allowing us to enter into a moving reality in which the sense of ourselves is preserved in change, such poems effect a liberation beyond praise.

JOHN BARTH / *Test Borings*

Very well, love had its place in my researches—but what a
bother, to take a mistress! The time for final examinations was
approaching, which everyone took and precious few passed; it
was the seventh semester of my quest for the old sheepskin; I
was anyhow past thirty, years behind the others, a bachelor in a
rented room with my books and instruments; no man could say
what I might be asked when my turn came; all day and half the
night I wore my eyes out learning everything.

If my room was satisfactory—in the turret of a rowhouse just
like its neighbors, block on block—the fellow I shared it with
was not. We are paired in this quarter of the University by
WESCAC, the mighty computer: at matriculation time everyone's attributes are coded onto cards which are then matched
automatically on the basis of complementation—a homely farm
girl with a svelte young piece from the Main Mall, and so forth.

Not in itself a bad idea; but show me the program that hasn't its doubtful side. I came into this campus with bad eyesight and an ugly birthmark, was never robust, cursed with a gimp; all this was duly punched into my card, I signed my papers, paid my fees, the gadget riffled and clicked. I went to my lodging and found there not the comely, clear-eyed, cheerful engineer I'd rather expected (myself being given to fits of brooding and conjectures at times more brilliant than practical); in fact I'd drawn no proper student at all, but Croaker, the great black athlete, All-Campus candidate, a mindless brute that ate raw hamburger at the Coach's orders, never wore a stitch except to go out, picked his nose, took what he pleased, urinated in the shower bath, danced and farted, rolled his eyes, bared his teeth, and had his way with a parade of coeds. Often and often when I had problems to think through, or wanted only to rest, I would discover Croaker at his business with one of the girls—perhaps a cheerleader with crimson letter on the breast of her pullover. The wretch never troubled to draw the blind: from my perch on the outside stairway I was obliged to watch them at their rut: how the smaller, pink beast feigned displeasure, even threatened alarum; how her ape of the woods merely grinned, and naked himself already, had at garter and hook; put her in a trice to the fearsome roger; whereat, coy no more, she'd whoop. And the worst was, we must share the same bed. Hard enough to relax in the odors of perfume and sweat while he snored and pitched beside me; more than once, when sleep at last gave respite from all thought, I would be roused by Croaker's heavy arm flung over me; caught up in prurient dreamings he mistook me for his prey, and I must either wake him (no easy task) or lie revolted in his hug till the dream was done.

Now then, he was not all bad. I never begrudged him his scholarship; brains aren't everything; studentdom must have its circuses. The whole body attended the games; I watched them myself, cheering with the rest. Croaker was a splendid supple animal after all, full of power and grace; it could lift my spirits to see him leap about the room or chin on the shower rod or lay waste half a sorority with his sable cannon. We were not always at odds. Though the smell of raw hamburger retched me, he saw to it I never starved; except in his most obstreperous humors he fetched and carried virtually at my command. In return—why deny it?—I filled out his scholarship forms, reconciled his bank statements, schooled him in the simplest etiquette and hygiene (not to defecate in classrooms, not to rape on streetcorners), and did his homework. I devised little tasks to make him feel useful and regimens to keep him fit; sometimes even I chose his girls, for left to himself he'd as lief mount somebody's poodle or the Dean of Studies. Let a bright young baggage from Theater Arts refuse me her company or turn away from my port-wine mark and thick eyeglasses: I would point her out to Croaker on the sly, and by week's end have the pleasure of seeing her boggle at his awful tup.

In sum, he could not have survived long in the University without my help, and I in turn would have found life insupportable had Croaker been shot to death, say, by the father of some ruined sophomore or lynched by the White Students' Council. However much, then, I might despair at his grossness and he perhaps at my inhibition and relative frailness; however much we each might yearn at times to live alone, or with a roommate more congenial, at our best we muddled through, strange bedfellows, who in any case were bound by the strictest of leases, which our landlord would not break before its term. And so strong a thing is custom, I soon could not recall having ever lived without him; it was as if we'd been together from the beginning, for better or worse. What is more, if our relation was at best uneasy, we came more and more to depend on each other as time went by. My affliction, a kind of infantile paralysis, worsened; I took to a wheelchair; Croaker delivered me to and from classes, even learned to take dictation and type out reports. For his part, he had got along before by a kind of instinct, which when he saw how better he fared with my assistance he either put by or clean forgot. I wrote out his answers to quizzes, told him when and what to eat and how to dress, made a quite presentable monkey of him, all things considered; I even learned the art of football for his sake and tutored him between matches in his forte, the Belly Series. All of which the professors, athletic directors, and students came to accept, grudgingly or not; to get Croaker they had to take me; to get me (who had my own kind of scholarship and notoriety) they must put up with Croaker; it was a package deal, we were inseparable as two old fags or ancient spouses.

II

Let them poke what fun they would at my poor eyes, that led me into cul-de-sacs and wrong toilets: some things I saw even then more clearly than most did. The first principle of University life, for example, I clasped to my heart during Freshman Orientation and never lost sight of after, not for an eyeblink of time, how clamorous or brave soever the voices that denied it. On all sides one heard old platitudes and half-truths—as that the unexamined life was not worth living, that the truth should make one free, that understanding was its own reward. *Cum laude* graduates, even professors, were not above urging one to greater efforts with such slogans, wherefor I early decided that either like all virtuosi—artists, athletes, yea Croaker himself— they ill understood the secret of their own greatness, or else they found it practical pedagogy to dissemble with us, as a child may best be lured from the cliff-edge by promise of sweets, when in fact his rescuers are candyless and want only to save his life. For whatever the case in academies of fancy, one thing alone matters in the real University: to avoid the torture of remedial programs and the irrevocable disgrace of failing out to the Dean o' Flunks. In short, to pass. Except this, what has importance? Very well to preach me the therapy of swimming for my shrunken legs, or its intrinsic pleasure; thrown overboard I care only to reach the shore, whether by sidestroke or astride a dolphin. To be sure, the Examiners are above corruption and intimidation; no candidate ever bribed or threatened his way to glory; to attain it one must know the Answers, nothing else will serve. There is the sole and sufficient ground for prizing knowledge: all other preachments are, if not mere sentiment, hollow consolation for the failed—who are *ipso facto* inconsolable. Get the answers, by any means at all: that is the student's one imperative. Don't speak to me of cheating; to cheat could only mean to pass in ignorance of the answers, which is impossible. Otherwise the term is empty, inasmuch as the end of passing determines all morality: what tends thereto is good, all else is evil or indifferent. Nothing could be simpler in theory than the ethics of student life.

But I don't suggest that the practice is without its difficulties! In the first place no one knows for sure what he'll be asked, or whether his answers will be acceptable. No two candidates are quite alike, however similarly trained, and no graduate, professors included, can know more than that he himself was asked so-and-so, to which on that occasion such-and-such reply proved acceptable. In consequence one discovers among them numerous hypotheses about the nature of examination, which even as an underclassman I was able to sort into two general categories: one holds that while the questions are different for each candidate, the Answer is the same for all; the other that while the Question never varies, the answers do. Whether in either case the variation is from age to age or candidate to candidate; whether it's a difference in formulation only or actual substance; whether it's radical or infinitesimal; whether the matter or the manner of the candidate's response is of more significance, the general tenor or the precise phrasing—these and a thousand like considerations are much debated among the faculty, many of whom, one sadly concludes, are more interested in academic questions of this sort than in the ultimate ones which in principle they should prepare us to confront. The students themselves must be pardoned for being in the main more realistic, if wrong-headed: desperate for straws to cling to, they're forever badgering their professors with down-to-campus queries: Will we be asked this in the Finals? Does attendance count? How much credit is given for class participation, for extracurricular activity, for washing blackboards and beating erasers, for a neat appearance and respectful demeanor, for improvement over bad beginnings? Not a few are persuaded that independent thinking is the *sine qua non,* even when naive or erroneous; others that verbatim responses from their lecture-notes are what most pleases. Some, of a cynic or obsequious temper, openly flatter their instructor's vanity, hang on his words as on a prophet's, turn the discussion to his private specialty, slap their knees at his donnish wit, and rush to his lectern at the hour's end for further converse. "What *other* courses do you teach, sir?" "Is your book out yet in paperback?" The coeds, particularly, are inclined to hope that a bright smile may make up for a dull intelligence, a firm bosom for a flabby argument, a clear peep for a cloudy insight. And more's the justice, not one of these gambits but has succeeded—in some cases and to some extent. Given two young ladies of equal merit and unequal beauty, who of us has not seen the fairer prosper? Who has not observed how renegade genius goes a-begging, is actually punished, while the sycophant's every doltishness is pardoned? A term's hard labor in the stacks, an hour's dalliance in Teacher's car—they come to the same. Who opens her placket may close her books; she lifts her standing with her skirts; the A goes on her transcript that should be branded in her palm. . . .

Yet all this is vanity. The Examiners care nothing for transcripts, only for answers. Campus legend is peopled with model students who never passed and mavericks who did; of those tightly fleshed and loosely moraled queans, some go dressed in white gown and mortarboard to be diplomaed out of hand; others are led shrieking down the Lesser Mall to be thrust beyond the pale forever. No theses so contrary that history won't feed both, and I soon induced, as might any undergraduate with his eyes open, that the whole collegiate establishment—its schools, departments, and courses of study, its professorial rank and tenure, its administrative apparatus, its seminars, turkey pens, elms, and alma maters—was but one more or less hopeful *means*; the most organized, surely, and hallowed by custom, but a mere alternative for all that. Its very advantages are not without their own perniciousness: faced with a Department of Moral Science and one of Swine Research, each with budget, offices, and journals, one comes inevitably to believe in the real separateness of those subjects—as if one could fathom hogs without knowing metaphysics, or set up as a practicing ontologist in ignorance of porcinity! Worse, within the same department one finds the Duroc–Jersey men at odds with the Poland–Chinas; the Deontological Intuitionalists and the Axiological Realists go to separate cocktail parties. Yet one must choose curriculum and major, ally oneself with Vienna Circle or Marburg School, dissertate upon *The Navigation of Sinking Vessels, Coastwise and Celestial,* or *Foundation Planting for Crooken Campaniles.* . . . Alas, the finals are comprehensive, the Examiners care not a fig for your Subdepartment of Rot Research, one wonders whether they know of its existence. Our Schools and Divisions, what are they but seams in the seamless; our categories change with the weather, not so our fates. In vain our less myopic faculty preaches general education: they have not only the mass of their colleagues to contend with but the very nature of the institution. Bravely today you devise something interdisciplinary: perhaps a pilot survey of Postlapsarian Herpetology and Pomegranate Culture ("Dilletantism!" cry the pomologists; the natural historians, "Thin Soup!"); by tomorrow there will be a Department of General Education, with a separate Division of P.H.P.C., and in time an additional Division of P.H.P.C. Education to train instructors for the first. There's no end to it.

Yet mind, I mean no disrespect for the colleges, certainly not for old New Tammany, which I loved then and love yet. (Why else have I returned—in tears, I grant you—like a rescued sailor to the water, in fond hope of saving others?) A wart on Miss University were nonetheless a wart, and if I will not call it a beauty mark, neither would I turn her out of bed on its account. Teachers forget their business; the University does not. There is a spirit here, a wisdom in the stones, as it were, that no amount of pedantry or folly quite dispels. I hear the pledges singing in their cups truths deeper than they know:

> *Wander we down College Mall,*
> *Old as time its elms withal.*
> *Broad as hope and dark as fate,*
> *It leads us to Commencement Gate:*
> > *But ah, but ah,*
> > *The Gate is strait,*
> > *And the Mall is not all . . .*
> > > *Ah! Ah!*
> > *Strait is the Gate,*
> > *And the Mall, not all.*

For those with eyes to see, the campus abounds with voiceless admonitions to humility. Not for nothing are Staff and Faculty equally privileged, so that groundskeepers and dormitory cooks earn as much as new professors; not for nothing does custom decree that our trustees be unlettered peasant folk, and that they select our Chancellors not from the intelligentsia but by lot from among their kind—tinkers and tillers and keepers of shops. For the same reason one observes among the faculty not gray-beard scholars only, their cowls ablazon with exotic marks of honor, but men of the people: former merchants, aspirant statesmen, gentle carpenters, and husbandmen. It is fit that our library be more modest than our stock barns, our stock barns than our skating rink, our skating rink than our stadium. Was not Enos Enoch, the Founder's Son, by nature an outdoor type, a do-it-Himselfer who chose as the original trustees the first dozen people He met; who never took degree or published monograph or stood behind lectern, but gathered about Him

whoever would listen, in the buckwheat valleys or the wild rho-
dodendron of the slope, and taught them by simple fictions and
maxims proof against time, which now are graved in the lime-
stone friezes of our halls?

Not the cut of your coat, but the cut of your jib.

All's fair that ends well.

Milo did not pass in class,
Nor did he fail in jail.[1]

[1] The allusion is to one of the early diplomates of Remus College, an ances-
tor of Croaker's, from whom Milo Park, New Tammany's present stadium,
takes its name. Book IV of *The Acts of the Chancellors* tells us that Milo
matriculated in a provincial Remusian Ag school with the modest aim of
studying dairy husbandry; but though he covered himself and the Remusian
Complex with glory for his athletic prowess, and became the inspiration of
a dozen sculptors, he repeatedly failed to qualify for Candidacy, for the
reason that a certain heifer named Sophie, assigned to his care, refused to
eat the experimental feed mixtures he prepared for it. Certain of failure,
Milo turned on the four-year-old animal in a rage one evening, killed it
with a single sock, and carried it on his shoulders across most of West
Campus from the old Stock Barns to the Chancellor's Residence, where
he left it high in a young red oak. For this outrage he was fetched to
prison by the Campus Patrol, who, however, were unable to remove the
beast from its perch. Seeing it next morning, the Chancellor asked how
a heifer had contrived to climb his oak tree, and being told of Milo's
offense, so far from exhibiting anger, he smiled and remarked, "There is
one way to raise a cow." He then convoked the entire Department of
Animal Husbandry and inquired whether the ablest among them had ever
got a heifer up a tree or knew how to coax one down. When none replied,
he ordered Milo released from Main Detention, dismissed the charges
against him, and passed him without further examination, the power of
Summary Bond and Loosement being still vested in the Chancellory in
those days.
The incident, and thus the epigram, has been variously glossed. Philo-
castrus the Younger (in *Comment. Act. Canc.*, Vol. 2, p. 438 ff.) formulates the classical interpretation: "Excellence is nondepartmental"—i.e.,
greatness is what counts, irrespective of its particular nature. Opposed is
the influential little treatise by Yussuf Khadrun, *De Vacae in Arbores*,
which holds that ends, rather than means, are the Examiners' primary concern: that the excellence for which Milo was rewarded lay not in his
athletic record but in his radical (and in the final sense practical) solution
of an apparently flunking predicament. To the objection that treeing the
cow was not a solution of anything until the Chancellor made it so by
rewarding it, later Khadrunians have asserted that Milo's victory was not
over the problem on its own terms but over the terms of the problem—

Learned Founder! Liberal artist! Dean of deans and coach of coaches, to whose memos we still turn in time of doubt: stand by us through these dark hours in Academe. Teach me, that am thy least professor, to profess no thing but truth; that am thy newest freshman advisor, not to misadvise those minds—so free of guile and information—thou hast committed to my trust.

---

that is to say, over the directive "Raise this heifer" in its conventional interpretation. As Fanshaw and Smart ask (in *The Higher Pragmatism*): "What did the Examiners care about experimental pasturage or the physical well-being of Sophie the heifer? In one sense everything, in another nothing. Milo's bold gesture made his failure the Department's failure; as the Chancellor's aphorism reminds us, too eager pursuit of solutions may blind us to the Answers, which are at least in some cases to be discovered by strange means indeed, and in strange places." Hugo Krafft takes a similar stand in his brilliant and exhaustive, if sometimes oppressive, *History of the West Campus Cattle Barns from the Founding to the Thirty-Seventh Chancellory*, and like other semantically oriented interpreters makes much of the first chancellor's fondness for word-play as a pedagogical device. The Neo-Philocastrians, to be sure, like the Scapulists they derive from, have never sympathized with pragmatism, higher or lower, and are inclined to be skeptical of the close textual analysis made popular by Krafft's followers; in general they still maintain that virtuosity, rather than net achievement, is the key to Commencement Gate—whether the performance wherein it is manifest be in itself "admirable" or otherwise. Thus Bongiovanni cites the examples of Carpo the Fool, an early freshman who knocked himself senseless in a fall from the parallel bars and was for several years thereafter the butt of campus humor, and Gaffer McKeon, "The Perfect Cheat," who confessed to never having given an uncribbed answer during his brilliant undergraduate career. Both men passed.

But the West Campus Philocastrians identify virtuosity with particular excellencies, while their East Campus counterparts, if so various a group may be thought of collectively, tend to speak of it with a capital V, as something distinguishable from virtuoso performances. Thus the old East Campus table grace quoted by Dharhalal Panda:

> With Milo, Carpo, and Gaffer,
> I live alone alone:
> Four fingers of a hand.
> May I, with Sophie or any other thumb,
> Grasp Answers as I grasp this food;
> Eat Truth; and on the Finals know
>   I feed myself myself.

Among the rash of modern researches into the political and economic life of the early University one finds frequent mention of Milo and the heifer—I think particularly of E. J. B. Sandry's scholarly analysis of the old enmity between the Divisions of Agriculture and Athletics in Remus College. Yet while one welcomes new light on studentdom's history from

Help me to grasp they rules; make clear thy curricular patterns as the day; thy prerequisites unknot for me to broadcast with the chimes. Enlighten the stupid; fire with zeal the lowest percentile; have mercy on the recreant in Main Detention and the strayed in Remedial Wisdom; be as a beacon in the College Senate, a gadfly in the dorms. Be keg and tap behind the bar of every order, that the brothers may chug-a-lug thy lore, see truth in the bottom of their steins, and next day find their heads a-crack with insight. Be with each coed at the evening's close: paw her with facts, make vain her protests against the advances of learning; take her to thy mind's backseat, strip off preconceptions, let down illusions, unharness her from error—that she may ere the curfew be infused with knowledge. Above all, Sir, stand by me at my lectern; be chalk and notes to me; silence the mowers and stay the traffic that I may speak; awaken the drowsy, confound the heckler; bring him to naught who would digress when I would not, and would not when I would; take my words from his mouth who would take them from mine; save me from slip of tongue and lapse of memory, from twice-told joke and unzipped fly. Doctor of doctors, vouchsafe unto me examples of the unexampled, words to speak the wordless; be now and ever my visual aid, that upon the empty slate of these young souls I may inscribe, bold and squeaklessly, the Answers.

---

whatever source, one cannot but regret the deprecatory tone of these investigators and the glib iconoclasm especially manifest in their handling of traditional anecdotes. Sandry's suggestion, for example, that the Chancellor saw in the Milo affair an opportunity to ". . . pull the collective beard of the Ag Hill Lobby" (sic) as a gesture of mollification to Coach Gaius, who was miffed at the large appropriation for new mushroom houses, is more exasperating by reason of its partial truth than plainly lunatic hypotheses (e.g., that the Chancellor's hand was forced, there being no other way to untree the cow, or that the whole incident was cynically prearranged by Milo and the Chancellor, or by the Division of Athletics, or by the Office of Public Information, for publicity purposes).

Perhaps the best general work on the whole matter is V. Shirodkar's *There Is One Way:* as the title suggests, he approaches Khadrunianism and Philocastrianism by way of the ambiguity of the Chancellor's observation and attempts to combine, or at least subsume, the major traditions into what he calls Mystical Pragmatism. The result, alas, is more syncretion

Every athlete is an athlete—hence the lure of varsity games. But in all studentdom, where is the student? There is no discipline any more. Rules we have a-plenty, but no one minds them; system in abundance, but no order. Time was, in the great days of West Campus, one durst not fall asleep in the classroom lest he

---

than synthesis, but Shirodkar's historicosemantic schema, here appended, belongs in every undergraduate notebook:

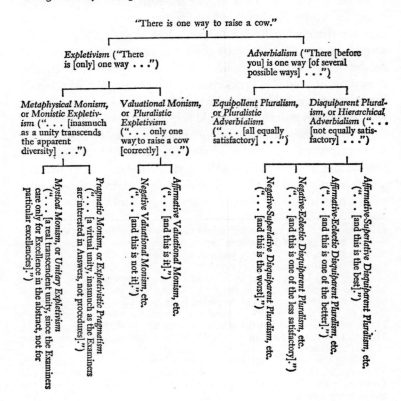

"There is one way to raise a cow."

Expletivism ("There is [only] one way . . .")

Adverbialism ("There [before you] is one way [of several possible ways] . . .")

Metaphysical Monism, or *Monistic Expletivism* (". . . [inasmuch as a unity transcends the apparent diversity] . . .")

Valuational Monism, or *Pluralistic Expletivism* (". . . only one way to raise a cow [correctly] . . .")

Equipollent Pluralism, or *Pluralistic Adverbialism* (". . . [all equally satisfactory] . . .")

Disquiparent Pluralism, or *Hierarchical Adverbialism* (". . . [not equally satisfactory] . . .")

Mystical Monism, or *Unitary Expletivism* (". . . [a real transcendent unity, since the Examiners care only for Excellence in the abstract, not for particular excellencies]. ")

Pragmatic Monism, or *Expletivistic Pragmatism* (". . . [a virtual unity, inasmuch as the Examiners are interested in Answers, not procedures]. ")

Negative Valuational Monism, etc. (". . . [and this is not it]. ")

Affirmative Valuational Monism, etc. (". . . [and this is it]. ")

Negative-Superlative Disquiparent Pluralism, etc. (". . . [and this is the worst]. ")

Negative-Eclectic Disquiparent Pluralism, etc. (". . . [and this is one of the less satisfactory]. ")

Affirmative-Eclectic Disquiparent Pluralism, etc. (". . . [and this is one of the better]. ")

Affirmative-Superlative Disquiparent Pluralism, etc. (". . . [and this is the best]. ")

be poled by the sergeant-at-arms. Quizzes were severely proctored, the very word struck terror; attendance was compulsory, and the penalty for disagreeing with one's professors was to be caned on the library terrace or have one's eyeglasses smashed. The several colleges then were not distinguished by location alone but by their whole attitude toward the nature of education and the Finals; professors caught lecturing outside their home quadrangle were liable to burning upon a pyre of their own textbooks. Student rivalry was intense: time and again the ranks of Divinity scholars sallied forth to reduce the East Campus; quarter was neither asked nor given in the Thirty Terms' Riot. Corruption, to be sure, was rifer then than now; it was also more open. The very esteem in which professorship was held drew to it the unscrupulous as well as the worthy: there were Deans of Colleges who could not read or write, department chairmen who had never passed the Finals and made no secret of their disbelief in the Examiners. Professors became mere vendors of spurious answer books to the superstitious; the tutorial and office conference were thin pretexts for fornication; what went on at the teas and conventions will not bear repeating.[2] Small wonder the lecturer's authority deteriorated; the sit-

---

Pragmatic Monism, Shirodkar maintains, comes to quite the same thing as Equipollent Pluralism, and Valuational Monism to the same as Disquiparent Pluralism. That this correspondence (which may be merely verbal) is ground for synthesis seems doubtful: the old Department of Dairy Husbandry may, it is true, be assigned with equal justice either to Negative Valuational Monism or to Negative-Superlative Disquiparent Pluralism; but what meeting of minds can be hoped for between Negative Valuational Monism and Positive Valuational Monism, or between Mystical Monism—my own position—and any of the others?

Heifer House, which generations of modern freshmen have been surprised to find is no stock barn but the office of the Campus Patrol, stands where Sophie's Oak once stood. The exact site of the tree is marked by a brass disk let into the floor of one of the auxiliary detention rooms.

[2] Those sincerely interested in pedagogical history may consult either Suebo's *Deaneries of the Middle Period* or Wittemberger's tract *Against the Tutors*, both available in the New Tammany Library's vaults on a need-to-know basis.

uation cried out for reform. One can only rejoice at the great tide of interest in extracurricular matters that then surged across the campus, and which the deans' offices, to their own detriment, tried to stem. Soon the only bonfires were at pregame rallies; Hotel Administration majors intermarried with girls from the Division of Fine Arts; juniors in Mushroom Management sang excerpts from the *Classical Quarterly* as they forked their dung. Already in the dramatic monographs of Quivero one finds hints of the doctrine of Examination Without Certification—or as he called it, Passage Without Transcript. More significantly, the *Eclogues* of Thibaudoux, his pupil, display no interest in the Finals at all; the poet turns his back alike on Commencement Gate and the South Exit, and speaks yearningly of a (fancied) Precollege era when handsome morons chased ill-read nymphs down the malls of primeval elm forests. Both the Ag Hill Covenant and the so-called *Pax Universitalis* are fruit of that troubled season; in vain one scans their legalistic clauses for the fire of Pearsall's *Burning of North Lab*, for the tang of Krumm's *Lecture to the Alchemists* on the night they stormed Tower Hall and emptied Main Detention. Is it not that, as in many another hybrid, distinctive flavor has been compromised for endurance and wide appeal? The course of subsequent events might have been predicted by any disinterested history major: Examination Without Certification was anathematized by the same Intercollege Council that approved of Certification Before Finals; intercurricular dining halls sprang up in every quad; yearbook bindings were embossed with the slogans of Mid-Percentile Baccalaureatism—"Every undergraduate his own advisor"; "Good doctors need no proctors"; "Fewer quizzes per quarter or quit."

The West Campus community we live in today is the child of this passionate begetting; its ills and strengths derive together from its mixed ancestry. Perhaps the soundest view to take of our present situation—indeed, of the student condition itself—is neither the fatuous optimism of the *General Prospectus* nor

yet the veiled despair of the *Ismist Antimanifesto*,[3] but the
tragic view. No one these days need die for the curriculum of his
choice: alas, would anyone be willing to? The passion that exalts
is the same that persecutes; if the new Auditorium has no Flog-
ging Room beneath it, neither has it a soaring Campanile above.
Never was our enrollment greater, or our average student less
concerned in his heart for the Finals. We have ceased to kick
the child who fidgets while we lecture: is it not that we also care
less strongly than we ought whether he passes, or believe less
strongly that our words will be his Answers? Our present Chan-

[3] An indictment of Paragraph 12 of the Academic Contract, which obliges
every employee of New Tammany College to declare his faith in the Examiners and his loyalty to the College Senate. The *Antimanifesto* was printed
and disseminated early last decade by a group of disaffected philosophy
majors who somehow gained access to the photocopy room of the Library.
Ismism, as their collective positions have come to be called, is quite fashionable now in certain strata of the student body, and has gained not a few
adherents among the faculty as well. More an emotion than a philosophy,
Ismism's main tenets are that all systematic explanations of the University,
such as expletivism and adverbialism, are posterior constructions reducible
to terms and categories existing in the mind of the theorist only, not in
the University itself; that they are, consequently, invalid except as self-
contained systems (i.e., "isms"), but perfectly valid explanations of the
hypothetical (*ismatic*) University which is their actual subject. Thus far,
saving the curious flavor of that last assertion, Ismism is little different from
such respectable theories of the University as unitary expletivism. But the
Antimanifesto goes on to deny the possibility of piercing this "ismatic
screen" to the nonconceptual *Universität an sich*, which "like the shade of
Aeneas's father, defies embrace." There *is* a kind of reality one may lay
hold of, however: the reality of the conceptual University, of the "ism-as-
ism." Finals may be passed, if at all, only when the Candidate achieves
the "Ismistic [called by some *Beistic*] Vision"—i.e., when he understands
that he himself, as knowable, is a term in the hypothesis whereto he sub-
scribes: not *merely* a concept, but *truly* a concept, with the special but
authentic reality of a dream or shadow. Thus set forth, Ismism seems
reasonable enough. But the Ismists in fact, like their wilder progeny the
Beists, are desperate spirits, at their best mere rationalizers of a situation
they really feel to be hopeless, at their worst sarcastic self-despisers eager
to project their own shortcomings onto the nature of the University. So
far as is known, no professed Ismist has yet confronted the Examiners—
whom also he must regard as "merely and truly hypothetical"! They are
lost intelligences, I fear, more in need of love than logic; the sad smart
children of West Campus rationalism, endeavoring like their forebears to
think their way to Commencement, but unable to believe in either their
vehicle or their destination.

cellory has the vices of its virtues, precisely. To gain this, we have sacrificed that; the pans remain balanced for better and worse. . . .

Nay, rather, for worse, always for worse. Late or soon, we lose. Sudden or slow, we lose. The bank exacts its charge for each redistribution of our funds. There is an entropy to time, a tax on change: four nickels for two dimes, but always less silver; our books stay reconciled, but who these days can tell heads from tails?

And as with the profession, so with the professor: I too shall fail. Only a handful will attend me; the rest will snore in the aisles, make paper airplanes from my notes, break wind in reply to my questions. I know they will steal my lunch and breathe on my lenses; expose their privates in the cloakroom, traffic in comic books under the seminar table. My voice shall grow hoarse, the chalk break in my hand. I know what seniors will murmur in the stacks and juniors chant at their torchlight rallies. A day approaches when the clerks in Tower Hall will draw up forms; the iron tools of Main Detention are oiled and ready; it will want but a nod from the Dean of Students to set my advisees on me in a pack. They will not remember who ordered their schedules out of chaos and put right their department; who routed the false dons from committees, established the Course, and set down this single hope of studentdom, the New Syllabus. Those same hands that lovingly last year put off my rags—will they not flip a penny for the cap and gown they dressed me in? Rank and tenure will be stripped from me; my protégés and assistants will curse the day I named them beneficiaries of my policy. Naked, blind, dishonored, I shall be coasted on a rusty bicycle from the quad. Past the farthest Model Silo, beyond the Forestry Camp and the weirs of the Watershed Researchers I shall make my way, in lowest gear, to the first spring of the last freshet on the highest rise of Founder's Hill. There in a riven grove one oak stands in the rock: its top is crowned with vine, its taproot cleaves to the spring beneath. At that day's dusking, when lights come on in Faculty Row and my enemies raise their bourbon, I'll make a goblet of my hands and drink cocktails from that spring. My parts will be hung with mistletoe; the oak will yield, and the rock know my embrace. Three times will lightning flash at a quarter after seven, all the University re-speaking my love's thunder, and it will be finished. The clap will turn me off. Passed but not forgotten, I shall rest.

WILLIAM BRONK / *Two Poems*

ON A PICTURE BY VINCENT CANADÉ

Pop did a triple self-portrait: three heads,
small and close together and much alike.
This was like him; he did himself to look
for something and look again, as anyone else
looks out the window a hundred times a day
just to look again at the same scene.
We try it. Well, we check the weather, the time,
the season. All that. The way we look, on trips,
at places, when what we really mean to see
is neither home nor here, but where we go
sometimes asleep, which is what we mean by place.
The strongest sense we ever have of place.
We know it isn't here, but nevertheless,
we try it, we try it. As if some day, one

attitude of infinite attitudes
at last, might make a place of here.
                              But all
Pop's heads looked like him, each in its own way.
Practice in looking at paintings shows us how what
we see can be said to look: as painting looks.
And this is a reason for painting, to say it so,
to limn the real, limit, illumine it.
Ahh! Flummery! Pop knew more than that,
knew better than to try to say the world or himself.
Those heads, like glances out the window, are to say,
"Listen, I have been here looking all day, all day
and every day; I have been here looking all day."

THE ELMS DYING / *and my friend*
Lew Stillwell dead

They are stripped and broken which were so beautiful,
gray-groined, graceful, which held the balance so
between lifting and lowering, they were the dancers who,
at the height of a rise, hovered a little aloft,
hung in the air, arms hanging, easy, poised.

So often the focus of such attentive awe
as we feel for the natural world, passing, they grieve
the fields for us, force us to find
elsewhere solace, such as anyone finds
where there were never elms, nor misses them.

Oh, it matters. It is not to say but what
it matters, but these dyings, yours even, say yours:
the riches of the world are infinite and it
is prodigal. What is terrible is
—not any death diminishes the world.

Or time. The way we push it: wishing next week
would come, or a year from now. Throwing away.
Does it matter so little? Isn't it rather that
we have it? Always. We have it. That there is no
diminishment. Never. Nothing. Help us. Help!

PETER SPIELBERG / *Back to Back*

A SHORT VIEW OF THE LONG

OF MARRIAGE IN ONE ACT OR THREE

SCENES (WITHOUT AN INTERMISSION)

I

The apartment, which may at one time have been one large room, is now divided into two rooms: a kitchen and a combination living and bedroom. The kitchen is the smaller of the two, yet it is large enough without being overcrowded to contain a chrome-legged, red Formica-topped kitchen table with four chairs to match as well as the usual gas range, oven, double sink, and eleven cubic foot refrigerator. On the wall above the stove and sink, the kitchen cabinet, painted the same color as the kitchen walls, extends to the ceiling, providing storage space for canned goods, nonperishable foods, and other staples. The portion of the wall cabinet above the sink contains dishes and glassware. There is no broom closet. The mop, straw broom, and dustpan are kept in the space between the refrigerator and the wall. The floor, covered with brown and white marbled linoleum, is clean, although it does not appear to be so because the linoleum is old and worn unevenly. This is also true of the rest of the kitchen. The obviously new pieces, the dinette set and the refrigerator, contrast sharply, point up the shabbiness of the rest of the kitchen. Yet, though it doesn't look it, the old, chipped, water-scarred sink is as clean as the new refrigerator. A visitor might think the floor dirty and expect to have the soles of his shoes stick to the linoleum; but this fear would be foolish since on a closer inspection one could see that the kitchen has recently been scrubbed, that the mop in the space between the wall and the refrigerator is still wet.

The wall which divides the kitchen from the living room–bedroom does not extend the full width of the apartment, but ends approximately four feet from the wall at right angles to it. No door separates the two rooms. The entrance to the apartment is at the extreme left, opposite the kitchen, in the wall which is at right angles to the wall which divides the apartment into two unequal halves (the smaller half contains the kitchen, the larger half is used as a combination living and bedroom). The rectangular space between the kitchen and the apartment's door, approximately four by eight feet, could be considered a foyer of sorts, since it does not properly belong to the living room, nor is it part of the kitchen. This feeling is further created by an old-fashioned clothes tree which stands to the right of the entranceway, blocking a visitor's direct view into the living room.

There is no toilet in the apartment itself, but there probably is one which is shared with the neighbors in the hallway outside.

The husband is sitting at the kitchen table with his back toward the wall that separates the kitchen from the other room. On the other side of the wall, in the combination living and bedroom—although it is now serving more as a bedroom than as a living room—his wife is reclining on what appears to be a homemade, combination couch and bed, a three-quarter mattress on a low wooden platform. Her back is propped up by a number of small pillows. If the wall separating the two rooms were removed, the back of the husband would touch the back of the wife.

The kitchen is brightly lit by a fluorescent ceiling fixture. The bedroom is dark in comparison, dimly lit by a goose-necked desk lamp which is standing on the floor next to the bed with its neck bent into an inverted U, its head touching the floor, so as to allow only a minimal amount of light to escape. The woman on the bed wears a white slip, no stockings.

Two or three minutes of SILENCE (perhaps as long as it would take a slow reader to read the above paragraphs out loud). The length of the silence as well as the depth is accentuated by an occasional creaking from the bed, caused by the wife as she moves a fraction of an inch higher up on the bed, pressing her back tightly against the wall as if to keep the pillows from slipping down. Yet the movement is hardly perceptible. The sound it makes, the wobbly wooden legs of the platform rub against the wooden planks of the floor, would ordinarily go unnoticed.

The man has not moved at all, not even his eyes, which seem to be looking down at the spread-open newspaper on the kitchen table before him but which are actually not focused on the print.

At first, the wife speaks louder than necessary, her voice cutting into the stillness, startlingly shrill, excruciatingly so, in sudden contrast to the interrupted silence, "Do you know what *Liebestod* means?"

The husband does not look up. He remains bent over, right elbow on the table, resting his head on his right hand.

The wife speaks as loudly as before: "Did you hear me?"

"I hear you." He does not speak as loudly as his wife, yet she can obviously hear him without any trouble.

"Do you know what *Liebestod* means? Capital *L*, small *i* before *e*, *b-e-s-t-o-d*."

"No."

"Can't you guess?"

"I'm not a dictionary."

"The death of love, a stalemate."

"A what?"

"A deadlock, a standstill, a dead end!" she adds, her voice again becoming shrill.

"That's a stupid thing to say."

"No. That's what the word means."

"What are you reading?"

"Nothing."

"What made you think of the word?"

"*Liebestod?*"

"Was that the word you asked me about?"

"Yes."

"Why?"

"I saw it in the Sunday crossword puzzle."

"SO?" Although he says "so?" and not "so what!" the tone and the implications are the same.

"I thought you might be interested . . ."

He does not respond.

"Are you?"

"I'm not."

The woman's lips move, but her words cannot be heard. Or if the words can be heard, they are spoken too low to be intelligible. Even an eavesdropper, in the same room with her, would not be able to unscramble them. Still, the gist of them is clear: her anger is communicated by her tone and by the abrupt way she changes the position of her legs, uncrossing them, and then recrossing them, so that the top leg is now the bottom one.

When the wife completes her motions, the husband begins his. (During this activity she sits completely still, just as he did while she was moving about.) He turns to another page in the newspaper, folding it carefully, silently, spreading it neatly out on the table. Then he reassumes his former position, bent over, resting his head on his hand, looking down, but not really reading.

The wife recrosses her legs (as above), pushes herself further up on the bed, taps the fingers of her right hand against her right thigh. The sounds of these movements are amplified beyond their normal volume, so that one can clearly hear the scraping sound of thigh against thigh, the swish of flesh rubbing against the satin slip, the rat-a-tat of the fingers, the rasping of fingernails as one is briefly caught on her slip, the groaning of the bed's (the wooden platform's) rickety legs.

"Stop it!"

The woman freezes; all motions and noises stop.

"I'm not doing anything."

"You were."

"No! I wasn't."

"All right," he retreats to avoid a dispute.

"I keep slipping down."

"All right!"

"The pillows are too small."

"Try keeping still."

"I can't."

"Try."

"I can't. I'm not like you. I'm still alive."

"All right."

"No! It's not!"

"Forget it."

"No!" she slaps her open hand against her thigh. "You're horrible! Cold, just like a dead, bloated white fish. You sit there reading your old newspaper, not paying any attention to me. I might as well not be here."

"I'm tired today."

"You're always tired, or you have a headache, or stomach cramps, or your eyes are burning, your ears are throbbing . . ."

"You exaggerate."

"Or you smell things, hear things . . ."

"All right."

"Something is always bothering you. If not one thing, it's another."

"And you?! You're either munching or scratching! First you yawn and then you stretch . . . then you eat—you crunch and slurp and gurgle—then you have to have a smoke and a drink. Never one without the other! So you puff and sigh and smack your lips. . . . And when at last I think you're sufficiently fed and watered and orally comforted, you begin all over again. You rub your scalp and attack your hair as if you were molting. You gnaw at your nails. Your legs twitch, your toes jump, your fingers drum. . . . It doesn't stop. Never. . . . You can't even sit still."

"I'm bored."

"That's not my fault."

"You don't talk to me any more."

"I said, I'm tired."

"Why don't you tell me something? Say something."

"That's unfair! Why should I invent stories to entertain you all the time?"

"You used to."

"I can't any more. I used them all up."

"Just talk a little."

"I wasn't married then. . . ."

"A word or two," she pleads.

"I'm too tired."

He pushes the newspaper away from him with his left hand, across the table, but still remains in the same position, now looking down at the bare red tabletop before him. His wife who may have heard the rustle of the paper asks, "What are you doing?"

"Nothing."

"Are you tired?"

"No."

"What?"

He repeats his answer, louder this time: "NO!"

"Why don't you come to bed?"

"It's too early."

"Last night you went to bed right after supper."

"What did you do?"

"I sat in the kitchen."

"All night?"

"Yes."

"Why don't you go to sleep now? You must be tired."

"I'm not sleepy. . . . Are you?"

"No."

"Are you going to read the paper tonight?"

"No. I'm tired."

"I'm sick of you!"

She rearranges the pillows which she has been leaning on. Her movements cause the bed to squeak. The stridulation is again magnified. The husband stiffens in his chair, but manages to control his anger for the moment. He grinds his teeth. His wife cannot see this, although she may be aware of it. She now pulls her slip, which has crept up, down, smoothing the material over her thighs. Still not comfortable, she adjusts the straps and then rubs one bare calf against the other, wriggling her toes as she rubs.

Throughout her movements, the husband has been sitting rigidly in his chair, not moving, his teeth clenched. Suddenly, he bangs the wall between the two with his fist and yells at her, "Stop it!"

"What?"

"Stop rubbing your feet together!"

"I wasn't," she maintains.

"Stop it! You're driving me mad!"

"I'm jumpy. . . . You make me nervous."

"For God's sake, don't pick on yourself! I can't stand this any longer."

The lights in the apartment go out.

II

The wife is in the kitchen. The double-hung window is wide open, both panes pushed to the top; the polka-dot curtains have been moved aside, revealing a view of the backyard and the kitchen windows of other apartments in the building opposite. She wears a full white slip, no panties, no stockings. Her good breasts are pushed outward by her black brassiere, which may be too small for her. The straps cut into her shoulders. The back of the bra is visible above the slip. The combination of the black and the white is odd. It seems as if she has black breasts. The rest of her body is very white, except for the dark area of her pubic triangle, which can be seen clearly through the white slip. Again, the contrast of black and white is startling. Even more so, when one remembers that she is obviously a natural blonde. Perhaps she dyed her pubic hair black.

She moves about in the kitchen on bare feet, taking a jar of mayonnaise from the refrigerator, a box of saltines from the cupboard, a glass, a knife. She opens the refrigerator again to get a tomato, which she bites into immediately, sucking the juice greedily. Some escapes her and drips on the floor. She puts the bitten tomato down and opens the cracker box, tearing the waxpaper wrapping, removing a cracker to cover it with mayonnaise. The first cracker breaks in her hand under the pressure of the knife. She lets it fall and picks up another cracker which she manages to cover without breaking. But as she is about to bite into it, she changes her mind and puts it down on the table uneaten. She looks at the wall which separates the kitchen from the next room.

In the other room, the husband is lying on the bed-couch. He is awake, fully dressed except for shoes, which he has removed and placed carefully at the foot of the bed, his back to the kitchen wall, propped up by a number of small pillows. His head is a little to one side, inclined to the right. The goosenecked lamp is still in the same position, the room dark in contrast to the bright kitchen. He remains motionless, except that from time to time he runs his hand through his white hair. Yet he is not old, certainly not much older than his wife.

She now sits down at the kitchen table, her back to the wall, and once more lifts the cracker to her mouth. This time she takes a bite, chewing slowly. Each bite sounds sharply in the otherwise silent apartment. She puts the remainder of the cracker down, picks up the glass, and goes to the refrigerator. Opens it. Takes a bottle of milk from the refrigerator, leaving the door open, pours herself a glass, and then looks up at the wall which separates her from her husband.

"Are you asleep?" she calls softly.

There is no answer.

"Are you asleep?" she asks again, louder.

The answer comes swiftly and loudly. "Leave me alone. Damn you! You filthy bitch. Stop it!"

She in turn turns and slams the refrigerator shut.

"Filthy bitch!"

She responds by pouring the untouched milk down the drain, but resists the temptation to smash the glass, and instead sets it down softly. Returning to the table, she sits down, her back to the wall. On the table stand the open mayonnaise jar, the cracker box, a half-empty milk bottle. She pushes the crackers away from her, crosses her legs, and leans back in the chair until her blonde head touches the wall behind her. She tries to keep still; hands in her lap, one holding the other down. After a while, though, her legs begin to twitch. She wriggles her toes. Slowly, maybe without being aware of it, she partially uncrosses her legs, sliding one leg down the other, slowly rubbing one bare leg against the other, back and forth.

"Are you awake?"

His voice is low, fighting for control: "Leave me alone."

"I'm lonely. I have to talk to someone."

"All right. . . . I know," his voice seems kind, yet the softness is forced, painful, as if each word cut his lips, "but I can't talk. I'm sorry. I don't feel well."

"Do you love me?"

"Of course."

"Then why don't you ever tell me that you do?"

"It's hard to talk."

"I love you."

"I know."

"But why do you stay in the other room? Why does everything I do irritate you?"

"Not everything."

She begins to cry.

"Don't snivel."

She tries to stop, smearing her tears across her cheeks with the palms of both hands. When her sobbing has subsided, she looks up at the electric alarm clock on top of the refrigerator and calls to her husband in a voice still husky from crying, "It's time for your lay. Do you want to do it on the kitchen table or on the bed?"

"In here. It's cleaner."

She gets up, turns off the kitchen light, moving smoothly in the sudden darkness toward the other room, whispers, "We should have a baby."

III

The bright fluorescent light cruelly illuminates the shabby kitchen, revealing grease-smeared walls, a chipped sink in which unwashed dishes are piled, the broken door of the refrigerator. The window is shut. A brown, water-stained, paper blind is pulled halfway down. A winter wind rattles the window, throwing sleet like pebbles against the panes. Three of the four gas jets of the stove are lit to provide warmth. The oven door stands wide open.

The HUSBAND fully dressed in a black suit and black tie sits at the kitchen table on one of the torn red chairs, his back to the wall which separates the kitchen from the combination living and bedroom. He has aged noticeably. His hair is white (but it has been white for a long time, since he was a child). He wears horn-rimmed glasses which seem to give him a lot of trouble; he removes them every few minutes, puts them down on the table, and vigorously rubs his eyeballs with the palms of both hands. Otherwise, he sits rigidly, staring at the dish-filled sink across the room, his head tilted slightly to the right as if he has difficulty in holding it upright.

The WIFE sits in the other room in a wooden rocking chair which has been placed on the same spot where the bed was before. The bed has been moved across the room. The rocking chair in which the WIFE sits faces away from the kitchen. Her back is toward the kitchen. If the wall separating the two rooms were removed, the chair on which the HUSBAND is sitting and the chair in which the WIFE is sitting would almost touch.

She holds her CHILD in her lap. It is a male child, yet looks and talks like a ventriloquist's dummy. (The part should be played by a midget.) He is dressed in a suit which seems un-suitable to his size and age.

The WIFE, it seems, has not aged. The dim light of the down-turned goose-necked lamp shows no wrinkles, no sagging of her high breasts. Her bare legs are smooth and long beneath her white slip. Her natural blonde hair is as blonde and natural as it has always been. She seems somewhat taller, but this is prob-ably an optical illusion caused by the difference in size between her and the CHILD and by the fact that she is wearing a pair of red spike-heeled shoes.

CHILD: (Speaks in the artificial, high-pitched voice of ventrilo-quists' dummies.)   Mama, can you tell me?

WIFE: (Answers in a resigned, tired voice.)   What?

CHILD: Mama, can you tell me what's up?

WIFE: (Sighs.)   I give up. You tell me.

CHILD: The sky's up!

WIFE: (Somewhat annoyed, she bounces the CHILD somewhat violently on her lap, but this does not bother him. He *laughs loudly, pleased with himself. She raises her voice to speak to her* HUSBAND *in the kitchen.)* What time is it?

HUSBAND: You have another ten minutes to go.

WIFE: Are you sure the clock is right?

HUSBAND: Yes, it's electric.

WIFE: What are you doing?

HUSBAND: Nothing.

WIFE: Are you resting?

HUSBAND: Not much. How can I? with him chattering like a monkey all the time.

WIFE: It's normal. You can't expect a child to behave any differently.

CHILD: (*whining voice*) What's normal, Mama? What? . . . Ma?

HUSBAND: Stop that whining!

CHILD: What did he say? . . . What did he say, Mama?

WIFE: (*soothingly*) Never mind. Just try to keep quiet for a few minutes longer. Papa needs his rest. Sshhh. (*She strokes the* CHILD's *head. He moves closer to her, playing with the hem of her slip. He remains relatively quiet during the next few minutes. Yet, although he does not talk or scream, he constantly hums and whispers to himself. His babbling should be as ever-present as background music in films. When his whispering becomes too loud, his mother shushes him. From time to time, when he pulls her slip too high up her thighs, she automatically pushes his hands away and pulls the slip down. Soon, though, he has it up again.*)

WIFE: (*reassuringly*) That's a good boy.

HUSBAND: (*half under his breath*) I don't think it's normal.

WIFE: What?

HUSBAND: He and you . . . and us . . . and . . .

WIFE: (*interrupting*) Don't start that again!

HUSBAND: It's not!

WIFE: Let's not talk about it any more!

HUSBAND: Fine! I'd rather not talk at all. You started it.

WIFE: (*after a minute or two of silence [see stage directions above]* . . .) What are you thinking of?

HUSBAND: (*violently*) Nothing! Stop checking up on me! Or in on me. Or whatever you're trying to do. . . . Rather, take care of your brat.

WIFE: Damn your eyes! (*She hisses her words.*)

CHILD: What's the matter with his eyes?

WIFE: Never you mind.

CHILD: (*Turns his head and shouts in the direction of the kitchen.*) What's up, Uncle?

HUSBAND: (*The reply from the kitchen comes back swiftly and clearly.*) Shut up! And don't call me Uncle.

CHILD: (*Mimics in a singsong voice.*) Put up or shut up. Shut up or put up. That's what's up!

WIFE: (*Shakes him again, more violently than before.*) Quiet. Your father is trying to rest.

CHILD: I won't!

WIFE: Please.

CHILD: Won't, won't, won't . . . (*chanting*) If you do or if you don't, if you will or if you won't . . .

WIFE: Stop it! (*She clamps her hand over the* CHILD's *mouth, and then suddenly SCREAMS, taking her hand away quickly.*)

HUSBAND: What happened?

WIFE: He bit me.

HUSBAND: Can't you control him? (*His voice shows his desperation; he strains, pulls at the words, and finally whines like the child.*) This is unfair. I can't even have any peace on my hour off. . . . Just keep him quiet for a few minutes longer. That's all I ask.

WIFE: I'll try. (*She bounces the* CHILD *more gently on her lap and hums to him. This seems to quiet him down. He snuggles closer to his mother and hums along with her.*)

HUSBAND: If only he would sleep sometimes! But never, never. . . . Have you ever seen him shut his eyes? Even for a moment?

WIFE: (*agreeing*) No.

HUSBAND: There! (*He pounces on her admission.*) You admit it, then! It's unnatural! And you can't convince me that it isn't.

WIFE: (*vehemently*) You're the one who's not normal. You're the one who can't live with people! Neither with the child nor with me. It wasn't any different before we had the child.

HUSBAND: Then why did you bother having one?

WIFE: We both bothered. Remember? Don't blame it on me. He's your child also. Half and half. He looks more like you than like me.

HUSBAND: Nonsense! He takes after you. He has your personality, your temperament, your insensitivity . . .

WIFE: Don't speak like that *devant l'enfant!* He's listening to every word.

HUSBAND: (*sarcastically*) Oh, excuse me. How stupid of me! How absentminded can a father get? to forget his only begotten son! Damn it, I must be becoming as callous as my surroundings. Will you ever forgive me, Mother?
The WIFE *does not answer. All is quiet for a few minutes.*

HUSBAND: (*Coming to a decision, he announces his intentions.*) I'm going to the toilet.

WIFE: Again?

HUSBAND: I have to shit.[1]

WIFE: Go ahead, but you'll have to take him with you.

HUSBAND: (*resigned*) I know.

WIFE: I wish you wouldn't take so long in the toilet.

HUSBAND: (*indignantly*) I don't go for my pleasure, you know. I don't go there to read or to jerk off, the way you do. —I mean the way you go there to read—I'm not even allowed that luxury! (*on the defensive*) I get through as fast as I can. I have to wait for the toilet seat to cool off! Don't I? You can't expect me to sit down when it's still warm, when it's still damp from the preceding occupant?! . . . Besides, what does it matter to you? I take the boy with me whether it's my shift or not.

WIFE: I don't want him to catch cold. It's a horrible, unsanitary hole. And that cold draft which comes out of it . . .

HUSBAND: I survive.

WIFE: It's not a cheerful place for a young child to be spending so much of his time.

[1] In the theatrical production directed by Mme. A. Kulpa, the word *crap* was substituted for *shit*.

HUSBAND: It hasn't affected him any that I can see. (*More to himself:*) He was born that way.

WIFE: How do you know? You wouldn't know. We could both die and rot away, and you wouldn't even notice—as long as we did it quietly . . .

HUSBAND: You couldn't! You'd fidget in your coffin.

WIFE: That's a horrible thing to say.

HUSBAND: It's true, though.

WIFE: But I can't help it.

HUSBAND: You can try.

WIFE: I do.

HUSBAND: (*Grimaces and shrugs his shoulders.*) I'd better go now. But if you're so worried, why don't you keep him here while I go to the toilet by myself.

WIFE: Oh, no! Don't start that again. We agreed to this arrangement. It's the only chance I have to eat anything.

HUSBAND: All right! But, for God's sake, get him ready quickly. And remember to clean up after yourself when you've finished eating. The whole kitchen is filthy enough already. Just wipe yourself and flush when you're through. It's such a simple, civilized rule.

He gets up from his chair, but has some difficulty walking since his shoes stick to the kitchen linoleum. He is, therefore, forced to walk in an unnatural way, lifting each foot high before placing it down again. Wincing each time he crunches a broken cracker underfoot, he moves to the clothes tree in the foyer, puts on a pair of high galoshes, a thick muffler, his winter coat with a fur collar, and a soft felt hat.

In the meantime, the WIFE *has also left her chair. She*

gets the CHILD *ready, wrapping him in a wool blanket. The* CHILD *is obviously used to this procedure since he does not protest. He cooperates, making himself comfortable, smiling. His mother leans over the unmade bed on which she is preparing him and kisses him.*

CHILD: (*Returns the kiss, smacking his lips loudly.*)   Mama—

WIFE: (*affectionately*)   Baby—

HUSBAND: (*who has been waiting impatiently throughout this exchange of kisses, stamping his galoshed feet while putting on a pair of black mittens*)   Damn it, I'm waiting!

WIFE: (*Hurriedly picks up the wrapped* CHILD *and rushes over to her* HUSBAND.)   Here. (*She hands him the* CHILD *as he opens the hall door. He runs out, slamming the door behind.* [N.B.: *The timing is very important here and should be rehearsed carefully so that it absolutely clicks. The* HUSBAND *and* WIFE *should neither touch nor look at each other during this split-second meeting. The exchange of the* CHILD *should remind one of a Mack Sennett comedy.*])

Light down and out in the living room. The kitchen light becomes even brighter (if this is possible), spotlighting the WIFE, *who stands legs apart, hands smoothing down her slip over her thighs, facing the audience and the closed door. The black brassiere which she is wearing beneath her slip shows clearly through the white material. Also visible through the thin material is her pubic triangle, but the pubic hairs are no longer black: they are gray. Otherwise she is an extremely attractive female.*

Suddenly, she turns and dashes further into the kitchen, frantically opening all the wall cabinets, drawers, the refrigerator. She takes food out, seemingly indiscriminately: canned fruit, sardines, Spam, beans, celery, carrots, two bottles of milk, a jar of mayonnaise, a loaf of white bread, an open box of saltines, pickles, a piece of cheese, and a huge chunk of raw meat. The top of the sink and the kitchen table are soon piled high with food. She searches for a can opener in the drawers and in the sink, but finds none. She gives up her search and tears open the package of bread, takes out a piece from the center, and then drops it and instead reaches for a handful of crackers and the cheese. As she is about to cram the food into her mouth she looks up at the wall which separates the kitchen from the combination living and bedroom, as if expecting to hear her HUSBAND's *voice. She waits, listens. . . . Slowly, she puts the food down, keeping only a single cracker in her hand. She puts the whole cracker into her mouth, chews slowly. The noise of her chewing is excessively loud. She stops chewing and sits down. Her cheeks seem bloated, filled almost to overflowing as if her mouth were stuffed full with food (yet she has only put one small cracker into it). She is breathing laboriously, her breasts rise and fall noticeably. She clenches her hands and puts them in her lap. After some time, she crosses her legs. Her slip has crawled up, revealing her white thighs. One of her red high-heeled shoes slips off her foot and falls to the floor. Then slowly, probably not realizing what she is doing, she uncrosses her legs and begins to rub one bare leg against the other, back and forth.*

CURTAIN

AUTHOR'S NOTE: Although this work—I once fondly (that is, in the archaic sense of the word—foolishly) thought it to be well within the short-story genre—was not originally intended to be trod upon the boards, I have let myself be persuaded by sundry friends and critics to allow what was once perhaps a closet drama of sorts to be performed as a legitimate one-acter (or as a not-so-friendly friend and critic chooses to call it: *a water-closet drama for the stage*). Yet let overenthusiastic thespians be warned: the work may not be acted by professionals or by amateurs without the written consent of the author and his agent!

KAREL VAN HET REVE / *In Turgenev's Hometown* / translated from the Dutch by Vera S. Dunham and Milorad Margitic

Precisely forty years after Pasternak, who was there in September of 1918, the author visited Turgenev's native region. This is the way it went. A small bus pulled up, the suitcases were loaded in the back, and our group took off to the station. Dr. D., our East German friend, was not feeling well, and I gave him my seat. I also carried his suitcases to the train. Our organizer was called Pavel Nikolaevich, a name which was easy for us to remember since it was just the other way around from Nikolai Pavlovich, a most unpleasant tsar. Our organizer, on the other hand, was a very nice man. He had not distributed train tickets to us, because a special car was reserved for our group. He left it up to us to enter our own car, and somewhere in the middle of it, we, the three Dutchmen, seized a compartment, sharing it with a Miss H. Right away she told us, in English, about an adventure she had had in Turkey and which slips my mind now. She was very pleased with the hospitality we were enjoying here and told us also that she had been invited by a Mr. and Mrs. B. to visit Yugoslavia for a few days. She had, gone, therefore, to the Yugoslav Embassy in M. to apply for a visa, and there she had been advised of a regulation requiring that the application be accompanied by several passport photos. As it turned out she did not have any with her.

"I told them," said Miss H., "that I had no photographs. They said I should have them taken. I told them that for photographs I should have to go to Gum, where everyone in M. and all the *kolkhozniki* of the M. district have their photographs taken, and that by the time my photographs were ready my Soviet visa would have expired. You know what the Yugoslavs did? They gave me a visa without a photograph, and they sent a special telegram to their frontier post, so they know I am coming without a photograph. Are not the Yugoslavs marvelous?"

We said that it was "very nice" of the Yugoslavs. Then, just as had happened when we entered the train in B., loud music resounded from the speakers in our compartment, switching sometimes from Russian to Western European songs. Among the latter was a hit seldom heard now in the West, *Marietje vrijt / Met een huzaar / Een hele tijd / Wel haast een Jaar*. On the basis of my Russian experience, I had said the previous time to J. that the music could not be toned down but that toward midnight it would stop by itself. J. had then found the button and reduced the music to silence. This time I tried to find the button on the basis of J.'s Russian experience. H. tried. J. tried. Miss H. tried. Several members of the Academy of Sciences of the U.S.S.R. tried, but in vain.

In the meantime other participants in the forthcoming celebration began boarding the train. A particularly nice gentleman, small and elegant, was pointed out to us, and he turned out to be the famous B.E., two of whose books I had not long ago discussed in my classes. Also a small fat man, wearing a cap, shoved through the passageway. This, we were assured, was O., another literary figure of world renown. Some other people boarded whose identity we discovered only later—for instance, old B., the author of a history of Russian literature of the eighteenth century. His was the first scholarly work I had bought after the war in the now defunct bookshop *Republiek der Letteren*. He had small red cheeks and wore an embroidered skull cap. He seemed, or rather was, friendliness itself.

A gay mood reigned. During the congress . . . I am going to pass on gossip from the hallways now. Gossip is the only source of interesting information in Russia, and one adjusts accordingly. One should accept nothing as truth in Russia. On the other hand, one should reject as untrue only the obviously absurd. One subsists, thus, on a mixture of *Dichtung* and *Wahrheit* without ever knowing whether one deals with the one of the other. Upon returning to the paradise of exact information —the West—one sighs with relief, although it must be said that rumors have their charms also.

As I was saying, during the congress, officials had somehow kept their eyes on their own scholars in order to rap them on the knuckles if they chummed too much with the foreigners. The watchdogs were recruited from among the scholars themselves. After the congress, surveillance was discontinued with that peculiar nonchalance we are inclined to consider typically Russian.

The men who were pushing through our car were in very high spirits.

"Why did this idiot A.S. attack that nice young fellow v.d.E. so viciously?" asked one loud man of another.

"Yes, wasn't it insane? And, what's more, such a nice young man and such an interesting paper." (This referred to our friend and compatriot v.d.E.)

"S. is a neurasthenic—" and that was the last thing we heard of that conversation. The Russians still use this pre-Freudian term.

More travelers arrived and among them V., the president of the congress, a member of the Academy. The Russian tradition, according to which there must always be a person in front of whom others grovel in the dust, had made him the great man of Russian Slavistics. And at the congress it was possible to distinguish the creepers from the more independent minds according to whether they quoted V. or not. If someone wanted to say that the second case of *stol* in Russian was *stola*, he had a choice between two formulations, namely: "The genitive of *stol* is *stola*" or "As it is rightly pointed out by Academician V., *stola* is the genitive of *stol*." This V. now made his entrance with his entourage. And at this late hour there arose a whispering and angry grumbling. In his simplicity, our organizer had left it to the participants of the celebration to distribute themselves over the thirty-eight sleeping compartments. The best place, in the middle of the car, was not reserved for the Academician V. Russians and those who think otherwise had been permitted to crawl simply pellmell into the compartments. The danger thus existed that the less trustworthy foreigners would spend the night with the less trustworthy Russians. And what foreigner is trustworthy, let alone a Russian? Again a piece of gossip. . . . What else should I, however, rely on so long as the State Publishing House does not issue a *Who Was Who in Siberia?* Had not Academician V. himself served his ten years in Vorkuta? He was there by mistake, as it later turned out. But that does not alter the fact that surveillance of such a person must be considered necessary. It seemed to us that the scholar K. was his bodyguard. The art of discovering collaborators of the secret police in a group of Russians is but feebly developed in the West. I here impart completely free of charge, for the benefit of those who in the future might profit from it, the results of my rather humble experiences, collected in the course of ten years. I found only a few distinguishing characteristics. Taken one at a time, they may mean nothing, but taken together in twos and threes might indicate something which must then be rounded out by intuition. At that point one still possesses as little certainty as before, but at least one has executed a piece of research. In fact, the uncertainty is increased, because it is now a Socratic one, that is, of a higher order than uncertainty *tout court*. So the Russian who fulfills in a group of Russians the function mentioned above sometimes possesses the order of the Red Star. He is sometimes not quite or not at all a confrere of the other Russians. It is not quite clear to Western confreres what his business might be. He has not published in the field at all, or he has published very little. Furthermore, he lacks the hesitation which sometimes keeps his colleagues back from a simple and cordial contact with foreigners. He smiles, settles at your table, starts a conversation, and tells jokes.

Suddenly the radio turned silent, as the train pulled away from the station. Many travelers were now chatting in the passageway, but because we did not personally know anybody except M., and because it was late we retired for the night. Officially the autumn had not yet begun, but it was unusually cold for the time of year, and by midnight the thin blankets in which we tried in vain to keep warm were supplemented by horse blankets. The next morning the train was still rolling. I believe that the special place we occupied in the group had already become obvious to most of our traveling companions. Unlike Miss H., we did not enter into conversation with highly placed persons. The three of us sat mostly together. We laughed quite a bit, so that we were more like schoolboys than scholars who must uphold their rank. Our car had two conductresses for its thirty-eight sleeping compartments. They made the beds, straightened the carpets in the passageway and served tea. One of them stormed our compartment, shouting "Hello, boys and girls, here is the guest book!" We offered her a seat, and she showed us the book in which previous passengers had jotted down their impressions of the journey and of the service. Since service was beyond reproach we wrote a few friendly words, making it a point of mentioning the names of the conductresses. "How young you are and how cheerful," she remarked, and when thereupon we disclosed our age and that of our children, her astonishment was boundless. Because of our habit of generalizing on a large scale, we concluded right there and then that people turned old in Russia sooner than in our country.

Pavel Nikolaevich, our organizer, also dropped in on us for a little while. He sat down without ceremony. He said that we were to arrive in a half an hour and with pleasant informality asked us for a smoke. Because of this, we became very much attached to him. We offered him a cigarette and inquired about the city of O. He told us that it had been almost completely destroyed during the war, not only because of shelling but also because the Germans had blown up many houses in retaliation against intensive partisan activity in the vicinity. I got the impression that he may have been a partisan in the Kovpak detachment himself, but to keep the conversation natural I did not ask him about it. It could have made him uneasy, and the conversation would have become official for the rest of the trip.

When the train arrived at the station of O., a group of school girls stood waiting on the platform. They wore black dresses and white aprons, and each held a bouquet of flowers. When we emerged from the car under the whirr of film cameras and flash-bulbs, these girls pressed bouquets into our hands. They were magnificent fall flowers, and we were moved to tears. Surrounded by the youngsters, we left the station, which, by the way, was a large new building, a Soviet palace of the kind we had seen already in B. A number of imposing Zis and Zim stood ready to take us to the hotel, where we were given a very nice room adorned with flowers and a giant radio. As a good patriot, I tried to get Hilversum, but I didn't succeed.

At 11:30 we sat down for breakfast in the restaurant. The directress of the Turgenev Museum, a very active and friendly lady, told us that we would lunch at exactly 1:30, and only at our protest was this dinner canceled. It was here that the printed programs for the celebrations were distributed. I saw with a shock my own name at the bottom of the list of speakers of the "scientific session" of the afternoon. Well, in M., as I was being invited for the trip, I had indeed heard something like "Say a few words." I had, however, considered this to be something in the manner of a polite Russian gesture that both parties discreetly forgot. Now fear struck into my heart. For me to make a speech in Russian is obviously more difficult than to make one in Dutch. Not only Russians but also foreign colleagues would hear my stupid mistakes. There would not be enough time to prepare a statement and have it checked by a "native informant." Moreover, what was there for me to say? Before me were six speakers, all of whom would undoubtedly point out that Turgenev had loved his country dearly, that he wrote beautiful descriptions of nature, that his novels portrayed the Russian society of the last century, that his *Sportsman's Sketches* were an indictment of serfdom, and that "millions and millions" of people were reading him at this very moment. As the seventh speaker I did not feel I should repeat what was said by the six preceding ones, things that had been hammered into the head of everyone present ever since his tenth year. But then what? Fortunately, I remembered the first chapter of a book of essays I had once written, and I tried now to use it. In it I had begun with the somewhat cryptic remark that a writer must turn obsolete before becoming immortal. I realized immediately that it was impossible for me to formulate this thought in Russian in a way that I could be sure was correct and understandable. And with the rest of the speech it was even worse. I planned to attack my unsuspecting audience by means of the German reactionary philosopher Schopenhauer—and to do so after all the friendliness and hospitality I was enjoying, not to mention the freedom of speech I was being offered on this occasion and which I would seem promptly to be abusing so ungraciously.

My heart bled, but my less fine instincts won. Anyone who has for years read the same two or three pronouncements on a certain writer and who then speaks to a public who has never read or heard anything else cannot resist the temptation to say something different for a change. Moreover, there was also *Dr. Zhivago*. I had read the book several weeks prior to the occasion and had become obsessed with it. Smoking and sweating I paced up and down our beautiful hotel room. On my request J. and H. had left me. I groped for a pretext to discuss Pasternak in a speech on Turgenev. Finally, just before the celebration began, I succeeded.

The ceremonies began at three in the afternoon. We were taken in automobiles and let off at a square where a statue of Lenin stood with its back to us and where several hundred people were assembled. We climbed the stairs of a building and placed ourselves facing the public. The first rows were again occupied by school girls, who again carried a magnificent bouquet of flowers each. There was a lectern and a microphone. We perceived other guests behind us, among whom was the striking and somewhat disheveled head of the well-known writer E. There blew a grim Dutch type of wind, and no one looked to his best advantage.

The meeting, as it was explained to us, was devoted to the erection of a statue of Turgenev. Because our eyes began searching for the traditional white sheet with the release cord attached to it, it was explained that a competition had been set up for the statue and that the jury had not yet agreed on the winning project. In the meantime a first stone would be laid there. However that first stone was also not here yet, so that it turned out we were actually engaged in celebrating the occasion of the decision to place before long the first stone for the erection of a statue before long. All this was connected with the fact that Ivan Sergeevich Turgenev died seventy-five years ago. We did not understand all of this right away, and therefore we were asked how such matters were handled in our country. When we looked at each other, one of the Russians conjectured that in the West, in a ceremony such as this, one probably unveiled the statue itself rather than the pedestal of the idea of a pedestal. We were glad to be spared the need of making such a statement ourselves, because we did not know for sure whether it was correct, and moreover, nothing is more unpleasant than to praise one's country in front of foreigners. Abroad I speak unfavorably about the Netherlands as much as possible. This creates an atmosphere of internatonal fraternity. And that's what counts, after all.

In connection with this, the following anecdote might be instructive. In a bookstore in Moscow I fell into a conversation with a sort of publisher. He told me that a lot of money was paid for the preparation of a text of a classic author in Russia. Thereupon I told him that it was quite different in my country.

"For the translation of all the novels of Turgenev," I said, "I received a sum of money equal to the amount I should have paid a typist had I had the manuscript retyped by anyone but my wife. In that respect, you have it much better than we."

"Yes," he answered in a low voice, "but that's about all."

A man who was the secretary of the regional committee of the Communist Party, as we later found out, a functionary comparable to the gubernator before 1917, opened the meeting. On the opposite side of the square a brass band intoned the Soviet national anthem in a thin, provincial manner. We bared our heads, and the public followed our example. On this drab, chilly square, in view of the gray, interested crowd, I listened to the ugly anthem which I had so often secretly heard during the war and reminded myself that with the sounds of this song these people had chased the Germans from Stalingrad to here and from here to Berlin. I felt proud to stand among them. Had the anthem of the U.S.S.R. still been the International, I would probably have raised my clenched fist, according to the old usage.

Then came the other speakers, a docent at a local pedagogical institute, a *komsomol* leader, and a member of the Academy. Nobody spoke very long, which no one regretted, and when the meeting closed, the apparently inevitable took place. The school girls stormed the stairs and pressed into our hands one bouquet of flowers after another. There were more girls and therefore more bouquets than foreigners; some of us could hardly move. The building on whose steps we were standing turned out to be the theater. We were led inside, where we tried, in as discreet a manner as we could, to get rid of the flowers because it makes no sense in Russia to give flowers without vases. The experience of that morning had taught us that in our entire hotel there was not a vase to save even so much as one or two of our bouquets.

We were left behind the stage in a sort of waiting room, where we found bowls of grapes, apples, candies, and, I believe, pieces of sausage. On the wall was a painting in which a young girl in a broad-rimmed hat fished in a pond while conversing with a man.

"*Wissen Sie was das ist?*" I asked Dr. D. to show off.

"*Etwas aus Turgenev?*" he replied with hesitation. "*Rudin vielleicht?*"

I was glad that I could best at least one of the Turgenev specialists present here, and I told him that this was Liza from *The Nest of Gentlefolk* with Lavretzky.

Dr. D., who was also to make a speech in a while and whose stage fright probably increased because of his kidneys, which were not in good order, looked at me, shook my hand, and said with admiration: "*Gratuliere. Haben Sie das auf Anhieb gewusst?*"

Flattered by this East German praise, I walked up to the stage with the others. On it was a long table and two rows of chairs, behind which an enormous portrait of Turgenev hung from a curtain. Behind the curtain I could see the empty stage itself, always fascinating to me: stone walls, ropes, wings, and the like, with a gigantic portrait of J.S. lifted very high against the bare background, like a *deus ex machina* no longer in use but stored just in case. We smiled and exchanged glances. By then we had come into the blinding footlights, and the public began to applaud. With the modesty that befits the representatives of a small nation, the three of us took seats in the second row.

Once more the Party secretary presided. The order of the speakers escapes me now, but several of them testified that Turgenev had loved his country dearly, that he wrote beautiful descriptions of nature, that his novels portrayed the Russian society of the last century, that his *Sportsman's Sketches* were an indictment of serfdom, and that "millions and millions" of people were reading him at this very moment. Meanwhile I looked nervously at my small piece of paper. Of the foreigners, M. and G. both spoke in French. Except for them, only H. understood anything. In most refined and animated French, G. gave a description of Bougival, the country house of the Viardots near Paris and the way it presently looked. All this was read from a paper.

The audience listened politely but looked tired, and the Party secretary announced a break of ten minutes, which we spent mostly in the Lavretzky room, smoking and drinking tea. In my nervousness I turned to A., asking him whether the first sentence of what I was shortly to say was correct Russian. He said that it contained perhaps a deep thought, but the meaning of my argument remained hidden to him. In turn it remained unclear to me whether the obscurity was caused by the thought itself, by the faulty Russian formulation of it, or perhaps—for one becomes frightfully suspicious in that country—by A.'s reluctance to understand my argument, let alone share it.

E., the well-known writer, was one of the speakers before the break. He had quoted in his address the poet Tiutchev, the contemporary of Pushkin, a friend of Heine, and one of the greatest poets of the nineteenth century. The following passage appears under the date of April 10, 1855, in the diary of the sister of the son-in-law of this poet shortly after the death of the already mentioned unpleasant tsar, Nikolai Pavlovich: "Everybody feels more or less relieved. F. I. Tiutchev has named this period very justly 'the thaw.' But what will follow it?" Now it is known that E. is the author of the novel *The Thaw*, which takes place shortly after the death of S. It had made quite a hit in Russia as well as in the West. It might not be impossible that the term *Thaw* was borrowed from that relatively obscure diary published in 1913. I thought it might be interesting to see E.'s reaction on discovering I had noticed his borrowing it. I approached him, forgot to introduce myself, and said:

"I.G., you just quoted Tiutchev. Have you by any chance borrowed the title of your novel from him? According to V.A.'s diary, that was the name he gave to the period shortly after the death of Nicholas I."

Blinking and listening wearily, E. heard me out and answered as follows: "The diary was sent to me later. I did not know that Tiutchev had used this word. A writer sent me this quotation later. I have not borrowed the title from Tiutchev. The situation, however, is the same." Apparently, then, not only was the borrowing I had discovered not a borrowing but what's more, I was not the first to draw his attention to the coincidence.

The meeting resumed. Again it was pointed out that Turgenev had loved his country, had described nature masterfully, had vituperated against serfdom, had painted the society of his time, and was now read by "millions and millions" of people. Fortunately, there were exceptions. Suddenly the old B.E. stepped in front of the footlights, saying that he had no speech to offer but a present which had remained in his bookcase for many years but which actually would be better placed in the bookcase of the Turgenev Museum. He showed the audience a German translation of Aeschulus of the first half of the last century purchased by him, E., for three rubles from an antique dealer. The latter must have been either extremely kind or extremely stupid, for on the flyleaf could be clearly read: *I. Turgenev*. Moreover, Turgenev had corrected with his own hand misprints in the text which were recorded in the errata on the back page. He had even, *en passant*, taken out a tiny misprint from the errata. Under applause, E. handed this book to the directress, who, blushing with joy, accepted it gratefully in the name of the Museum.

Meanwhile, time did not stand still. Only too clearly did I hear the secretary of the Communist Party of the O. region call out my country, my function, and my name. Greeted by a ripple of polite applause, I stumbled out of the row of chairs. Walking toward the lectern, which was violently illuminated, I tried to joke a little further with our East German colleague Dr. Z., whose turn was coming soon after and who was as fearful as I was. The desire to make himself loved by his fellow men drives a human being to do strange things. I myself undertook to elicit this love by the unusual means of making a provocative speech in which the holiest belief of many of those present might be injured. I spoke thus:

"Mr. President, Ladies and Gentlemen, dear comrades. It is a great honor and a great pleasure for me here in O., in the city of Turgenev and amid his compatriots, to testify publicly to my admiration and respect for this writer. Much has been already said about him here. Allow me to add a few personal words. Every writer must turn obsolete before he becomes immortal. I hope that my colleagues are not going to be angry with me if I say that in this respect great writers such as Tolstoy and Dostoevsky have not yet proven their immortality. Their genre—the long psychological novel—still exists. But Turgenev's genre, the short novel with love, moonlight, country estates, and gardens in the spring, alas, does not exist any longer. Nevertheless, Turgenev is still read, a proof of his immortality. In still one other respect Turgenev can be distinguished—one could almost say advantageously—from Tolstoy and Dostoevsky. (You understand that I will naturally say nothing bad about these two.) It is his restraint. Turgenev understood the art of adhering to what the great German writer Schopenhauer called the *alte Regel der Weltleute,* that *parler sans accent,* that speaking without emphasis. Turgenev does not shout at you, he does not want to convince you that he is right, he does not prescribe to you what you must do and how you must live. He tells you simply: live. Therein he resembles the hero of a Soviet novel which I read a few weeks ago. With some justification, as it seems to me, this hero says: 'Man is born to live, not to prepare himself for life.' "

If my memory is correct, the directress of the Museum was

thereupon given the floor. With touching simplicity she pointed out that actually we had to be grateful to "our beloved Party" for everything we had. Then A. thanked all the speakers, especially the foreigners, and the Party secretary closed the meeting. We left the podium and were again served tea in the director's office. The well-known writer E. came up to me, said a few friendly words, and asked whom I had quoted. I told him. Not a muscle moved on his face. He said that he had read the book. How he had gone about it he didn't tell me and I didn't ask. However, he wanted to know in what edition I had read it. When I said that it was in French, he replied that he had heard that the French translation was not bad. I said that my quotation may have been inexact because I had to translate the sentence from French back into Russian. E. thereupon observed that certain writers gain in translation—for example, Dostoevsky. His work contains here and there poorly written pages, slapped together out of necessity, which sometimes a good translator can somewhat improve. I then told him about J.M., who had replaced in his translation of *Crime and Punishment* the language errors of Dostoevsky with similar Dutch errors in order not to do violence to the original. As for Pasternak, E. said that he had to warn me that he did not belong to his opponents.

"I tell you this because in my opinion when he introduces the speech of common people in *Dr. Zhivago*, they speak the language of 1905 and not that of 1919–20. This is disturbing to the Russian reader, but in translation this drawback disappears."

At this moment B.E. joined the conversation. "Your observation about obsolescence and immortality is very correct," he said. "Take Walter Scott. His genre is obsolete and so are his books. While Turgenev's genre has also become obsolete, his novels have not."

E. pointed out also that the fact that Turgenev did not intrude on the reader was indeed something that distinguished him from Tolstoy and Dostoevsky. Chekhov possessed this quality in an even greater degree. By way of the French translation of *Dr. Zhivago*, Turgenev's sojourn in France, and the French speeches of the afternoon, the conversation turned to France. And E. thought it remarkable how many Russian writers hated that country. He gave me examples. Since again the occasion presented itself to disavow the West, I sardonically agreed with him, joining Fonvizin, Batiushkov, and Turgenev against de Gaulle.

Talking and sipping tea, we chanced into a sort of foyer where young people asked for our autographs, which we signed sometimes in Latin and sometimes in Cyrillic script. It was there that a vague young man shook my hand with the following words:

"You spoke a true word. I thank you."

One more gentleman came up to me, and since I incline toward exaggeration, I began to feel almost a hero and Turgenev's special representative on earth. "What you said about life," this man said, "is very true. And that it finally was said is most useful." I thanked him for his friendly judgment, and he asked me whether what I had said was also my own idea. I said it was.

With this the festivities of the evening were not over. We were now asked to take seats in the hall in order to enjoy a program which was described by the Russians with the word *concert* and which in the Netherlands might rather be called "spectacle coupé." The program consisted of songs, dance, music, and a declamation and was provided by local amateurs. It opened with a group of peasants from Spaskoe, Turgenev's former country estate. This was most appropriate because Turgenev himself, when entertaining foreign guests, had his peasants perform just such songs and dances for which, according to an old custom, they were recompensed by "half a bucket," that is half a bucket of spirits. In colorful costumes, their descendants were now lined up on the stage of the theater in Turgenev's birthplace. One wondered which of them could be Ivan Sergeevich's great-grandson and whom among the girls he would have taken as a mistress. The most picturesque part of the spectacle were two toothless women of gypsy appearance. With grins on their faces, they fired the youths on by shouting and clapping their hands. Our hosts were fearful that due to Western snobbishness we would hold in contempt this somewhat rustic performance. But this was not at all the case. We enjoyed it all very much, and we let our approval be clearly known. We assured the organizers who were surrounding us that we preferred by far these *kolkhozniki* to professional artists brought from M. The public in the hall behind us was less naïve than we and now and then laughed mercilessly over a false step or a false note. A local poet stood now in front of the footlights and glorified in the style of "Dutchmen wintering in Nova Zembla" the legendary origin of the city of O. The performer was a healthy young man but already corpulent. He went about his job with great earnestness and gave the impression that the foundation of his native city moved him deeply. He declaimed in the manner of someone who performs the Dutch social-democrat poem "Who Is It that Turns the Black Furrows into Undulating Grain?"

It should be noted here that the organizers of the evening's program made a lucky hit as far as the choice of the presentations was concerned but committed two errors. First, they had every number announced by a muscular lady, with an enormously high bosom, garbed in an ugly, shiny, long black dress. After every number, she marched up the stage, stared furiously at the audience, and in an embittered voice betraying inexplicable resentment, announced the next presentation. Her tone was supposed to inspire awe, but it had a chilling effect on an audience that was otherwise receptive. The second error committed by the organizers was that in their simplicity they put before us the best they had to offer in the beginning instead of saving it for the end, so that the quality of the presentation declined as the evening progressed.

We found the performance of a peasant family especially striking: father, two daughters, and a young son. This foursome, stuck in their Sunday best, sang in harmony the famous song *Step', Da Step' Krugom*. The father, blushing from embarrassment, looked above the heads of the audience, and due to obvious anxiety, sank a good half of an octave, just about what I would have done in his place. Slowly, falsely, and with deathly seriousness, they sang about a coachman who dies in a deserted steppe and with his last strength charges his friend to bury him "here, in the deserted steppe," to take his horses to his father, to take greetings to his mother, to say a word of farewell to his wife, and to hand her his wedding ring: "And say to her / that she should not grieve / that she should marry another man. / Say for me / that I froze to death in the steppe / and that with me / I have taken her love."

After that, a less famous but much more tearful piece of corn was sung by a fat young woman; marvelous also was a chorus of six young girls who had attempted to dress alike. In a provincial town of similar size in the United States the six girls would have worn identical dresses purchased specially for the occasion. In the Netherlands one would not have gone quite so far in the attempt to make everything as alike as possible. The shoes would have been all black, all with high heels, but not all of the same style. All skirts would have been black and of the same length but not of the same cut—no more than the blouses. How expensive and how scarce shoes and clothes were in this country was clearly demonstrated by these six girls. Their appearance testified that they had done absolutely everything in their power to make an entrance on the stage in uniform dress. However, their white blouses were each of a different model, and some underwear was blue, some was pink. The skirts were uneven in length, material, and cut. Some wore broad belts, others narrow. Low and high heels stood pellmell, and one girl wore brown shoes.

The performance of a little chanteuse, who was to have been accompanied on the piano, was touching—and brought forth a salvo of laughter. Her accompanist played the introductory bars, and as the chanteuse was inhaling air in order to start, the accompanist stopped where she was and fled into the wings. Perplexed, the chanteuse followed her example. And with a dead-pan expression on her face, the announcer marched up to the podium and called the next number. Turgenev himself, whose gigantic portrait still formed the backdrop for the stage, was not forgotten. The big choir sang one of his favorite songs, and the same poet as before recited one of the "Poems in Prose," namely, "The Threshold." It is a short piece of prose in which in front of Turgenev's inner eye there appears a young woman at the point of crossing the threshold of an unknown and threatening destiny. A voice warns her. The woman in question was doubtlessly meant to represent a Russian revolutionary in the seventies of the last century. Turgenev knew very well that many a person braves prison as well as the gallows if he knows that there will be witnesses of his heroic deed. Therefore, Turgenev has the voice ask the young woman whether she knows that it is possible that no one will be grateful to her, that no one will know anything of her fate. "Do you know it?" the voice asks. "I know it," she answers and crosses the threshold. "Fool!" cries a voice. "Saint!" cries another. Our poet recited this with much feeling. I wondered whether there was anyone in the hall who considered that this poem could apply today to a woman who would turn against the present administration with the same determination and the same contempt for death as the one who stood model for Turgenev's poem. I had to leave this question unanswered.

We were taken back to the hotel in buzzing Zims. There we were served supper at about ten o'clock. The three of us sat somewhat in the back and rejoiced in the special favor of the waitresses. Whether it was because of our nature, our national-ity, or our youth we did not know. Perhaps it was because we were pleased with everything. Everything we were served we found excellent, while some guests, remembering that they were on an expense account, composed their orders with great care and insisted on caviar and similar delicacies. We were satisfied with bread, butter, cheese, and tea. According to Russian concepts, this is not a meal but merely an introduction. As a reward, the nice waitresses brought us pastries which we had not ordered. Alcoholic beverages were also served, and from different tables loud exclamations reached us.

"They will be drunk in five minutes," said a somber Georgian who was sitting beside us. Indeed, several celebrants had already become somewhat loud. With the aversion which grips social-democratically educated Dutchmen in such situations, we observed how a forced and unelegant gaiety came about in a somewhat overheated little group around the Party secretary. We were sorry to see how academicians, who in our field of knowledge surpassed us by far, did their best to make a cheerful and loyal impression on the Party secretary, a man who was bereft of any intellectual sensitivity, who constantly stank of liquor, who had watery pig's eyes, and who seemed to exercise the *jus primae noctis* in the whole region of O.

The Georgian related to us the customs for a festive meal in his country. One begins there with a serious debate out of which results the election of a table president. The president starts out by making a toast, let us say, to a foreign guest. After that people naturally drink. In turn, each one of the table companions must make a new toast on the same subject but without repeating anything that was said before. While we were having this conversation in O., C.E. was himself participating in such festivities in Georgia and told us later that this ritual was taken very seriously there. If the president toasts the children of the honored guest, the other table companions try to find out something special about these children, so that when their turn comes, they can say something new. When the speeches are finished, a debate is opened in order to analyze without mercy all the tricks, repetitions, and long-windedness of the speakers. Considering that after each toast one must drink bottoms up, it is understandable that a Georgian celebration requires a great deal from body and soul and that the disorganized shouting, which we were witnessing, was not fit to raise to a degree higher than was recorded in the newspapers the admiration, as it is officially called, of the Georgian people for their Russian "older brothers."

O. came to sit at our table. He was also somewhat flushed. Following the habit of many congress participants, I had presented him with a reprint of my article "The Silence of Krylov," a title which had repeatedly made me a target of the mockery of the other Dutch participants. Under the roar of the festivity, O. started to develop for me his theory about the role which Krylov's father had played in the history of the origin of Pushkin's "Captain's Daughter," namely, the fact that Captain Mironov, a character in that story, could have been inspired by Krylov's father. The latter was also a poor little officer who took part in the struggle against Pugachev. "Who is the hero of this book?" O. asked gravely. Earlier critics had claimed that it was Griniov, the good, unspoiled character, described by Pushkin with some irony but also great sympathy. Others have said that it was Pugachev. O. rejected both theories. According to him, the hero was captain Mironov, stuck someplace in the steppe "with a man and a half and a single horse" to defend a pretty rotten society against rebels who in many respects had the right on their side. Both the tragic and the heroic in this character are expressed in the fact that with death in front of his eyes, he remains loyal to his fatherland, to the Russian state which is ruled by Catherine *for better or for worse*. He and not Griniov is the hero, for he is the incarnation of Pushkin's ideal. His point of view is that of Pushkin when Pushkin wrote the book: loyal to the Russian state although he had many objections to it. I told O. that I understood his approach, although I was especially reminded of a letter which Krylov's mother wrote after the death of her husband. She sent it to St. Petersburg. It was a request for a pension or some such, a document which in its semipeasant, semiofficial phraseology is completely imbued with the spirit of that fort, that small band of worthless soldiers, a wooden enclosure, and one cannon described with so much mastery by Pushkin.

More than with the relative correctness of his view, I was struck with O.'s inclination at all cost to find a "hero" in such a story. Were not, each in his own way, Griniov as well as Pugachev and Mironov and even Catherine the heroes of this story? Why must there absolutely be one character in a book behind which the author stands completely? It seemed a typical Russian, a typical Soviet conception. But I did not tell him that. Neither did I tell him that his theory was supported not only by the text of the novel and the facts of Pushkin's life but also by the attitude of the Russian literary historians toward their authorities, a position which resembles Pushkin's under Nicholas I. Their attitude is marked by loyalty toward the state, some features of which they consider an evil, but a necessary one. Since it is necessary, it is to be accepted and even defended. However, if one does not know a person well, it is not easy to talk about such matters.

Other celebrants came to visit us at our table. K., whom we suspected of being there not just for purposes of scholarship, paid his respects, and we fell into conversation also with a little old lady, a Tolstoy specialist who had just finished a study on *War and Peace* that dealt with the problem of its origin. For that purpose she had read the manuscripts, a performance which filled us with awe, for alone by the hand of Tolstoy's wife there exist something like six or seven manuscripts of the entire book. The old lady told us the total number of pages which she had examined—tens of thousands, I think—and told us with pride that she knew why Prince Andrey had to die.

"You don't know that," she said, "but I do."

And she smiled most kindly. In order to do something in return, we informed her that two of Tolstoy's letters were preserved in Amsterdam.

A very tall and very old Lett was part of the group who

wanted nothing better than to waltz. It seemed to us that approaching death made him decide to enjoy life as much as possible in the time remaining. One encounters old people with a similar exaggerated inclination, though usually toward tasty food. As soon as he heard music being played close by, the Lett tried to find a partner among the female participants or among the service personnel. It was in the nature of things that he approach J. and ask her for a dance. They disappeared behind a row of columns where, according to what I heard later, he tried to persuade the orchestra to play a waltz. At the same time, he conversed with J. in a most peculiar German. After imploring the orchestra a long time there resounded at last the much familiar sounds of "On the Hills of Manchuria," a hit of 1906 or thereabouts which is still popular. All these things had the effect of fatiguing us, and we retired.

Next morning we were driven to the Turgenev Museum, 11 Turgenev Street. The sun was shining, and O. looked like a Russian provincial town no matter what the period. It was difficult to imagine that during the war this city was almost completely destroyed, because so many buildings seemed to be standing there from 1840. This look of age was no doubt due to the severity of the climate, poor construction, and inadequate maintenance.

A very eager young woman guided us all the way through the Museum. We were shown Ivan Sergeevich's manuscripts, first editions, translations. We were shown his shotgun, his library, the desk at which *The Nest of Gentlefolk* was written. We were shown everything with expert commentary and with boundless love for a man whose memory was preserved here. This devotion to the memory of a great man had already very much impressed us during our visits to the houses of Tolstoy and Mayakovsky. Aside from the exhibits, the Museum contained a number of paintings by two local brothers who apparently earned a substantial livelihood in depicting Turgenev. One saw him in the company of Belinsky and in the company of characters from

Sportsman's Sketches; one saw him a few moments after the completion of *Fathers and Sons*, standing at an open window and looking out gravely and hopefully, as if he were expecting at any moment to be awarded the order of Lenin.

"Il y a quelques étudiants qui désirent vous parler," said G., emerging suddenly. He took me to the garden. The paths there, just as in a Turgenev novel, were strewn with sand. While I was working on my Turgenev translation, that sand had furnished me with considerable difficulties because I did not understand what sense it made to strew sand on a garden path which, I had thought, naturally consisted of sand. Fortunately I had stuck to the text. For now I saw that covering garden paths with yellow sand lends them neatness and color. Three students were sitting on a bench in front of two plaster statues of, in turn, students.

"We would like to meet you," said one of them. "We liked your words about Turgenev last night more than what we usually get to hear."

They introduced themselves and under the promise of most strict secrecy asked if I were willing to tell them what Soviet writer I had quoted. I told them.

"Oh," they said. "We thought it was Dudintzev."

"I have indeed read that book," I said, and added that there were even two Dutch translations of it published.

"What do you think of Dudintzev?"

"Sociologically very interesting, but from the point of view of literature nothing special."

"That's what we think too, but there are people who praise him to the skies. Do you know that *Not by Bread Alone* made a big impression on youth?"

I said that I knew. They asked how I had read *Dr. Zhivago*, and said that the quotation I used was taken out of their very heart. Then they asked me the flattering question of how it was that I knew so exactly the state of their minds. I answered that if you read Russian newspapers and books for ten years, you gradually got an idea of what was happening in their country.

Actually this was a very peculiar answer because one looks in vain in Russian newspapers and books for an indication of what is happening in the Soviet Union. However, anyone who regularly follows the press gets some idea of what's going on in the minds of people who depend on such a press. That's the way I meant it, and that's also the way they understood it, for we all lowered our eyes for a moment, a clearer sign of international contact than an embrace or a handshake.

"No, Ricky, wait. Please won't you just," she said. "Won't? A moment. Touch this," she said. "Not the glove."

Conrad didn't want to, but he couldn't endure another scene. He shrugged out of the leather; the cold cracked down across his knuckles.

"Now here." She took his wrist. "Up and down."

The slender trunk of the birch was sheathed in ice, liked oiled gun metal under his fingertips. The texture of the tree was gone, hidden; the places where he could see the coated bark peeling back were only dimples and nodes in the ice. He looked from the tree to her.

"Now touch this." She thrust his hand between the parted skirts of her leopard jacket, underneath the cashmere sweater. "You can't feel anything, can you? Ricky?"

"Of course I can. Don't be smart."

"My skin," she said. "You can't feel the grain of my skin, can you?"

"Your skin hasn't got a grain. Don't be ridiculous. It's smooth."

"Like ice?" she said.

"It's—"

"Like ice?" she said again, and leaned the weight of her body against his hand. Her breath was smoky beneath his chin; the wind was in her hair and blowing it across her face. "Is it like ice? Really? What do you know about my skin in your mind?"

Conrad blinked his eyes. Over his shoulder he saw the gas station attendant's freckled, hooded face staring their way. The family in the station wagon on the other side of the pumps was staring their way.

"Give me your other hand," she said.

"Julie, please stop this. Make sense."

"Give it." She caught at the hem of his other glove. "Take that off and touch me. I want to—"

"Julie, the whole world's gaping." Conrad was fumbling the bare hand back into the glove.

"Bashful." She was laughing. She got her fingers in among his, snarling his with the glove, defeating him. "You're embarrassed. Aren't you a fool?"

"Well, all right." He ripped the glove free and turned away. He heard her laughter and her boots with the same abrasive noise on the gravel of the filling station. There was a bubble of sweat sliding in the small of his back like a needle. The cold had burned his fingers; it was stiffening the muscles under his eyes. The air about him stilled, and his breathing covered every other sound. He was sucking his tongue against the rage, and he felt helplessness jelling his body, setting it like plaster. Then she slammed in through the door of the car behind him, and the explosion of that sound cleaved the air about him like a melon.

Conrad was paying the attendant; the dollar bills were brand new, adhered to each other. He couldn't manage them through the black leather. She was watching up at him through the sealed windshield. All of Vermont, the white and green of Vermont, was reflected on the glass, with her face spectral behind them. Her leopard jacket lost its yellow in the glass, and her eyes went down to green. Her skin was gray, her mouth went down to green. Her hair was green. The blue of the car's paint turned green like dollar bills and he ground the dollar bills between his thumb and index finger. They had no fiber, were slippery against the glove leather. The attendant was concealing his sneer badly. Conrad wanted to slap the attendant's face; he felt he could do even that to protect her.

In the car, he snapped the seat belt across the front of his quilted nylon windbreaker.

She looked on, amused. "Do you feel entirely safe now, love?" she said.

He twisted the ignition key and the hammering of the V-8 brought the Pontiac alive. In the rearview mirror he saw the attendant leaning in near the open window of the station wagon, sharing a smirking confidence with its driver. Conrad took the transmission to first gear, punched the accelerator against the firewall, let the clutch spring up. The torque hit the macadam of the filling station with a whoop of tires, spewing back gravel like shot. And the Pontiac lurched onto the roadway, a blind and an overpowering thing.

The snow had been plowed up in drifts to the height of a man on either side of the two lanes. The shoulder markers barely thrust above the peaks; the tassels of cotton cloth that measured a seven-foot depth were plastered down with frost, did not hail the slipstream of the Pontiac. The seams in the concrete thudded up through the tires, through the links of the suspension and the frame of the car with the mesmerizing regularity of a pulse. The speedometer's pointer jabbed and stuck at the 5 in 65 as if pinioned. There was a steady, hypnotic whistle of draft across the automobile's canvas top.

"Did you have your revenge on those people?" she said. "Aren't you a baby?"

Conrad said: "You could put the seat belt on, you know. It doesn't cost you anything."

"Why should I?" she said. "Give me a good reason. Go ahead. Just, Rick, for God's sake, you're getting so stuffy."

"It's my brain," he said. He put a cigarette in his mouth; she took it. He brought a second one from the pack on the dash and thumbed the lighter in.

"What's the matter with your brain?" she said.

"Statistics," he said. He was going to explain it; but he stopped himself, and made a joke of it instead. "The seat belt raises my chances for survival. I can't keep from reasoning." He wasn't saying it right; he wasn't saying it lightly enough. He glanced over toward her. "Excuse me for having a mind," he said, and his voice died out in despair.

"Machine," she said. She plucked the lighter and put it to the end of her cigarette until the tobacco glowed orange with the lighter's coil. She lit his. "Take your right glove off," she said, and blew the drag his way.

"Don't start that again." Conrad wound his wind wing ajar; their fine smoke vanished through it, and the roar of the wash sucking was a tone higher than the hiss of the canvas top.

"You don't want reality to charge in here and bust up your neat little bigotries, do you?" she said.

Conrad slouched in the grip of his bucket seat. "Look, we're almost there," he said. "Behave."

"Go on and take your glove off." She pushed the front of her jacket open and freed the cashmere sweater from the tops of her slacks. "Ricky, do it. Please."

He knew he couldn't refuse her. He threw the glove at the crotch where the windshield met the dash and thrust his bare hand into the grasp of her miniature two.

"What do you think now?" she said. "Ricky, what?"

His fingers felt the swell of her belly, the pit of her navel and the furrows of skin that poured into it. The skin was smooth as he had said it was. He thought of the ice winding on the birch tree. The ice was smooth. Then her skin was nonsmooth, rough. The gravel driveway of the gas station had been ragged, rough. Her skin was nonrough. Ninety-eight point six. Ectoderm. The sense in his fingers rose until it was razor-fine. Her belly sang down the nerve work of his arm in pointillism. Cobbles of tissue punctuated with follicles' pits. The seams in the concrete registered like fists beating on the Pontiac's hood, the wind sighed, whined through the crack in the open vent. She pushed his hand down under the tops of her slacks. Warmer. $NaCl + HOH + NH_4 + OH$. Sweat. Slick. He clung to the steering wheel with his other hand. The frilled fringe of her pubic hair. Fur: rough. Skin: smooth. Gravel: rough. Ice: smooth. Semirough. Demismooth. Grain and texture. Define.

The roadway was like a channel between the drifts of snow. Like the harbor of her snow-white thighs. Platitude. Her milk-white thighs. Platitude. Her nonwhite thighs. Thigh-white. Belly-smooth. His own hair-darkened thighs and belly. His thighs were not thigh-white; his belly was not belly-smooth. Then her thighs were: her-thigh-white. Impossible language. Her her-belly-smooth-belly. Absurd. Wind shriek, engine scream, gearbox chatter, concrete rumble, boom, bam, bang, whizz, ping, crack, clunk, clank, ting, pow, zip, hiss.

"Rick, do you love me even now?" she said.
She said:

"Riky, dew yoo luff me?"

"Rickee, du yew luv me?"

"Riquie, doo yu loff mi?"

The noises of the car in flight were: boom, bam, bang, whizz, ping, crack, clunk, clank, ting, pow, zip, hiss. Onomatopoeia. Valid language.

His fingers parted her labia, touched heat, dampness. There was a sound, he knew, a splash when his fingers touched that wet. He wanted to hear that sound. He should put his ear to her vulva. A finely tuned ear. Hear that sound that was like no other sound in the universe. Hear it as he heard the road sound through the balls of his feet, as he heard the wind sound that was partly the tingling of the draft on the hairs of his auricular canals. Like the singular color of her thighs and belly, an unreproducible sound. An index-finger-touch-vulva-damp sound. "I touched the moisture of her vulva with the tip of my index finger." Dry language that somehow turned loose a Niagara in his brain.

And dimension also: not merely vulva-damp. Vulva-love-damp. Vul'və-luv-damp. All their lives together compiled by a monosyllable. Hello. Courtship. Carnations. Satin dresses. Hair spray. Brassiere. Language like incantation. Phonemes to morphemes. Sounds to conjure with. Our waltz. Cointreau. Cigarette. Music. Scotch and water. Affair. Clasp. Clench. Kiss. Loss. Hip to hip. Loss. Thigh between thigh. Loss. You were right, love. You were right, love. My history with you is packed into the sound between my finger and your weeping vulva. Splash.

Conrad heard that sound. Like the car noise, the wind noise, the road noise. All the sensations whirled in him with reason in a grand cacophony, and the muscles in his bowels folded shut in a fist. His body trembled, and he sucked his tongue against the agony of wanting her. And the memory of the sense of helplessness at the filling station came back to him in resonance with his desperation to ram his body into hers. There was a truth in her that was beyond logic. And the rage to have her and the rage to protect her were identical, inseparable. The same. They were the same, and they were irreconcilable, he knew. Terror and a terrible confusion rained down upon him like drums.

In the ski lodge her cheeks were pinch-pink before the glow of the fireplace. The night pressed solid to the high glass windows, impenetrable as the color of her hair. Mountains and trees moved in the darkness outside, bending and swaying while the wind swam among them like whales. Her skin was smooth in apposition to the fireplace brick; even the nub of her sweater seemed smooth. The stretch of her ski slacks ran without crisis from where her body became legs to the snares of her calfskin boots. She was holding a Manhattan, and its color matched her mouth.

Conrad had watched the sprawling blond boy of twenty or so edging across rooms all afternoon, homing on the bare ring finger of her left hand. In range at last on the couch beside theirs, the boy said: "You'll love the hill. Try the Vista Trail." He was sitting so that Conrad could see the ski patrol patch on the shoulder of his white sweater.

"I know I'm going to love the hill," Julie said. "Ricky, don't you love hills?"

"I don't know," Conrad said. He didn't want to be belligerent, but he couldn't have the boy involved. "I guess I don't care much for hills, Julie," he said.

"Who's your friend?" the ski patrol said, and flexed the muscles in his neck.

"That's my ex-husband," Julie said. She looked at Conrad out of the side of her face.

"Julie, stop it," Conrad said.

"He follows me around," Julie said. "He starts trouble wherever I go."

"Well, that's not quite true," Conrad said. His palms were becoming sticky; he held both of them to his glass.

"You see, he's afraid I'll have affairs," Julie said. "He doesn't want to lose me. He doesn't believe in divorce, even when two people have no future together. Do you believe in divorce?"

"You bet," the ski patrol said.

"You are a horse's ass," Conrad said to the boy, and felt immediately a fool.

The ski patrol sat back. He put his highball glass on the polished oak floor. "Say, hold—"

"Don't pay attention," Julie said. "Ricky was an athlete once, and he's very dangerous to fight with."

The ski patrol looked from Conrad's side of the couch to hers. "He doesn't look as tough as—"

"That's the secret," Julie said. She stretched out, resting herself on one elbow so that her hair poured into Conrad's lap. "He doesn't look it, he doesn't want to face it, but underground in Ricky there are alligators and spiders. Devils. Violence."

"Julie, it's late," Conrad said.

"Devils and violence," she said. "Under the veneer of rationality. A primitive thing lives in Ricky. But he has corsets on his mind to hide it."

"Well," the ski patrol said. "All the same, he looks—"

"Like an orchid," Julie said. She set her glass down on the floor and leaned toward Conrad, arching her arm over her head to put her fingers in his hair. "He won't admit to anything he feels," she said. "So he's a madman. A maniac."

There was a yoke of perspiration under Conrad's shirt and turtleneck, bracelets of perspiration where they closed at his wrists. The instant the boy seemed hostile, Conrad would have to strike out at the base of his sternum, double him over, slap him across the ear.

"Break something for our friend," Julie said to him. Her voice was liquid, coaxing.

Conrad cleared his throat; he made a pass at gaiety. "What, for instance?"

"Break a chair. Chop through a tabletop. Split a board with your elbow. Then tell us what it's like."

The ski patrol picked up his drink. He seemed to be gathering himself to rise.

"Wait," Julie said. "You've been stalking me all night."

The boy blinked; shuffled his feet.

Conrad said, "We'd all better turn in."

"But he has been stalking me, Ricky. You saw him."

Conrad opened his hands. "Julie, it's midnight. We want to get an early—"

"Suppose I told you that this man here is annoying me?" she was saying to the boy.

The ski patrol looked at Conrad and then, cowed, away.

"Suppose I told you, help me, would you, please? This man is being terribly rude. What would you do?" She smiled at the boy. "You know that people like me, people like me always give their boudoirs to their heroes, don't they?"

"Well." The boy shrugged.

"I'm not worth a broken nose?" she said, straightening. "Are you going to sit there saying I'm not worth a black eye and a headache?" She wheeled on Conrad. "Ricky, are you going to let him say those things about me?"

"Julie." Conrad fingered the wool of her sweater. "Julie, Julie, it isn't going to work," he said.

She subsided against the couch. Conrad looked across at the ski patrol. "What's your name, my friend?" Conrad said.

"Gerry Lynch."

Conrad felt the perspiration pouring around his neck and into the gullies above his clavicles. "Go to bed, Gerry," Conrad said softly. "It's almost midnight. Go on." He motioned with his head. "Go on."

The ski patrol stared at him.

"Go," Conrad said, and waved the back of his hand.

The boy looked at Julie; she closed her eyes, settled on the couch and raised her heels to the edge of the elevated hearth.

"Go ahead," Conrad said again, and a silence lingered in the emptiness that the boy left.

The groups that had been chatting in other corners of the room began to drift downstairs to bed and Conrad was alone with her. The fire sank away to ashes and a final glowing fringe on the charred logs. The heat dissipated, the light fluttered and passed. The sitting room of the lodge settled into quiet, and darkness rolled under the beam ceiling, filling the room to brimming. The lamps had been extinguished, and there was only the dim gleaming of the lobby beyond the rear door. Their shadows slowly crept down the room's rear wall. At last the fire came juddering to cold.

Julie hadn't moved. Conrad wondered if she were dozing. He reached toward her, and his hand was trembling like tiny bells. Just in the instant before his fingers would have collided with her lips, her mouth pulled back into her cheeks and she said, "Entropy."

Conrad hung as he was, reaching from God to Adam.

"Will you love me even now, Ricky?" she said.

Conrad didn't answer.

She said, "I know you're here. Even without my eyes open. Don't make me open my eyes and crash all this as if it were china dishes."

"Julie, I'm doing the very best I can," Conrad said. "The very best."

She smiled; her mouth grew narrow and long in a meticulous bow. "You're a poet, Ricky," she said. "Like Oscar Hammerstein was a poet. You have absolute laws and so you have pop sentiments. You have certain knowledge. You're stuffy and soporific. You're a believer. And honestly, Rick"—her face rolled his way, but her eyes remained locked—"that's a tedious way to live."

"Because I believe in keeping promises?" he said. The darkness was cooling off. Even the last electric bulb burning in the hall outside the sitting room seemed to be wavering. "In things like keeping your vows?"

"You're discussing marriage now, aren't you?" she said.

"That's right."

Her face rolled away from him. "Ricky," she said wearily, "you will surely dance among the angels."

Conrad didn't say anything.

She sat without movement for a while. Then she said, "You're crying, aren't you?"

Conrad couldn't say anything.

"You think I'm out of my mind, don't you?" she said.

He couldn't talk. His throat was swollen closed. Gummy saliva filled up his mouth. His nose was running. He couldn't make her silhouette out clearly.

"Ricky, I want you to know that no one but you ever laid me."

"There's nothing wrong with." Then his voice split in the middle of the words and the muscles in his legs pulled and he was standing. "I'm just a human being, Julie. I'm just an average man," he said. "I can only take so much."

"You're a chemical engineer," she said. "You're well-paid and you're attractive."

"If I can't always cope with you it isn't because I'm not trying," he said. "But I'm used to reason and to logic. I've earned everything we own with logic."

"Machine," her voice said.

"I have to reason," he said. "I have to plan, understand things." Then he brought his hands in front of his face and drove his fingertips into his forehead to dull the thumping.

"Assumptions," her voice said. "You're always making assumptions. Come to bed and screw me in the present tense, and I wouldn't give you one drop of spit for all your assumptions and plans."

Like a cat he turned to her place on the couch. He didn't want to grab into her like an animal, but his arms were moving and his legs were moving. He was going to debase himself if he touched her like this, shame himself, humiliate himself. He fought his appetite, fought back whatever was primitive in him. He couldn't let himself revert to savagery; he couldn't let himself be decimated.

His foot struck her glass, crashed it over in shatters. He tried to adjust his balance, lost his equilibrium. He was falling. He tried to recover, stepped sideways, slipped again. Then he let his body go and fell at her place on the couch with all the force of his frustration.

His chin smacked down on the wood of the couch's frame. She was gone. And then her presence was beside him, so close that he could feel the heat of her through the chill of the room. "No suffering you can do can make any of your stupid plans or assumptions holy," her voice said at his ear. "Come to bed with me, Ricky. Let that be enough in itself. Come to bed with me." She took his hand and led him toward the light in the doorway.

He followed awkwardly: threading his way between the sliding planes of shadow that were draped over the furniture of the sitting room. There was a throbbing in his chin and a sympathetic swollen feeling over the back of his head like a skull cap. In the cellular lobby of the Inn the single electric fixture seemed to swing from the ceiling like a pendulum, as if his visual acuity had trebled so that he could discern the sixty-cycle-per-second beating of the element in its bulb. He followed her down the bare, complaining stairs with the veined, splintering weft of the dry wood coming through the rubber soles of his après-ski boots; along the corridor through the hips of the Inn where the recessed spotlights poured yellow on the deck paint of the concrete floor; silently to their bedroom's door, with the notion of her hips ricocheting between the walls of his thoughts with the *ping* of an overinflated basketball. The cobbled texture of your skin. My pebble-grained love.

Her sweater was over her head, suddenly a formless, weightless tangle of animal fibers in the passionless embrace of a chair. Her brassiere with its stressed cups and halter like the high ironwork of a bridge. The latticework of pain in his jaw. The cones of her bosom brought to conformity by the spandex stitching. $\frac{1}{3}\pi r^2 h$. Volume. Her stretch pants, now listless, shapeless. Her straining nylon stockings and the stays of her garter belt. The pounding over his head like an umbrella.

"Ricky, you don't look well."

Her nude body. Correction: naked.

"Ricky, why don't you take your clothes off? Did you hurt yourself?"

The trellis of pain in his jaw. His clothes made her naked: his nakedness would make her nude.

Her hands were scrabbling down his chest like the feet of squirrels. The turtleneck up over his head; a dark journey, like dying. The piles of slacks about his ankles, hobbling him. Nude, nude. With the whole lifeless room of dead artifacts about them. So that they became alien, the only breathing, heat-giving things in the room. And they moved about, making no real contact with the room or any of its parts. When the lights were put off, they drifted.

Conrad shut his eyes and tried again. But the darkness had no structure, no form, was inexpressible, resisted language, terrified him. Her fingernails went through his back like talons.

He lay awake long afterward and found that his judgment had been hasty; there was light in the room after all, off the snow outside, through the netting of curtains. There was enough light for him to see the shape of her body rippling under the blanket beside him.

There was a numbness throughout his maxilla that had replaced the pain; the hurt had left the parietal area of his skull. His eyes were open. He could make out lamps, a dresser, a desk, closet doors, doorknobs. He knew the world by doorknobs. He was relaxing. He eased his head against the pillow; the springs of the mattress reapportioned their thrust to the configuration of his body.

The light from outside threw the pleated pattern of the curtains on the ceiling like the bars of a graph. The crests of the pleating were umbra, its troughs were fair, contained even the beginning of color. Upstairs in the light of the lamps and fireplace of the sitting room, Vermont had seemed a country of blackness, imperturbable, incomprehensible. Now, in his own darkness, Vermont gave Conrad light, radiated, became intelligible.

He lay there, observing. The pattern of light and shadow made the plane of the ceiling discrete. Fine dark lines, finely etched lines. His mind filled up with numbers, like the functions of numbers on the x and y axes of a graph. "The locus of an equation in x and y is the collection of all those points in the plane whose coordinates satisfy the equation, and no other points." $S = k$-Boltzmann log P. $PV = 1/3Nmv^2$. $KE = 3/2nRT$. Conrad was singing himself to sleep. $P = (Nmv^2)/V$. He was sinking away. Numbers danced along the graph. Pure, path-of-a-point lines without measurable thickness. $\triangle p \triangle x = h$. All his neurons were singing. $Bqv = m(v^2/r)$. $hf = mc^2$. And the lines budded, grew other lines. Lines lacing lines. More lines against empty white. Spokes of lines, flights of lines, webs of lines coming in from the vertical and the horizontal. Lines weaving together and exhausting the emptiness, filling it. And the darkness that all the lines created lulled him. It was bulging. It was full of mind.

In the morning, Conrad dressed before she awoke. He showered, and came out of the shower with the scent of her still clinging to him. He tried to cover that with deodorant, with a splash of aftershave lotion on the chest of his sweater. He left their bedroom with the morning still baffled by the curtains.

Upstairs, the dining room of the Inn looked west toward the ski slopes. The sun came back off the snow, superheating the room. There were families and groups of two and three surrounding most of the tables. Among other places, there was room for him at the table set deepest in the corner where the two walls of glass met. The ski patrol boy was seated there. Conrad moved instinctively toward that familiarity, and took the chair opposite him.

"Good morning." There was a Pyrex coffee carafe over a candle in the middle of the table. The cloth was checkered red and black, stiff from a repetition of washings. Conrad looked at the boy; the boy seemed confounded.

Finally he said a grudging "Hello."

"You have to excuse Julie," Conrad said, falling into the litany of coffee pot and creamer, two level spoons of sugar. "She isn't herself," Conrad said.

The boy didn't answer him; he dug into his cereal bowl and seemed as though trying to give the impression of being exasperated.

"You don't work here the year round, do you?" Conrad said. He found the candle carafe was only decoration; the coffee was cold.

The boy was looking at him. He had a round, adolescent face. His nose was red and had peeled slick. The boy said, "No."

"You go to college, I suppose," Conrad said. "This is between semesters for you, isn't it?"

"That's right," the boy said.

Conrad changed his fingering on the handle of the coffee cup; he folded his legs under the table and leaned back in the bentwood chair. He listened to the boy chewing his cornflakes, watched the articulation of his clumsy, thick fingers and the uncertain path of his loaded spoon. The sunlight made the dining room very stuffy. Conrad shifted his weight in the chair.

"My wife hasn't been herself for some time now," Conrad said.

The boy began to look at him, and then carried on with his eyes over Conrad's shoulder.

"Julie would want me to apologize for both of us," Conrad said. "So I hope you'll." He broke off there.

The boy went on chewing his cereal. He sipped at a glass of milk. Some of the milk ran over his lower lip, into the cleft of his chin. He dabbed away the dripping with an effete, almost coy flick of the checkered napkin.

Conrad couldn't control himself. "Neither of us paid any attention to it at first," he said. "How could we know anything about—"

The boy stood up, balling his napkin. He pushed his chair aside and went around the table, out of Conrad's sight.

When Julie came upstairs, it was after eleven. Conrad had been trying to read a stale copy of *The New York Times*, but the ink on the newsprint refused to congeal into words. She had the leopard jacket on and was carrying his windbreaker. She wanted him to take her for a ride into the hills. He said he wouldn't mind; but that she should get some exercise. Otherwise, she'd go back to New York as pale as she had left it. She called him a fetishist.

Outside, there was a skin of frost on the windshield like heavy dust. Conrad started the car and left the choke nursing the cold engine while he attacked the frost with a plastic scraper. It came off hard at first, gradually easier as the car's defroster began to throw warm air at the base of the glass inside. She was already within the car, and as he scraped he exposed piece after piece of her to the light like a jigsaw puzzle, until she was full-face, staring at him, blinking.

He discovered her every morning of their lives that way. Either it was as the sleep gradually left his eyes or as he glimpsed her moving between bed and shower and closet and dresser and vanity. The function of her was etched in outline in his mind, and every day he observed her afresh, waiting for her catechism of movements to color all the familiar blank spaces. There was something missing in him until her morning smile fleshed out the skeleton of his recollection of her.

She was smiling. "It's marvelous country, Vermont."

"Yes?" He slammed the door of the car shut after him and locked it.

"I said it's marvelous country."

"Yes," he said, and glanced over at her. "Yes, it is. Do you want to do your seat belt up? Julie?"

"Why should I? Just give me one good reason." Then she

leaned over and touched him. "Ricky, please don't be a prig today, will you?"

"Well, it doesn't cost you anything," he said. Then he blew a breath into the palms of his gloves and applied it to his face. He didn't want any more unnecessary arguments. "You just can't lay around while we're up here, Julie," he said. "You know we planned this so that you could have some exercise. It will do you a world—"

She was laughing. "Rick, stop." She shook her hair out. "Drive us up into the hills," she said. "A long way. And don't be so sensible for a while. I want to smell the white and green."

They drove a long way: all afternoon. Several times they passed through towns that were only a few stores and a post office clustering into the crevices where a north–south road crossed one coming from the east. There was always a padding of snow on the roofs of the frame buildings, and every weather-cock they saw was frozen pointing to south. In the end, they found a half-cleared road that broke away toward higher ground. The car climbed it with snorting and flinching, until the country leveled off and the road was entirely under snow. When their way ended against a triple-laced guard rail, they were just under the summit of a treeless, drifted hill.

"Let's go back," she said. "Try another way. I want to go higher."

"If you want to go higher, walk," he said, with some small laughter.

"You're talking exercise again, aren't you?" she said.

"Yes," he said. He twisted the ignition key and the engine died in burbling.

"Well, fine," she said. She opened the door of the car and the evening cold came in upon them. She swung her boots out and Conrad heard them on the parchment crust of the snow. "Aren't you coming?" she said. She pointed upward, toward where the whiteness ended in a blue that was dropping into purple.

Shade was in the valley that held the last brief town they had passed through. A few lights were coming on. The wind behind them was bitter, slapped at the sleeves of their jackets. There was snow on the wind.

Soon her hair was sparkling in the last twilight with the moisture, and there were dots of white in her eyebrows and occasionally on her lashes. The night edged up about their feet, mingling with their shadows.

Once she looked up at him through the driving of flakes and said: "Everything is falling, Ricky. Ricky, everything is falling earthward." She stuffed her gloves into her pockets and cupped her hands before her to clutch the feel of the snow.

P. N. FURBANK / *Worlds*

How true it is that when I arrive by an unfamiliar train at a part of England that is new to me, I cannot prevent one part of my mind from suggesting that the people there are absolutely foreign. I see the same jeans, and head handkerchiefs, and navy-blue suits over green pullovers, and I know what attitudes I usually have to them, but I cannot call on them for the moment. If I talk to people on the train or in the street, shyness can intervene to make me feel like a stranger hurled from a different planet, different in all his outlooks and motives, who is only barely, by a prodigious linguistic effort, able to make his simple needs known to them (and also, perhaps, a stranger who has, for once, a chance to exert a charm and distinction that in his everyday life he would long have despaired of). For the moment I have converted my surroundings into a brand-new, foreign, and self-contained whole, a strange and disconcerting new amalgam with its own unique chemistry, which I am tempted to call a "world."

Again, when I come to the *same* place, a place that I know, like a part of London, by a different route or in a different context, something opposite but similar takes place. I push out of a crowded restaurant late in the evening into a Soho street, and it is the same street which I visit every day at lunch time. But I say to myself, a little puzzled: "This is where I feel so-and-so, surely? And now to be expected to feel something different! I don't know how I'm going to do it." And I try out which is best, whether to prolong my present state of feeling, and paint the scene anew with it, or go back to the lunch time pattern which has time-honored authority to support it. It is like, but perhaps the opposite of, reading the same novel in two different editions, with different illustrations; yes, it is really seeing the same set of illustrations attached to different novels.

It is from this second tendency that so many of my misjudgments of character arise. I remember that when I returned to Cambridge, after some uncomfortable years as a private in the army, there was at my college a tall man who wore a British Warm overcoat and a buff waistcoat with metal buttons and grew the kind of bushy mustache that I associated with majors. Now, everyone made fun of this fellow, who could not speak without muddling and making *faux pas*. His eyes were blinking and uncertain, and he walked about in a wandering, harassed fashion. I could see him exactly as my friends saw him; and yet I could never clear my mind of the doubt that there was some mistake, and that if I were alone with him the magisterial military symbols might not suddenly reassert their proper meaning.

It is the same with our dealings with our friends. For some of us there is no worse nightmare than that all of their friends should be brought together in one room. "They belong to different worlds," we say to ourselves. It is not merely that the friends wouldn't get on. It is that we feel that if they came together, we ourselves should suffer some appalling fission, as the separate selves which we have created fought hopelessly to occupy the single body at the one moment.

Everybody, I think, has these various experiences from time to time. They were ones to which Proust attributed great significance. There is a passage in *The Guermantes Way* in which, to the eyes of the youthful narrator, the Princesse de Guermantes and her friends in their box at the *Opéra* seem so many marine deities, composed of, and inhabiting, an element different in every atom of its substance from that of the remainder of the audience. They swim in a "somber and transparent kingdom," bounded by their eyeballs—from which he has no more right than a stone or mineral to expect any sign of human recognition.

Again it was cardinal for the narrator in *Swann's Way* that nothing could ever bridge the gulf, the essential and unresolvable difference, between the Méséglise (or Swann's) Way and the Guermantes Way. They were "sealed vessels"—between which there could be no communication.

> I had invested each of them, by conceiving them in this way as two distinct entities, with that cohesion, that unity which belongs only to the figments of the mind; the smallest detail of either of them appeared to me as a precious thing, which exhibited the special excellence of the whole. . . . I set between them, far more distinctly than the mere distances in miles and yards and inches which separated one from the other, the distance that there was between the two parts of my brain in which I used to think of them, one of those distances of the mind which time serves only to lengthen, which separate things irremediably from one another, keeping them for ever upon different planes.

The remainder of *Remembrance of Things Past* shows the narrator gradually discovering that the "sealed vessels" do, after all, communicate. Time and time again he discovers that social "worlds" which he had supposed mutually exclusive touch and overlap, thus ceasing to be "worlds." Indeed it was his acquaintance with Swann (and thus, in a sense, Swann's Way) which led him, circuitously, to the inaccessible kingdom of the Guermantes. Finally, in *Time Regained*, at the moment when he is about to be introduced to Gilberte's daughter (the fruit of the union of the Swann and Guermantes clans), he perceives that, like a crossways in a forest, she represents the meeting point not only of the Méséglise and Guermantes Ways but of innumerable other "ways." "Certainly, if only our hearts were in question," he reflects, "the poet was right when he spoke of the mysterious threads which life breaks."

> But it is still truer that life is ceaselessly weaving them between beings, between events, that it crosses those threads, that it doubles them to thicken the woof with such industry that between the smallest point in our past and all the rest, the store of memories is so rich that only the choice of communications remains.

One of the things in common to all the phenomena I have been describing (and which one can call thinking in "worlds") is that they are irrational. They represent a primitive and prerational mode of thought, one which reappears under all kinds of disguises, some beneficent and some pernicious. Proust saw that, in his own case, it underlay his profoundest insights and his grossest delusions. It was for him an essential factor in imaginative creation, and equally, in his social existence, it was the very basis of his snobbery. And one should remember that it is a kind of thinking which finds a natural expression in anti-Semitism. As Sartre points out in his *Anti-Semite and Jew*, it is an essential part of the mythology of anti-Semitism (a mythology which Jews often subscribe to themselves) that any resemblance between the things a Jew does or possesses and their Aryan counterpart is illusory. A Jew's culture, his success, his love are only "Jewish" culture, Jewish success, and Jewish love—a sort of fairy gold not to be confused with the real thing. Living in the midst of Aryan society, and to outward appearances a full member of it, he is forever shut out from its "real" existence. He inhabits a "world" which coincides physically with the world of his Aryan neighbors but brings him no nearer to participation in it.

And what has to be said about all such convictions is that the person entertaining them *knows better*. He knows, with the rational part of his mind, that the Princesse de Guermantes is made of the same material as the people in the stalls and the gallery. Thinking in "worlds" is only respectable when done in the consciousness that it is a paradox. And when people, when critics and journalists especially, talk about "worlds" literally and without irony, it is a sign that something is wrong. It represents either laziness of mind or some definite mental confusion.

It is clear that writers and journalists, at present, find it extremely convenient to talk about "worlds." The heading "The World of Music" catches my eye in the newspaper; and the article begins: "There are not many composers whose world is so full and self-sufficient that no one would choose to live in it cut off from outside contacts for long." One reads of "the Impressionists and their world," "the world of that Barrault film *Les Enfants du Paradis*," "the world of Japanese woodcuts," or "the world of Truman Capote," "the ideal machinery of the Tridentine world," and *Shakespeare's World of Images*. I feel distrustful of so many worlds being discovered or created and suspect that entities are being multiplied needlessly. It is as if one were to go about founding innumerable exclusive but illusory clubs which never attain definite premises or a settled membership but exist ever afterward as a name in the directory. No one seems to have much use for these worlds after the moment of their creation. They are like the "world" I create, out of shyness, on the train to Manchester and forget promptly when my self-possession returns. And what they amount to is a deliberate act of laziness. Being unwilling to commit himself to any noun of definite signification, however vague—even *spirit* or *ethos* would say too much—the writer falls back on a word which can be relied on to define nothing whatever and merely appears to draw a circle round the subject.

These are one of the two sorts of "world" one is always meeting in literary journalism. And the other is the kind of "world" which is meant when a critic says that a novelist "creates his own world." And the question in both cases is, why "world"?

It is a favorite theory of literary critics that a novelist should create a special fictional "world." "Mr. Davidson," writes Kathleen Nott in a review of a novel, "has created a genuine new world between American airfield and English harvest-field." Here the word *created* bears no great emphasis. She might as well have said that he "found" this new world. She is talking the same language as those who speak of "the world of Japanese woodcuts" or "the world of Truman Capote"; she has invented a nonce-world which will live for the space of an article and then return to the limbo of all other nonce-worlds.

More often the theory includes the notion that the world is the novelist's own, a unique one, his particular speciality. "With all her faults," it often goes, "we must admit that Miss —— has done what stamps her as a true novelist; she has created her own strange yet utterly convincing world." Lord David Cecil states it as a principle: "A novel is a work of art in so far as it introduces us into a living world, in some respects resembling the world we live in, but with an individuality of its own."

The novelist praised in this way is thought to secrete a certain unique coloring, of which he alone has the formula, and to impregnate his fictional "world" with it.

> In three novels, Thomas Hinde has built up a world that is original and disturbing, and wholly his own. And the deadpan style, economical almost to the point of transparency at times, the description more by implication than by facts and adjectives, is all part of it, part of the pared-down feeling, the curious sense of waiting, of significance, of a sort of spiritual pregnancy. . . .

And as his "world" is said to be "wholly his own," so his characters are said to have "a life of their own":

Its characters [those of *The Snowman,* by Charles Haldeman] are either grotesques or fragmentary consciences for whose conduct we receive little guide from the progress of the plot. Yet they fasten hold of our imagination with a bizarre tenacity and a precise life of their own. Ambiguities occur mainly in the moral world in which Mr. Haldeman requires them to live and in the images, like that of the snowman itself, by which he seeks to embody that world.

Now I will say at once that I think the theory that a novelist should "create his own world" is false. But what I am objecting to is not so much the idea of his creating a world as of its being his own. There is nothing wrong with saying, as Zola did, that Balzac created or fathered a world.

> Balzac remains for us, I repeat, a power not to be argued with. He imposes himself, like Shakespeare, by a creative *fiat* [*un souffle créateur*] which has fathered a whole world.

What this means primarily is that Balzac rivaled God in inventive power. He put an extraordinary abundance, an awful lot of things, into the *Comédie Humaine.* People do not, on the whole, say that Balzac created "a world of his own." The implication is that he seconded God's power, not that he constructed a rival creation to conflict with God's. If people do talk of the novels of Balzac (or Proust or Dickens) as rivaling the everyday world, what they mean is that they are tempted to sit reading them rather than make money or love on their own account.

Zola's remark can also be taken to mean—what is equally true —that Balzac aimed at getting the *whole* of something in: in his case the entirety of French society. It is something which became a much more precise ambition for the great post-Naturalist novelists. Proust and Joyce had a very clear determination to get the *whole* of something in—the whole of a single day in Dublin or the whole of one man's memories. The Naturalist novelists, like Zola and the Goncourts, by posing in the role of a scientist toward their material, were *ipso facto* prevented from depicting the whole of anything—for the whole of anything that is observed has to include the observer. The post-Naturalist novelists found the way on from Naturalism to lie in abolishing or incorporating the observer.

A further idea, however, comes into the talk of the novelist "fathering" a world, the idea that he makes it a self-contained whole; he gives it the unity and structure of a world. Frank Kermode, speaking of Lawrence, Forster, and Joyce, wrote:

> They all saw the novel as a world, not in a trite sense, but with very exalted notions of what wholeness is. They hated divisions, whether between thought and emotion, sense and spirit, form and matter, pleasure and value. . . . To make a world it is necessary, but not enough, to know this one; to bring its possibilities to being the artist has to put forth all his goodness. His world will have its myths, its politics, its sociology and psychology, as Pasternak's has; but it will never be devoted to illuminating their counterparts in life.

The operative phrase is *devoted to*, of course; Kermode is warning us not to regard the novels of Lawrence and others as psychological or political treatises. All the same there is something paradoxical here. *Aren't* the politics and the psychology in their novels devoted to illuminating their counterparts in life?

I think they are, and that the trouble arises from using the word *world* in this way. For why *world*? The world doesn't deserve the praise of being "whole" and a "unity." It is whole and a unit only because it happens to be all there is—so that it would be illogical to accuse it of any deficiency. It hasn't "a" structure, it has an infinity of possible structures. It is not a good metaphor for wholeness and oneness in the sense of symmetry and inner harmony—except for the fact that the earth, as opposed to the world, happens to be spherical.

Two quite different senses of the word *world* have got mixed up here. For evidently, novels are about the world; that is to say, they are about life and the visible scene, as mathematics are not. And if you can get a great deal of reality and human multiplicity into your fiction, you can perfectly well be said to have created a world, as Zola said of Balzac. But on the other hand, novels are objects in themselves; they have parts and limbs; and these, or their nice adjustment or organic relation to each other, make up what you can call an "organic whole" or an "esthetic monad." Or if you are Kermode, you may call it a "world." But, of course, *world* in this sense has nothing to do with the other sense of *world*—that is, what the novel is about.

What Kermode is doing is to mix up these two meanings. In talking of a novel, or any work of art, as an esthetic object he would be happy, I think, to speak of it, as Romantic and post-Romantic critics do, as an "organism." He would hold that the parts of a true work of art interpenetrate and form a unity possessing qualities not inherent in the parts—that, as in living organisms, any part of the work in some way contains the blueprint of the whole. Only in the case of the novel he changes his metaphor from *organism* to *world*. And *world* in this sense gets mixed up with *world* in the sense of what novels are about.

The two senses are not only different but contradictory— though also complementary. For viewed as an esthetic object, a novel or a play ought to be something self-enclosed and complete and internally harmonious, as should any work of art. But from the point of view of subject matter it should have quite different qualities; it should be unenclosed, outward-looking, and suggestive of endless perspectives. Henry James constantly came back to this distinction:

> . . . though the relations of a human figure or a social occurrence are what make such objects interesting, they also make them, to the same tune, difficult to isolate, to surround with the sharp black line, to frame in the square, the circle, the charming oval, that helps any arrangement of objects to become a picture. . . . The play consents to the logic of but one way, mathematically right, and with the loose end as gross an impertinence on its surface, and as grave a dishonour, as the dangle of a snippet of silk or wool on the right side of a tapestry. We are shut up within the action itself; no part of which

is related to anything but some other part—*save of course by the relation of the total to life* [italics mine].

If you write about the world, you are writing about something which is sprawling, multiform, and infinitely extensive. But if you say that a novelist creates his own "strange yet convincing world," you mean he has created something insulated and isolated, like a knot in timber rather than a figure in the carpet—something very unlike *the* world, that is, but which will somehow provide a substitute. And it will be false or unsatisfying precisely in what James calls "the relation of the total to life."

What James means by "the relation of the total to life" will be the same sort of thing in the case of a poem as in that of a novel. Every achieved work of art, indeed, is unique in this respect, that is to say, in the nature of its link with the real world. It is the most elusive, as it is the most important, thing about it, and nothing can be said about the question of such links in general terms. One should remember, though—and this represents a difference between fiction and poetry—that some novelists deliberately adopt a convention which reminds the reader that such a "relation of the total to life" exists. This is mainly a technical matter, and is described very clearly by W. J. Harvey in his *Character and the Novel*:

> . . . the novelist may so disguise the frontiers of his fiction that we sense beyond the story the continuum of life itself. In this way the reader's experience of fiction merges imperceptibly into other, "real-life" experiences just as, in actuality, one context of our lives overlaps with another. This disguise, this effect of blurring the frontiers of fiction and life, is again the product of art, whether naive or crafty. A crude example, I think, is the technique of montage used by Dos Passos in *U.S.A.*; we may contrast with this the author's addresses to the reader in *Tom Jones*. These may look simple-minded when compared with modern technical experiments but are, I believe, sophisticated and designed to produce quite complicated effects upon the reader. At first sight they might seem to be conventional devices artificially delimiting the area of the novel. But they have

the opposite effect, raising the novel to the magnitude of life itself and giving the fictional world a wonderful openness which is then played off against the formal intricacy of the plot.

There is, perhaps, something which superficially reminds one of the talk of a novelist "creating his own world" in the attitude of the Symbolist poet to the image—as described in Frank Kermode's *Romantic Image*. The poet in the Symbolist tradition felt that his poem was an autonomous object, an "esthetic monad," out of the flux of life and having no connection with utility or with discursive reasoning. And this was also Joyce's idea of the work of art: it is "apprehended as self-bounded and self-contained upon the immeasurable background of space or time which is not it," and the mind which apprehends it is arrested in "the luminous silent stasis of aesthetic pleasure." But if you talk about a novel in this way, you must be talking of what it has in common with a Symbolist poem—you are talking of its qualities as an esthetic object, not of what it's about; and in this sense any true work of art should be "a world of its own." The other strand of the Symbolist tradition puts us right. For, as Kermode has pointed out, the artist in this tradition has a fixed conviction that to create the image he has to turn himself into a homeless wanderer, with no place to lay his head. He cuts himself off from the common world, dooming himself to isolation and estrangement and possible madness; and yet, as a human individual, he has no place *in* the image or "world" he creates either, since by its very nature it excludes and denies his humanity. He is very far from coloring it with his own personality and desires; it is no private sanctuary for him, which is what is implied by saying a novelist "creates a world of his own." On the contrary he stands aloof, "refined out of existence, indifferent, paring his fingernails."

All the same, when a reviewer says that so-and-so's novel "creates its own world," it is often a genuine reaction. Only he is using the wrong metaphor. What he means is not that the nov-

elist is creating some rival to the real world, but that he is fenc-
ing off a part of the real world, with himself inside it, and con-
verting it into a playground, where in dilettante fashion he can
erect follies and rearrange nature as it pleases him. It is very true
that some novelists do this; and that is what is wrong with them.
For it is easy enough to make your own world if you falsify the
real world to do it. When a novel gets praised in this way, it is
often a hint that something has gone wrong. In the case of a
true novel, however small its chosen area, life, reality, and the
world stretch round it and you feel them there; nothing is excluded by the narrowness of the point of focus. But with another sort of novel, you feel that the author is not bringing all he
knows to bear on what he is writing. He *knows better.* He is
secluding some part of himself from the reader; there has not
been the collision of a complete personality with something
taken whole from life; and the book, as a consequence, though it
may have brilliant qualities, is somehow cut-off, self-enclosed,
and nonconductive.

For instance, there is the novelist who is said to re-create
childhood (a "child's world") with astonishing fidelity. The
reviewer praises his novel, and yet he is not really happy about
it. He calls it a *tour de force,* which immediately puts it in its
place; and he may go on to grumble that there have been too
many novels doing the same thing—except that this one is
different. What in fact is likely to be wrong with the novel is
that adult knowledge has not been brought to bear on the childhood experience. Think of L. P. Hartley's *The Go-Between.* It
was nearly a very distinguished novel. It *was* a distinguished
novel at the moments when, in rendering the boy's experience,
it simultaneously rendered the emotions, of beguilement and
horror and rueful hindsight, with which this experience returned to the middle-aged narrator's mind. It was essential to
dramatize the narrator as well as the boy; the novel existed in
the interplay between them, and it was by this perspective that
it led out into the world at large—this was the "relation to the

total of life." For whole long stretches, however—for instance, the scene of the cricket match—all you get is the boy's experience (or "world"). The novel thins out at these points, so that it remains only the sketch of the fine novel it might have been.

Something like this is true of Iris Murdoch. Her novels tend to begin very substantially, with figures solidly placed in a background and standing in the light of day, with other human possibilities and perspectives stretching round them as far as the eye can see. Then the shutters come down; the theater exits are closed, and the characters fall into their dance; the thing becomes a ballet of bloodless essences, in which characters act out their feelings overliterally—choreographically, as it were. Her people strike us as less solid and less rich at the end of her novels than they do at the beginning. A kind of falsity has set in as soon as the novel turned into "a world of its own."

Would not Ivy Compton-Burnett be another case in point, and a particularly interesting one? She strikes me as having, with a cheerful cynicism toward the pretensions of the novel, deliberately elected to convert a piece of the real world into "a world of her own." In her novels the shutters are down from the beginning. She is peculiarly a novelist who draws a circle and says, "Beyond that I shall not look." And it's in vain for us to look. Her characters materialize out of the void. One feels the presence of nothing outside the circle she has drawn, that country household in 1910; and what we find within it, not surprisingly, varies wildly in the kind of credence we can give it. There is some solidity and depth of observation behind her gallery of domestic tyrants, and the purest Wodehousian fantasy when it comes to her butlers. Her plots, as a recent admirer has admitted, are "servantlike," and her cynicism about the novel comes out in what she once said about them: "As regards plots I find real life no help at all. Real life seems to have no plots, and as I think a plot desirable and almost necessary, I have this extra grudge against life." It hardly seems to matter, so much has she insulated the "world" of her novels for her own ends—that is, the practice of a certain kind of wit. This is not to denigrate her. Her wit is a marvelous, superior, intelligent pleasure. She is a *philosophe*, a wit of the anti-Victorian school of Butler, Shaw, and Wilde, who has pitched her tent in the field of fiction and made herself as snug there as possible. Pit her against her fellow *philosophes* and she shines. It is only when you pit her, as critics have sometimes done, against Jane Austen and Henry James, that it appears how little you compliment a novelist in saying he "creates his own world."

HENRY H. ROTH / *My Spy Story*

I

Save for me, everyone has his own spy story—I know this to be the truth with the easy sureness that I know the name of my wife child and dog. I admit it and confess for this lack of knowledge clearly indicates the criminal failure of my life. Both personal and impersonal. For who is to say who is and who is not a spy—yet I have been unable to secure even a single confidence to hear such a marvelous, but not (my tragedy) uncommon secret. I accept the lack of many things in my life but with the wearing away of each year I have become weaker and weaker until this absence of a spy story impales me with unbearable pressure—now completely helpless I am forced to take a taxi to and fro work.

I am confident that spies number in the millions—since spy stories must then abound everywhere it is perfectly logical for me to seek one out, claim it, caress it and perhaps by ritual of seizure even begin the purifying of my soul. But it is only logical on one level; I have this weariness that is smothering me, my affliction passes undetected my screams are so muted they can only suggest yawns.

Can one tell by Christmas cards how many potential friends (spies) one may draw upon?

My wife is a great one for setting up displays, but alas not of herself she is always dressed in sackcloth yet our house is filled with bonsai trees, lemon trees, planters hang at every height; there are mooseheads, gay abstracts, sombre watercolors and pornographic etchings. Each December my wife places seasonal cards in the living room above the fireplace by mid-month the cards have become things which have run amuck into every room, they are in closets, fill three bathrooms, some are even nestled in the garage; I can only sob out into this chaos that is my family, my life—*and not one of those signed names I do know or do not know has ever shared his spy story with me.*

I turn to her stepping out of sackcloth preparing to enter a NEW YEAR'S PARTY GOWN, she is unbelievably white and soft and lush, her nipples point accusingly at me, her cunt yoohoos to me. I touch her gently and she shrivels up, puts away my hand and evening gown with the same gesture and covers herself with sackcloth . . . she smiles, she cries, she laughs and she torments, "You haven't had an erection in three years, why is tonight any different from any other unsatisfactory evening?" I want to tell her that each night is different, each moment is precious because we'll never have that exact moment ever again but she has exited.

I began to watch her not with the usual anticipation of what she was planning for supper or what room she was going to thorough-clean; instead I observed like a philosopher, I eaves-dropped on her conversations and twice followed her.

The Christmas cards were of no avail, I searched each name for a clue, a sign, I even called a few, invited some to lunch, others to parties but there was not even conversation possible.

Beware of those who send CARDS, they are as sterile as the inside of a nun's pocketbook.

My child! What could he whisper to me? After all Hitler had a complex system of young stool pigeons, my boy could have been a Goldwaterian while all the time posing as a liberal child. Instead I learned to my astonishment that he was twelve and not ten and he was in the sixth grade and not the fourth.

During my search I looked most carefully at those with whom I had daily contact . . . My milkman supported ailing parents and a family of four and keep my wife very happy he leered.

From my wife I gleaned other things, she had lovers at least three now, at least thirty since our marriage and she possessed the vilest tongue I have ever overheard. But was she a spy? She had done a splendid job of deceiving me, perhaps her mind belonged to another country, perhaps I could even turn her in. One night I took her by force, she bit me, I slapped her, she opened her mouth to cry but I shoved my fingers into her throat causing a slight retching; with all the excitement, the stench of her vomit, her breasts slapping against me like tidal waves I did have an erection . . . afterwards I whispered screw you and she tried to tear my eyes out.

II

I chose to return where I was born, where I might see if my parents were spies, they had concealed so much from me practically everything, so they might indeed have been involved in some sort of half-hearted espionage. I walked about my old neighborhood, the streets as filthy as I remembered, the numbers of the buildings corroded in the sun, everything was of course much-smaller than I recalled, also the neighborhood was now completely colored. I stood quite still at a street corner refusing to budge though the light was green, a message flickered to me WALK FOOL WALK . . . but I was immobile as if paralyzed by the glare from the flashlight affixed in the palm of the GREAT PROSECUTOR. My parents were not here; they lay rotting side by side still holding hands in a mass family grave in Forest Hills. The colored people were watching me with compassion, I only wished I could pitch a tent on this sidewalk and live with them and compare tortured tales. Instead I took a subway and got hopelessly lost.

My dog was clever but could not speak or rather could not be persuaded to share articulately his knowledge and secrets. Since my attack my wife watched me very carefully, never turning her back always keeping her legs crossed. I was forced to turn elsewhere. My dry cleaner's wife had just died, he was going to marry the alteration lady, he beamed both in shame and pride. Not an interesting man. I once attempted to talk with a crosstown bus driver but he almost punched me.

Things thickened out now, a gigantic pudding texture had engulfed me. I would have permitted the matter to lump there if not for the fire in the den. My den, for it is a small windowless square that no one in the family wished so I claimed it. Once there had been a busted desk with many drawers filled with my old letters, several stories both short and long, one or two essays, many poems and at least twenty diaries . . . all were destroyed in the blaze. It was not a very big fire but the Community fire department pulled out a hose that would have cowered a nuclear holocaust and watered the room down to a degree that I'm confident flowers will sprout up from the charred wood this spring.

My wife tripped over her sackcloth hastening to call the fireman and her lip was split, I only wished I had caused the flow of blood with my fist, my son watched the fire with unconcealed erotic delight, my dog now that the situation was in hand barked and barked . . . the den however was done.

I started the fire planning to sacrifice some part of me to God or gods and in return be granted a secret. Perversely in the eye of the fire I saw the truth, all those papers (there were thousands of pages it seemed) which I had thought enough to write words upon through the years were gone. And why? It was as if I had destroyed the evidence, hearing the clear faint knock of the police on the door (who else would knock) I had to choose—either swallow all that paper or burn it, it must not fall into their hands. So it was I who was the undercover agent hiding from everyone, never even telling myself—now it was too late I had destroyed my papers, my work, my assignments. I had my spy story and had been telling it to the world for forty years, living in a real dream. I was now awake, my ties were slashed, all the evidence that might prove interesting to myself was destroyed. Strangely I am not physically weak any longer, I now take buses instead of taxis and I have found a young woman who may love me for the time being. I spend creative hours with my son; my wife and I share our lot and since strangers never argue too much our house is free of tension (definitely she could not have been a spy), I bring toys and biscuits for my dog and try never to kick it. I am for the first time really in the swing of things; making money happily, behaving like a dutch uncle to my wife and son; screwing my secretary; taking full advantage of my credit card—however, I must confess I do long for those secret days and even more secretive evenings, those agonizing tense times, my spy times. . . .

PAUL WEST / *How to Marry a Hummingbird*

Cynthia Dougherty hated afternoons. Florida ones were the worst and this was the worst of those. She had to get through it, but she couldn't repeat the best trick she had thought of yet. She had, on that occasion, written down on a letter card most of the possible permutations of her husband's Social Security number and mailed it to him at the air base annotated, in grandiloquent banality, "From one of me to all of you." It had baffled Rob, who began baffled anyway, and she felt that somehow she had refined his mental predicament while dignifying her own. If only, he'd said, she had kept it until the evening— the card, of course. She thought of her bikini pictures and cutting out the clothed parts to send him, saying, "From the best of me," but she abandoned the idea. The afternoon was too hot for anything ingenious.

Stacked neatly in a minor architectural complex on the blazing face of her petit-point looking glass, the apparatus of calm awaited her need. The cylinder of suntan spray towered over her Winstons, the neatly folded book of matches called "Surefire," a pair of parchment-colored ear plugs, and one pack of gum with the red ribbon partly peeled away. She did some visual mental arithmetic, then checked the numbers by saying them aloud. It was probably the twelve thousand, seven hundred and eightieth afternoon of her life on earth.

Since one-thirty she had been idling on the baked lawn and wincing at the summer calls and incessant swooping curves of the backyard birds. Having slept only one hour the previous night she had the dazed, rebuffed feeling of not being within the envelope of her own body. She felt as if she were lying beside herself about three feet away; and beside herself also, she noted, in womanish rage. It had been Rob. Why any light colonel should spend four hours between midnight and light explaining, or rather shirking explaining, why he wasn't going to be promoted was beyond her. He had sat in the living room, occasionally getting near the point but then drifting off into the preliminaries of yet another deliciously confessed infidelity while she patted his knees or stood up and went to do superfluous polishing in the kitchen. Almost a whole bottle of bourbon had enriched his mumblings but had not blocked the usual résumé of his wasted life: the guilt about the saturation bombing he was decorated for doing in Europe, the guilt of skimming the girls of fifteen nations and having affairs, the guilt of telling her (who stood by him), the guilt of no longer wishing to touch her, the guilt of not pretending about that ("I could've, I could've, but I couldn't"), the guilt of—oh, just too much talk about guilt. They had gone to bed without even a curt goodnight, he to immediate drunken insensibility, she to a clock-watching, irritable vigil. Brian the boy, the four-year-old, always woke at six-thirty and pummeled her until she woke. He never had to pummel much.

For about a year this had been the pattern of two nights in five, and she had long known Rob would not be promoted: he was willfully insolent to superior officers. He got away with it; but getting away with it, as she told him, was getting nowhere. He had now applied for Vietnam in the hope, he said, of being killed, as he should have been during the war. It was either that or going back into the Church, which he had left informally in 1940. And there was guilt of that too. That was the guilt he enjoyed most.

"Look, Rob," she had insisted, "the war is over. Done. No, don't touch me. The bombs have *fallen*, you don't *have* to tell me about these girls," and then shouting, "I don't *want* to know!" Her voice had echoed out into the fetid, insecticidal-perfumed night. The ground-spraying vehicle had just gone past, and the air reeked of DDT that stung the eyes delicately and dried her voice into a shrill.

He had a long drink then. "Tar*ew*, hon'," he said slowly, meditatively, "but it brings us close. When I tell you, I mean. You listen and then I know it's all all right. Don't go," as she rose and made for the kitchen, there to renew her Diet Cola. "Don't walk out—just listen, don't talk. Hon'?"

She leaned round the half wall, stared him full in the eyes (he was twisting his neck to see her) and whispered percussively that she didn't want to listen. She was going to bed. "Talk," she opened her mouth wide as if preparing to receive a whole apple, "to yourself." Then she accidentally caught her glass against the wall. He laughed because he heard it smash against the simulated marble floor. She retrieved some pieces and threw them with short-distance violence into the gaping trash can; the lid had stuck as if giving a Nazi salute.

They always quarreled in such formulas as these. Their dispute had no heart in it but resolved itself into a verbal quadrille while each of them thought privately about other matters: Rob of the girl pick-up he had given money to for some minor operation, Cynthia of all the places she had been posted to with him and the long solitary nights she had spent in Rome, Oxfordshire, and Turkey (to name a few) reading those interminable Tolstoys and retreating into the too-soon-finished Spillanes. Words bounced between them, occupying the space but never reducing it. Last night his thickly fleshed face had gone beet-red and the sweat had beaded down from his sideburns while he toyed with the slight lever of his fly zip. It had gone on, neither of them feeling capable of breaking the pattern. After all, she mused, it was the only intimate bond they had remaining to them. Without it he would have cried and drunk more bourbon, and she, narrow and slender, chronically attuned to his moods and tics, would have lost a pose in which she saw herself, in wan hyperbole, as a hummingbird and even felt the part in her garish kimonos. She laughed at such an idea: it was fanciful and silly, not a grown woman's thought at all. But, strained and set quivering and given enough stimulus to self-pity, she let the thought in and watched herself vibrating in the night. "How," she thought, "you mate a hummingbird. Only a few know. Keep her in motion all night, wings whirring like mad, and above all don't let her escape to some other place or room where she might have a life that isn't all words and quarrels and hollow making-up (on lucky nights) just before dawn, always in words, but never through a real hard. . . ." Her head felt twice its normal weight as she sat down again on the floor beside his chair and let her hand float up to his. He was still in the pants of his uniform. Bourbon had stained the front, and her damp palm left a faint, balanced print on the fabric. "Use the glass," she admonished as he reached for the bottle, "use the glass. Don't lose your manners too."

Out on the lawn she made a deliberate, fist-clenching effort to stop remembering. She shook her head to dislodge the memory of the night and felt the steam-heavy air cling to her face before slumping away. "God," she thought, "I'm losing contact with *everything*. How do you stay sane all day with only a child to talk to?" She looked round for Brian, and not seeing him, sang messages through her nose in case he was near: "Brian, honey, don't you go too far away. You hear me now. Stay close to the house and close the refrigerator door if you use it. No, not *use*;

open it." Then she thought herself ridiculous, screaming self-corrections the boy was bound to misunderstand. But she had breath left, tension still not dispelled. So: "You hear me, lover?" Lover was not answering.

Only that morning, while she squeezed his orange for him, he had asked in his direct, ingenuous way, "Mom, is it this day or the next day?" She had reassured him it was today, Wednesday, but he hadn't seemed convinced, because he then accused her of "putting him on." So she threatened him with Sunday school; she would make this day Sunday and not a next day, which meant he would have to go and be like Jesus for two whole hours. That beat him. He drank his orange juice in a puzzled, metaphysical silence, committed to this day above all others and determined to be bad when she fell unwakably asleep as she always did in the afternoon.

The pool filter choked, then wheezed again into life. She was just going to call Brian again when she caught sight of him asleep, indolently plunged on a rubber mattress in the corner of the patio, the wet glistening on his back like snail's tracks. He was dreaming, she told herself, about invisible invaders he had killed or repelled with his spacegun until only a few minutes ago. It was now about three; her glance at her wrist didn't even take in the minute hand, and she wondered why she bothered to wear her watch. Her stomach told her the time. She scowled and picked up the suntan spray from the withered grass. The jet felt cool against her arms and legs. All she could hear was the pool filter, the canary from inside, the refrigerator hum and the *pss-pss* of the spray as she squirted. She lay down, rolling the back of her head to make a hollow in the blanket. The spray can felt like a hot-water pipe in her hand, so she let it fall. The afternoon had to be got through somehow. What could she do? A drink? No, that would just renew last night. She couldn't go and talk to Adèle next door because Adèle, fresh from Montreal on a permanent visa so she could obtain her divorce, had taken her three pampered children on a motor yacht with her boyfriend, the attorney from Washington who was down on a visit. Gorgeous, giggling, bird-of-paradisey, dynamic Adèle, who called her "Cyn" with a soft "C" and taught her how to use a lipstick brush, had deserted her, and with her had gone the funnel-shaped, floppy, ever-willing ears into which "Cyn" had slid the diffident rancor of the past four months while aching, ever so little, to touch her new friend, the broadness of her, the hard pulp of the calves, the nervous discolored lids of her narrow green eyes.

"No, I'm *not* that kind of woman," she had told herself when reviewing things one raining day, "I just love my friend. If that's a crime, or a kink . . ." Adèle had a college degree and talked about recessive genes. Rob always watched her, pushing his tongue under his right upper lip. Adèle had told her to refuse him, not to listen to his confessions. "It's a luxury for him; like my ex-to-be. Don't listen to him, and he'll like you again. You'll see." Cynthia had tried it and Robert hadn't come home for a week, although he had called her from North Carolina, affectionately too. But when he did come back he didn't touch her at all. And then Adèle had told her what to do next, but Cynthia hadn't followed or even wanted to follow. One morning, while making the instant at coffee time, she had asked Adèle again, but Adèle for once seemed out of counsel. "It's a young body he wants," Cynthia had announced, "it's the young body. He thinks he's getting old. And being with me makes him older than ever." Adèle had nodded, poking in her ear with a bobby pin as if truth had lodged in the cavity.

Now Cynthia was lying at peace, her veined, undernourished-looking legs crossed and her arms extended at right angles. She was prone and would be so for roughly ten minutes before going supine again with the same pattern of limbs. At least the birds, cawing and quarreling, made no demands. The grass was over ankle height; one hinge of the flimsy backyard gate was broken, and children had been infiltrating. A decomposing cardboard box brought sometime from the liquor store reposed at an angle on the crowded dandelions, announcing "Straight Bourbon

Whiskey 86 Proof" although they had brought home only two bourbon and six bottles of Chianti. She had tried to wean him onto wines, but the Chianti was still in the kitchen cupboard. An alien ball, more or less green, and a foot in diameter, was perched on top of the arbor. She cursed then, the broken power mower, her husband's indolence (he could bomb but not fix), the casual habits of the garbage men, and the inaccuracy of ball-tossing children. Then she felt able to relax.

She lay musing, mostly on her name and its odd beginning. Not the Cynthia part, as that was birthright and sacrosanct, a possession for which everyone respected her; but the "Dough" in Dougherty, as if she had caught on too late and discovered her spouse was a baker. But that was better than starting too early and thinking, on the strength of "Do," that he was a man of action, and then getting bogged down in "ugh." Starting later in the name she found "erty" a cheering compensation, dismissing "dirty" and the vulgar "purty" and concentrating on the way it thinned out the "Dough," stretched it out, turned it from loaf into *baguette,* from squat plebeian into long and thin and delicate-grained aristocratic bread fingers. Then she remembered how everyone said the word with a Scottish *ch* as in *loch;* she thought of phlegm—not cheerful imperturbability but expectoration on buses—and she wished with all her heart she could be just Cynthia.

Tiny gray insects kept settling on her arms. She dislodged them, but they kept returning. The faint down of her outer arms failed to trap or repel them, and when she was supine they landed on the unbrowned skin of her inner arm as if landing on silk. They nuzzled and bit. Again she flailed, and soon she was walking irritably about the small garden walled in by foliage and teased by the birds. She stood and attended: one bird threatened in a high, spinning snarl; another muttered from ground level in widely spaced single pleas—like vocal hyphens; and others, all of a kind, contended in tiny hysterical hisses.

Before she knew it she was stroking a nettle, safely, in the direction of the spines. Thrilled in a small way to be trifling with danger like this, she thought of her collections indoors of birds' eggs, butterflies, pressed flowers, and unusual stones. Their bedroom was full of boxes, full of her various collections. She dusted them every morning before dusting the rest of the house. The fragile hollow shells gleamed with her love; the wings of the pinned butterflies seemed grateful for reprieve from endless undulation; the flowers gladly gave up the stale chore of contracting and closing, opening and expanding; and the stones, she felt, dimly but positively, knew they were safe. The nettle obeyed her coaxing hand; there was no sting. But she was standing. She went indoors, past Brian, dragged out a collapsible chair and brought it to the spot where the nettles grew. Then she sat, reaching out again for the leaf, stroking it again and again until there seemed a current between her cupped fingers and its rough undersurface. Then, for no good reason, she lit a Winston and held the match flame under the leaf. The leaf lay still; the flame fattened and reached upward; the rim of the leaf curled and crouched, and then the flame began to sear her finger. She waved her hand against the humid air, as if snubbing and dismissing whole crowds of people.

The afternoon had still to be got through. When Rob was home she asked, "Is this all there is?" When he was away she asked, "What am I supposed to do with peace anyway?" They had been married eight years, and when she surveyed the chaste shimmer of the kitchen or the geometrical repose of the living room she was glad. But in the bathroom, alone with a fragrant soap called Harem and mingled scents of shaving lotion and instant lather, as well as the fur of towels drying in the direct light, she hated the throat-urging, disrupting tickle of small stools come upon in the pedestal after the boy had raced out to play. Again she stroked the nettle, caressing it and winning over all the capacity of the world to hurt: the unyielding needles, the bloodsucking clocks, the soured elations, the wasted vows, the constant menace of roaches, the untidy weather, the trouble on the lawn and in the bed, the way friends went off, the child slept, the match burnt her, the gum dried or softened, the way—the silly, showing-off way—Rob upset the boy, trying to make him— well, somehow rough. Brian was not only a boy: he was the king of the boys, as well as the king of the gorillas, dinosaurs, moun- tain climbers, monster-killers, spacemen, and underwater long- distance swimmers. He was (and this Rob sang like Popeye) Brian the Lion, and would give this title when asked who he was.

So, while Cynthia tried to interest the boy in her collections, which he liked in any case, Rob the father encouraged him to accept a grandiose domestic reputation. But when Brian told his friends of his prodigious roles in jungle and space, in swollen rivers and at anoxic altitudes, they jeered, and he wondered how to prove the truth. He was trapped between losing face with his friends, of whom he had few, being shy, and refusing his father's worship. He was baffled and upset to be king of so uncom- prehending, so badly informed a world; and the more baffled he became, and the more upset, the more his father fed him with myths entailing the crossing or purging of crocodile-infested rivers and the quick dispatch of arrogant giants. The more inept the boy felt when confronted with his growing reputation, the more his father made him a superman. Sometimes, at the men- tion of giants or monsters, Cynthia screamed, predicting for her son a colossal complex and a short, unheroic life in which he wouldn't even have time to learn how to blow an egg. But the boy stared and Rob guffawed her into silence. Then the heroic interlude went on while she retired to tidy her collection boxes.

On a sudden whim she went in, checking to see that the front door was locked. It wasn't and it wouldn't lock. Another thing to be fixed. Twenty-first Street North sailed neatly before her, quelled by the summertime and trimmed daily by careful, evening men with hoses, small knives, and pots of weedkiller. Crabgrass had no future here. The road shimmered and waited. She turned away, grimaced at the mess of her sodden hair in the mirror, and then walked, as if into a waterfall, into the first ring of the phone. As if the instrument itself had been dozing and she woke it. The sound set her trembling.

"Hel—" she cleared her throat. "Hello?" It had been hours since she had spoken.

"Rob. I'll be home early, Momma. I want to talk. I mean I think *we* should talk. About last night—this morning." He sounded hoarse and quite convincing, she thought.

"Please yourself. I can't stop you. I can't make you come and I sure as hell can't make you go. Come or go." She had not realized she had had even that many words in her this afternoon. "If you want. You'll probably forget anyway soon as you've had a drink. I don't see why you couldn't have said what you want to say last night. No, I don't. Look, don't interrupt, please. I got no sleep. I feel dead. I don't want to talk to anybody, you least of all. I don't really want to listen either because the more I listen the worse you get. No, it's the truth. Honest. You do. You go and do something—anything, any *aw*ful thing—just so you can come home or come back and tell me about it, and I don't, do not, repeat don't, *want to know*. Not any of it. If it's something new, then save it and spill it somewhere else where they don't care. I feel dead and I wish I were and . . . and—Just tell yourself I'm deaf."

She was out of breath, surprised, and faintly impressed by the amount and impetus of her indignation. He had tried to interrupt, and she had overriden him each time. But he would come anyway and he would talk. If she avoided him all evening and went to bed early, he would wreck some other night. Perhaps that would be better; always later, better. "Please yourself. You always do. I couldn't care, I feel just absolutely—" It was the absoluteness of blankness, for she couldn't finish the sentence. He asked about the boy, but it sounded as if he were asking from the radio mast of some ocean liner thousands of miles off, inching gently toward an exotic coast of pink castles, cool courtyards, and dark, dashing, olive-skinned, undrunk men.

"He's fine." She wrenched the comment from the side of her

mouth, glancing involuntarily through the large window that flanked the pool and wouldn't close properly. "He's asleep." She heard a sentimental grunt, a prediction that he would see her (that foolish idiom again, she winced), and then a sound as if the whole apparatus at the other end had fallen into an elevator shaft and life was extinct. She stared at the sweat marks, then killed the busy noise by sinking the receiver voluptuously back, the two rubber nipples being thrust home into the nostrils of the whirring animal. How she hated the phone with its demands on her voice. Your voice was never safe.

She went out again, unnerved. As quickly she came back. Then she went out again. She sat and stared at Adèle's washing as it swung minimally on the line. The small stringy plants by the house wall hunched and shivered as if some animal had blundered into them; but it was only the licking, furry July wind. Bees aimed at the flowers, found home, sucked dry, and reeled away like sailors. A black fly pestered her inner left ear until she flicked it away. She felt persecuted by miniature things. If only, she caught herself wishing, Rob were back. If only! She went silently hysterical at the thought. Then she had another thought and raced into the house, patio door clashing behind her, to take the phone off its cradle. The whine came at her unbroken, but it troubled her little. She felt as if she had turned on a dangerous jet of steam.

Moving to the lawn again she looked at Brian, black-haired, scowling, and sweating in his sleep. Gently, almost *en passant*—but she did linger a second or two—she raked her fingers across the velvet pad of his relaxed, bare belly, and he stirred, muttering. She clicked the patio gate behind her and again fell on the blanket. Her mind began to slow down. A few quiet moans later as if someone had intimately curled up with her, she fell asleep, sailing on another ocean this time, with a boatload of children who licked lollipops in tongue-tied unison.

She had been asleep only ten minutes when Brian stirred, shook himself like a wet puppy, and called, gently so as not to wake her, "Mom! Hey, Mom!" He half-smiled and sat up, gazing round the pool. He was safe, he knew. If any lion, or Monsky, the three-eyed monster with the machine gun sewn into his belly-button, should burst from the house, he, Brian, could be at her side in three steps. Then he went into the house, breathing heavily, stunning ogres with one glance from his electric eyes and burning guns from the very hands of hidden outlaws. He looked around, this time with his ordinary eyes. The house was untidy. He liked it neat, his heavy toys stacked right angle to right angle in the bottom of his toybox; then lighter things such as planes, small cars with fins, and pencil boxes. The heavy filling station was usually on the bottom, the lead soldiers and the plastic revolvers on top. He always set his comics in a gaudy block on top of everything. Today nothing was in place. So he set to and, after retrieving them, put his toys away, heedless of his possible needs in half an hour's time.

One day he had even tidied up the entire house, making the beds, washing down the patio, emptying the garbage, and collecting up the detritus of perhaps two days and fitting the orange peels, the matches from books of matches, empty cigarette packages, feathers, gum wrappers, fragments of toilet roll, small glasses that smelled of gasoline, pieces from hastily opened envelopes, fallen crumbs, and newly dead thousand-leggers. All this he had dropped into an old salt canister and tamped down with his clenched fist. Then he put the filled canister into the garbage can outside. Some days the house was neat in a military, hospital way; others it was a mess. Some days Cynthia let the mess accumulate, especially if she had had a bad night (two in five), and then like a Conquistador prevailed over the debris, reducing all to geometrical decency in a matter of hours. But Brian could never understand why all days were not alike. He liked the mess because he could tidy up; but he also liked the neatness because he knew where his toys were.

He went outside to the patio and slid down the steps into the water, holding on all the time. He felt cooler. Then he released his grip and leaned slowly forward, sinking to the bottom and lying there prone as if preparing to sleep. It was his newest trick and he practiced it for fifteen minutes or so, plunging up for air with his eyelashes stuck together into small black thorn shapes and his face pale green from the water.

When, for the first time, he threw his head back he saw the twig on top of the patio cage. It annoyed him and he stared at it, trying to melt it with a space stare. Then small rhomboids of light shuffling across the surface of the water caught his eye and, lower down, something else. He sank again to the bottom, his shape deformed by the depth. He groped, slowly, and then began to rise again until he burst from the water with wet seal's head and his mouth round as if someone had just unplugged a teat. Gasping and blinking he pushed aside a comical-faced red rubber mouse floating against his shoulder and looked at his hand. There, dull and green from immersion, was a cent, a penny. Without a sound he aimed and slung the penny at the twig on the patio roof. He missed and the penny fell to the bottom of the pool. A silver cigar-shape slid across the sky, the high upper sky, going south.

The twig stared at him, like the skeleton of some misguided, trapped rooster. After clambering up the filter unit in the back yard and getting nowhere at all, he fetched a box from the garage and set it up outside, but leaning against, the mesh of the patio wall. When he had climbed up, after one mishap in which the box keeled over and fell on top of him, he stood and stretched as high as he could. It was no use. He abandoned the box, jumped nimbly down, and ran to the garden gate. Cynthia's mouth was open for a quite audible snore, and the boy smiled, wondering what he could drop into it. The fence adjoining and supporting the gate was one of woven planks, woven inside, then outside, the square uprights. He soon gained the top of the fence and moved onto the top of the garden gate. From there it was an easy swing to the flat roof. All he had to do now was haul himself to the roof and shimmy across the empty bedroom to the screen over the patio and the pool. With small grunts he did this and tested the wire mesh with a soft hand. It held firm against his push. He moved off, crawling, trying the area before him until he reached the twig on the third section of mesh from the gate. Above him the sky blazed blue and the clouds had fled to the edges of the world. There was no jet and the canary was silent. The filter urged itself on, hoarse and tired-sounding.

He broke the mesh when he stood up. His squeal was simultaneous with his plunge head-first toward the water. The twig dropped into the pool and floated as if happy to land. Brian, however, stayed suspended, his foot caught against a loop of wire, so that his head swung a couple of feet above the water and his free leg swept the air groping for purchase. First his head swung round in an oval of panic, then in a faster oval of exploration which gave him no help. He waved his arms, trying to swing himself free. He was determined not to cry out and he had already bitten back the one involuntary sound that had begun. Calmer, he took a small time out to ease an itch in his groin, which he did none the less competently for being upside down; and then, being small and having suppressed any noise, he made water into his swimming trunks. The fluid trickled down from the fabric and the bow of white tape across his navel, some lodging there, and then across his chest to his chin where it dispersed.

Cynthia slept on, deeply into it now. Because he had been swinging about, Brian's foot began to bleed. The wire had cut his ankle, and the rent mesh was scissoring his upper middle foot. The blood dried in the searing light of the sun, only to flow again when he swung himself again in a vain effort to get free. Tiny spittle drifted into the pool and floated. Then a speck appeared on the ankle and touched the dried and the seeping blood. In the sky another speck appeared, stopped or appeared to stop, and slowly grew in size as it sank down. He felt a tickling and tried to kick, first with the trapped foot, then with the free one. The tickle continued. Then he tried to look upward but looked right into the sun and sank down again with a scorching retina image of the sun, the torn mesh, and the steel frame of the patio roof. He began to shiver.

A small black fly buzzed against his face and dive-bombed him from somewhere in the sun. Below him the water swirled and shifted, now achieving a faint meniscus, now going concave, but always hospital green and winking back at him when he blinked his tears away. No one came although the morning paper, delivered late, hit the front walk with a thump. He did not hear it and he could not have read it anyway.

The frail, nut-brown body dangled steady as a plumbline and seemed to lengthen in the shifting sunlight. His face grew mauve. On the line next door the dishcloths and towels dried and grew rigid. A sudden slight wind blew loose one corner of one panel of the patio door screen, and the loose corner flapped. In the house the refrigerator continued with its nasal hum and the canary began to sing again in an obbligato of brittle, high notes. From the surrounding houses came only the chirps and squeals of children being put to bed for naps or awakening; one child wailed lengthily until silenced by cooing ventriloquisms from a high female voice. Cars crunched on gravel and hurried by. One car, louder than the rest, had no muffler. The snort seemed to occupy the neighborhood even after the car had gone. Cynthia woke, relapsed, then woke again.

The pelican settled on the steel frame of the patio roof and arched its neck, surveying the distance. Then it poked its ungainly head into the rent in the mesh. After a pause, as if afraid of a trap, it nosed the boy's foot, which then scraped and slipped and silently fell downward, taking the stuck fruit flies with it after the body into the water. Cynthia heard the splash and screwed up her eyes against the sun. The pelican flew up in panic as the saw-teeth of water subsided and, circling once, batted its wings before seeking a current of air to idle on. The boy floated across the pool among the floats, plastic shells, and rubber animals.

Cynthia saw him, smiled, and stretched. Then she realized she had a beating headache and, while she was pondering the move to the house to find the right tablets, was amazed to see her son stumble up out of the pool, race to the patio door, and with a mounting scream run at her until he knocked her over, such was the force of his arrival. His foot was bleeding and he looked marble white or faint green. When she had calmed him in the house, he told her incoherently what had happened, and then she screamed too, stopping suddenly when she saw the boy begin to emulate her. She took him into his bedroom and sat with him after she dressed the cut on his ankle. There was no need to call a doctor.

Rob had parked his red MG with a declaratory "I'm-back" burst of the engine, hauled off his tie, and opened a can of Budweiser before he sensed anything different. He called loudly and heard a small response from the bedroom. When she told him, he stared woodenly, his head shifting forward, and suddenly raced out and jumped fully clothed into the pool, still holding the can of beer. He could think of nothing else to do. He could have done mouth-to-mouth on the boy, blowing the life into him, but there was no need of that. He insisted on calling a doctor, who came later that night and treated the ankle while Brian slept.

As all the implications of relief began to become real to them after the first, hallucinatory panic, they hesitated to look again at the living shape in the bedroom, primitively afraid it might rise up and strike them. As if he had been dead. Flies and moths poured through the hole in the patio roof; they filled the house, circling and squatting, bumping into eyes and flying into nostrils. The two of them sat unheeding. And while the boy rested in preparation for an even more marvelous tomorrow, she cradled Rob's head.

Next day he repaired the screen and drained the pool, thereby, she told him, making it even more dangerous. No, he told her; he had taken a day off and he had to do something. He spent the entire afternoon reading to the boy. Cynthia wept for most of the day but cheered up on a Martini about five. Brian fell asleep while watching a Western on the Early Show, and they both carried him in to bed, arranging his limbs with diligent, embalmer's care, and then rearranging until he half-woke and with sluggish petulance told them to lay off the blanket (which he called the "rampet"). They did, and then, over dinner, two TV dinners heated in recessed metal foil dishes, had a serious discussion.

Two nights later he touched her, and she wept with uncontrollable relief while he said something about "not leaving things to chance." When she told him, later that month, that she might be pregnant, he nodded several times and then laughed out loud. She bloomed and grew fey. He canceled his application for Vietnam. Brian found himself the recipient of many new toys. Adèle next door got her divorce but then told the judge she didn't want it and would he please not sign the papers; something had struck her, she said. Rob labored to be polite at the base; he even took Cynthia her breakfast in bed before he drove away in the mornings. And he began to cut down on the bourbon.

Their mutual reprieve lasted just over six weeks; and then she had to tell Adèle, still next door and beginning to dither again, "It's all started again, the same as before. Everything the same except it's worse now. I might have known, but I guess I didn't want to. So now what? Hey, Del?" Adèle's shrug said nothing. Adèle thought she had said enough, and Cynthia, in her slow-motion way, realized that nothing could be said. It was all beyond words, even beyond the sort of unspoken understanding they used to have. "I've tried," Cynthia told the blank TV screen, "I've tried too damn hard, just like I tried when I had Brian. Life's just one long squeeze—squeeze in, squeeze out, squeeze lemons, squeeze into clothes, cars, squeeze into *his* life —squeeze your courage or whatever it is. That's it: *screw* your courage. And as soon as something feels delicious, you look down and your fingers are all covered with slimy rotten banana. Well, I'm through with trying. It's time I did something else. Something for *me*."

Eventually, after a last two days of half-importunate tears from her and bullish reassurances from him, he left in an Air Force car with what seemed to her fewer possessions than were seemly even for a light colonel (the levity of that went through her like a shiver of wind). She waved lamely from the walk, locked the repaired door, lifted the receiver off the phone, and went to join Brian in bed, where she slept with him in her arms until about three-thirty. Her last thought before dropping off was, "Oh Lord, he'll soon be in school—once August's done with."

By the time she woke, her mind was made up, like something left to bake while she slept. With Brian following her, meek with sleep, she walked into the patio in her yellow one-piece bathing suit, not even bothering to slip the straps over her suntender shoulders, and padded to the deep end of the empty pool. Abruptly she stabbed her head sideways in annoyance, then stared down at the concrete. "Oh, that'll never do. I'll kill myself." She went back to the sliding plate of glass which was both window and wall and stripped the long plastic cushion from the chaise, hauled it to the deep end and lowered it into the empty pool. "What do you do when you don't have stairs?" she asked herself as if in a trance. "What else?" Not even what she thought was the echo of her voice unnerved her. This was retaliation; a piece of her own back.

She stood, jumped, winced, trudged across to the ladder, pulled herself up the steps and walked back to jump again. Each time she jumped, Brian croaked with joy and clapped awkwardly. On she went: stand, jump, wince, cross the pool, climb up, stumble round; stand, jump again. The eighth or ninth jump did something, not to her numb feet, or her jellied knees and ankles, but to all of her trunk. She felt a vague, tidal churning and sank to her knees on the cushion, sweat salting her eyes and the whole pool reeling about her. A sound like the wind flapping a flag—slapping it—came and went; Brian was applauding again. She mouthed a slack smile to where she thought he was, and tried to stop quivering.

"No, it's not that easy, is it? Where on earth did I get that idea from? Del? Oh, to hell with Del. I don't need Del for this. This—this's *Cynthia's*."

After she had flat-footed across the pool and into the house, she took a tumblerful of bourbon, told herself it was water, and drank it in four choking gulps. She ran the bath, reeling over the edge, until it was scalding, all the time murmuring "Good old Cynthia, good old Cin!" With a second tumblerful of bourbon she leaned against the wall, head lolling like a doll's, and dipped in a foot. Her squeal brought Brian in from the living room.

"Can I come in too? Hey, Mom?"

"Later on. 'Stoo hot for you, honey. Now you—you go an' tidy up the house—your toys. For later. Nice and tidy now."

Brian scowled. "Hey, Mom, will Dad bring me some—"

"Not tonight. No. But you go and tidy up for him. That's a good boy." She set the glass on the flat at the rear end of the bath and lowered herself, wincing, flinching, into the water. She burned. At once she ran in some cold and swished it backward. Then, with eyes closed, she gulped again, heaving her throat up but, somehow, keeping most of the bourbon down. And she thought, like a woman a hundred miles away, "Who told me about this? Why didn't I wait? I never know the answer to anything."

One thing she held to: a sentimental image of a small, over-sized silverfish-shape which she could rock in the palm of her hand. Somehow she clambered out of the bath, skimpily dried herself, made hamburgers without onion, fed Brian, smeared him with a face cloth, and got him into bed. Then she collapsed on the couch in her bathrobe, the phone still whining at her and Wagon Train, minus the sound, still on the screen.

She woke sore and hot, the hair matted on her forehead. In

the bathroom, bombarded by moths as she squatted, she discovered a faint show and thrilled with guilt. For ten minutes she stared at the flaky tissue, afraid, trying to love what she saw, but not certain how to feel or what to do. "I mustn't," she whispered, "Otherwise . . . I'll have to be careful now. My God, it's hot. And I hurt, and I feel sick."

The pool filled as she lay on her back under the clouded evening sky, head down and her legs splayed wide. A small tickle of lapping cold rose above the diameter line of her legs, just where the kneecap began to bulge. Water nosed at her loins and the cotton wad, spilled her hair sideways, and at the other end of the pool, floated the rubber mouse quietly toward her. Gently she cupped her hand, as if weighing something on her palm: wondering, hoping, waiting. Then, just before the water lay level over her belly, she forced herself to a sitting position, floundered to her feet, and went dripping into the house.

She soon found it, the issue of *Life* with full-page color photographs of embryos and fetuses. She stared at the six-and-a-half-week hunchback so much larger than life, and then went into the bathroom to check. Nothing, save stains. So she took the nail scissors and clipped round the outline from the bulbous head to the curling tail, folded the clipping neatly into four, with the hunchback inward, and with tender finesse laid it centrally in an empty cold cream jar from the bathroom cabinet. Then she screwed the lid on tight.

After five days the bleeding stopped and most of the nausea had faded. Still nothing. She had clipped on the third day. "That's it," she told herself, "I broke faith. I didn't wait. I took a changeling. If I hadn't, I'd have found it, wouldn't I? I wish I was honeymoon fresh. I looked and looked. Funny! It stood me up! I had a date and it never turned up. Well, I needn't feel so guilty, then, need I? I'll manage, now I know."

Rob was promoted full colonel soon after arriving in Vietnam. His regular weekly letter became the week's event. He always enclosed a second letter, written in large capitals, for Brian.

And she wrote punctually back, first her own reply, and then guiding Brian's hand for his. A pity, Rob said, about the false alarm. But no: *she* could reenter the Church; he wasn't going to. He hadn't time, anyway, not to mention inclination.

Safe and already dried into a buff-colored curl, the folded paper stays in the cold cream jar, never looked at, flanked by looking glass and jewel box, with Rob's letters to her neatly stacked behind it. Cynthia never sleeps in the afternoons now; and if she finds herself dozing or dreaming in the old way, reads the letters in chronological order. Rob sleeps little and, in his efficient, pessimistic way, has made a will. Adèle, readjusting to her husband in Toronto, no longer muses on Cynthia's gradual desiccation, having long ago (it seems to her), in a flush of defensive smugness, summed the whole mess up in one unuttered sentence: "Some women have no pride, no shame." The cent is still on the floor of the pool, and the water is still back to its usual depth. Brian is in school, the twig has blown away somewhere, and the pelican has not returned. If it ever does, elbowing in from the Gulf with its pale goiter, it will have to bear a living child in its beak and, to satisfy Cynthia at all, deliver it through the mesh into the pool.

Notes on Contributors

A. R. AMMONS is the author of several volumes of verse, the most recent of which is entitled *Tape of the Turn of the Year*.

JOHN BARTH, author of *The Sot-Weed Factor* and other novels, is at present teaching English at Buffalo. His new novel, *Giles Goat-Boy*, will be published this fall.

WILLIAM BRONK, born in 1918, is the author of two volumes of verse: *Light and Dance* and *The World, the Worldless*.

ROBERT BRUSTEIN is dean of the Yale University School of Drama. Among his works of dramatic criticism are *The Theatre of Revolt* and *Seasons of Discontent*.

JANE COOPER teaches at Sarah Lawrence College. In 1960-61 she received a Guggenheim Fellowship for creative writing in poetry. She is currently preparing a volume of verse.

MAURICE CRANSTON is the author of a book-length study of Sartre and has written many articles for *Encounter* and other periodicals. He is teaching at the London School of Economics.

STEPHEN DONADIO, a graduate of Brandeis University, is now continuing his studies at Columbia University and writing poetry and criticism.

HANS MAGNUS ENZENSBERGER is one of the best-known German critics and poets. He has published several volumes of verse as well as several volumes of critical essays and is the winner of the Georg Buechner prize for 1963.

IRVIN FAUST, whose first volume of short stories, *Roar Lion Roar*, appeared in 1965, is Director of Guidance at Garden City High School, Long Island.

P. N. FURBANK lives in London and writes criticism for *Encounter* and other periodicals.

STEVEN KATZ is presently teaching English at Cornell University. *The Weight of Agony*, a book of his poems that appeared in a limited, hand-printed edition in 1964, was reprinted last fall by the Eibe Press. He is now working on a novel.

JASCHA KESSLER, now teaching at the University of Southern California, has published several volumes of fiction and poetry.

ROBERT LOWELL's latest book is *The Old Glory*. He won the Pulitzer Prize for *Lord Weary's Castle* and the National Book Award for *Life Studies*. His work-in-progress is entitled *Near the Ocean*.

KAREL VAN HET REVE is professor of Russian literature at Leyden University, Holland. His essay in this book is part of his work, *Russland voor Beginners*, published in Amsterdam in 1962.

MORDECAI RICHLER was born and raised in Canada, and is now living in England. He is the author of two novels, *The Apprenticeship of Duddy Kravitz* and *The Incomparable Atuk*.

HENRY L. ROTH is a short-story writer and lives with his family in Rockland County, New York.

HAROLD SCHIMMEL teaches English at the University of Jerusalem. Several pamphlets of his poetry have been published abroad.

THALIA SELZ, whose fiction has appeared in *Partisan Review* and other magazines, lives in New York City.

STEPHEN T. SOHMER is twenty-four years old and lives with his wife and daughter at Mahwah, New Jersey. He is at present a copy-writer with the American Newspaper Publishers Association's Bureau of Advertising. "Entropy" is part of a book to be published in the fall of 1966.

PAUL WEST, who was born in England in 1930, was educated at Oxford and at Columbia, and has taught in Canada and at several American universities. He is the author of works of fiction and poetry. His collection of critical essays, *The Wine of Absurdity*, appeared late last year.